Introduction to Nanotechnology: The New Science of Small

Shana Kelley and Ted Sargent

THE
GREAT
COURSES®

PUBLISHED BY:

THE GREAT COURSES
Corporate Headquarters
4840 Westfields Boulevard, Suite 500
Chantilly, Virginia 20151-2299
Phone: 1-800-832-2412
Fax: 703-378-3819
www.thegreatcourses.com

Shana Kelley, Ph.D.

Professor, Division of Biomolecular Sciences,
Leslie Dan Faculty of Pharmacy
University of Toronto

Professor Shana Kelley, Ph.D. is a researcher, academic leader, and entrepreneur based in Toronto. She leads a team of 20 scientists and graduate students conducting research in the area of bionanotechnology. Professor Kelley received her B.S. degree from Seton Hall University in 1994 and her Ph.D. in Chemistry from the California Institute of Technology in 1999. She was a National Institutes of Health postdoctoral fellow at The Scripps Research Institute, where she was trained in molecular biology. Dr. Kelley began her academic career at Boston College in 2000 as an assistant professor and was promoted directly to full professor in 2006. She joined the University of Toronto that same year.

Professor Kelley has also cofounded 2 companies based on her work in biomolecular sensing. GeneOhm Sciences Inc. was a San Diego–based company acquired in 2006 by Becton Dickinson, which now markets the tests for antibiotic-resistant organisms that GeneOhm developed. Xagenic Inc. is a Toronto-based company that will commercialize a chip-based detection technology recently codeveloped by Professor Kelley and collaborator Ted Sargent, Ph.D. Professor Kelley currently serves as Chief Technology Officer of Xagenic.

Professor Kelley's research has been disseminated in leading scientific journals, including *Science, Nature Materials, Nature Nanotechnology*, and *Nature Structural and Molecular Biology*. She has published 70 original scientific papers and 10 reviews of her work, and her discoveries have been cited by other researchers more than 3000 times. Her work has been featured in *Scientific American* and *Nature Medicine* and on national television.

Dr. Kelley's work has been recognized with a variety of awards, including a 2010 E. W. R. Steacie Memorial Fellowship, an elite honor given to up to 6 Canadian scientists each year by the Natural Sciences and Engineering Research Council of Canada for research excellence. She was honored among Canada's top young leaders in 2009 and named to MIT's *Technology Review* list of the top 100 innovators in 2004. She has also received a National Science Foundation CAREER Award, a Sloan Research Fellowship, and a Camille Dreyfus Teacher-Scholar Award. ∎

Ted Sargent, Ph.D.
Professor and Canada Research Chair
in Nanotechnology
University of Toronto

Professor Ted Sargent, Ph.D. is a researcher, academic leader, and entrepreneur based in Toronto. Since 2009, Professor Sargent has served as Associate Chair for Research in The Edward S. Rogers Sr. Department of Electrical and Computer Engineering at the University of Toronto. From 2004 to 2006, he was also Visiting Professor of Nanotechnology at the Massachusetts Institute of Technology. He received his B.S. in Engineering Physics from Queen's University in 1995 and his Ph.D. in Electrical and Computer Engineering (Photonics) from the University of Toronto in 1998.

Professor Sargent leads a team of 25 scientists and graduate students conducting research in the area of nanotechnology. His research has been disseminated in *Nature*, *Science*, *Nature Materials*, *Nature Nanotechnology*, and *Nature Photonics*. His discoveries have been cited by other researchers more than 3500 times, and his work has been featured in *The Economist*, *The New York Times*, *The Wall Street Journal*, *Scientific American*, and *Nature Medicine*. He is a fellow of the American Association for the Advancement of Science and the Institute of Electrical and Electronics Engineers.

Professor Sargent is the author of *The Dance of Molecules: How Nanotechnology Is Changing Our Lives*, which has been translated into Korean, French, Italian, Spanish, and Arabic. Professor Sargent has addressed broad audiences on nanotechnology and its implications, notably at the Technology, Entertainment, Design (TED) Conference in 2007 in Monterey, California; on Parliament Hill in Ottawa; and at corporate, venture, and policy conferences around the world. In 2003, Professor Sargent was named to MIT's *Technology Review* list of top innovators under 35. He was also named to the 2005 *Scientific American* 50, an annual list "recognizing outstanding leaders in science and technology," for his contributions to flexible infrared solar cells.

Based on inventions developed at the University of Toronto, Professor Sargent founded InVisage Technologies Inc. in 2006. The firm won *The Wall Street Journal* 2010 Technology Innovation Award in the semiconductors category for revolutionizing the capture of digital images using its patented QuantumFilm technology. InVisage is partnering for manufacture with Taiwan Semiconductor Manufacturing Company, the world's largest semiconductor foundry, and will ship its image sensors in smartphones. Professor Sargent serves as Chief Technology Officer and is a Director of InVisage. ∎

Table of Contents

Table of Contents

Table of Contents

Introduction to Nanotechnology:
The New Science of Small

Scope:

Nanoscience is the study of how matter behaves when it is configured on the scale of the nanometer—1 billionth of a meter. It is a field that has seen tremendous progress in recent decades. The broad advance of nanoscience has enabled nanotechnology, the application of these new ideas in areas as diverse as medicine, sustainable energy, and computing.

Atoms are the building blocks of matter; like the letters of the alphabet that compose words and sentences, atoms are combined to make molecules, such as water, H_2O, and materials, such as droplets of water, crystals of silicon, and plastics. The qualities atoms bring with them—their numbers of electrons available for bonding, the atoms' characteristic size—underpin the resultant properties of materials that emerge. Carbon atoms' 4 electrons available for bonding are at the root of diamond's tightly bound crystal lattice based on a 4-nearest-atomic-neighbor collaboration.

The rules that govern the emergence of physical properties from combinations of atoms and molecules include—but also go beyond—the classical physics of Newton. They include Einstein's and Schrodinger's quantum mechanics, wherein electrons and photons behave simultaneously as particles and as waves. Thus, electrons, though discrete and countable in number, have a spatial extent. Like the string of a guitar or the head of the tympani, the media to which electrons are tethered can be tuned in size and shape, changing their resonant frequency. The result is nanoengineered materials whose size programs the colors of light they absorb and emit.

Computing has been one of the early playgrounds for nanoscientists and nanotechnologists. The early transistors that displaced the vacuum tube were not nanometer-sized, but they did evidence key qualities, such as the smooth flow of electron waves through the pure, perfect crystalline environment of silicon. As engineers strove to increase computers' speed and sophistication, they increasingly carved and connected transistors, first on the length scale of micrometers, and, today, of a few 10s of nanometers. Like computer chips, the lasers that generate the light waves that beam through fiber-optic cables rely on quantum nanoscale effects, as do new generations of image sensors for cameras and security inspection systems.

Medicine and biology are poised to benefit from growing dexterity at the nanoscale. DNA—the template from which proteins, organelles, cells, and ultimately, organisms are derived—is a coil of information whose double helix displays periodicity. Thus, precise interaction with the molecular basis of all life demands finesse on the nanoscale. Improved sensing of patterns, mistakes, and changes in DNA and proteins is allowing scientists to better understand the origins of disease and to catch such illnesses as cancer at the earliest stages, while they are still treatable. Nanomaterials that allow us to target specific classes of cells or certain structures within cells, such as mitochondria, allow drugs to be concentrated for maximum effect and minimized side effects. Designer nanomaterials are enabling visualization of tumor margins during surgery, allowing residual cells to be detected and surgical resection rendered accurate and complete.

Technology for sustainable energy is another field urgently needing rapid progress. Scientists are beginning to build flexible—even wearable—solar cells that efficiently capture the Sun's rays, both visible and infrared. These rainbow solar cells use nanoparticles' tunability to make optimal use of each slice of the Sun's broad spectrum. Just as importantly, nanomaterials are enabling improved means of storing energy—a critical part of turning the power of fluctuating renewable energy sources into a dependable and major source. Similarly, advances in materials engineering are allowing more efficient catalysis for the synthesis of industrial chemicals; flexible and highly efficient sources of light to replace the incandescent bulb; and, ultimately, new classes of photosynthetic analogs that enable direct solar-to-stored-fuel energy conversion.

In 1959, physicist Richard Feynman made his famous speech, "There's Plenty of Room at the Bottom." Underlying the diversity of applications in nanotechnology is a commonality of themes based on the physics and chemistry of the nanometer-length scale. For example, at the nanoscale, surface area becomes vastly larger and more important compared to volume, and this one difference affects everything from computer chips, to mitochondria in cells, to the design of better solar panels. Common scientific principles underpin many of the advances in the field of nanotechnology. Understanding these principles puts us in a position to experience how it is possible to engineer matter—safely and with increasing control and dexterity—in order to build and use new materials having designer properties that have never existed before and, thereby, to deploy them in a vast array of exciting and important applications. ■

The Crossroads of 21ˢᵗ-Century Science
Lecture 1

W e begin our journey into the nanoworld by trying to visualize the size of nanoparticles and looking at the advances in technology that have been achieved on this incredibly tiny scale. In the "top-down" branch of nanotechnology, matter is engineered on the nanoscale to a specific purpose; our dexterity on this length scale has enabled such innovations as computers, smartphones, and the Internet. Even more amazing is the "bottom-up" branch of the field, in which materials are engineered to self-assemble.

The Length Scale of Atoms and Molecules
- A grain of sand measures about 1 millimeter, 1/1000 of a meter; the cells in our bodies measure about 1 micrometer, 1/1,000,000 of a meter. A nanometer is 1000 times smaller than that.

- Optical microscopes are limited in their ability to resolve images by the wavelength of light, and the measure of that length is a bit smaller than a micrometer; thus, we typically can't resolve things that are smaller than that size. We need to turn to other methods to be able to visualize the world on the scale of the nanometer.

- To visualize individual atoms, we use transmission electron microscopy (TEM). A scanning tunneling microscope allows even finer resolution. Interestingly, TEM was invented around 1937 and the scanning tunneling microscope was invented around 1980, yet the two inventors shared the 1986 Nobel Prize in Physics.

What Nanoscience Enables
- We tend to think of nanoscience as a revolution that's unfolding today, but its foundations—the ability to visualize matter at the nanometer-length scale—go back many decades.

- In 1959, Richard Feynman, another Nobel Prize winner in Physics, proclaimed that there's plenty of room at the bottom. In other words, there's plenty of capability for us to increase our dexterity in manipulating matter on smaller length scales. Feynman envisioned writing the entire contents of the *Encyclopedia Britannica* on the head of a pin.

- Integrated circuits, such as those inside your computer, have billions of individual transistors on them, each of which is defined on the scale of the nanometer. It's only because we have the capability to understand the materials making up the transistor and can engineer those materials on the right length scales that we have been able to experience the computing revolution.

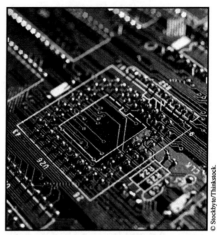

Our capability to understand and engineer materials on the nanoscale has enabled the computer revolution.

- In fact, it's because of our dexterity on this length scale that we can actually sense our world. A smartphone has a GPS, temperature sensors, and proximity sensors, and all of these are connected to multiple integrated circuits, which "talk" to the Internet through wireless communications. All of these capabilities are traceable to our ability to engineer matter toward a specific purpose.

- We've taken a vast array of semiconductor technology—a vast array of building-block materials—and combined it rationally to make devices that integrate many functions.

- The Internet itself is enabled by important advances at the nano-length scale, coming, in this case, from the field of fiber optics.

Today, we're able to send trillions of bits per second of information over a single glass optical fiber cable.

o A crucial piece here was the discovery of how to make glass so pure and perfect, so lacking in defects, that we're able to ensure that light launched into one of these fiber optic cables can travel thousands of kilometers without loss of power and, thus, loss of information.

o The sources of this light must be incredibly pure and provide a single frequency that's extremely powerful and focused.

o With these semiconductor lasers, we're able to make coherent beams of light that we can launch down an optical fiber to propagate information over vast distances.

• Some of this may sound incredibly difficult to engineer, and originally, it was. But what's striking now is that many of these innovations, such as integrated circuits or fiber optic communications, have actually reduced costs.

Top-Down and Bottom-Up Nanotechnology

• We can think of these advances in the field of integrated circuit engineering—computers, lasers, the Internet, and so on—as top-down nanotechnology.

• In the top-down branch of the field, we set ourselves on a design of a device or a material, and we then make an imprint and convey that imprint using a technique called lithography. This technique is used on a massive scale—but on a very small length scale—to generate billions of identical transistors and connect them together.

• However, one of the most exciting things that's going on today in the field of nanotechnology comes from the bottom up. In this approach, we use our understanding of atoms and their interactions to engineer materials that self-assemble.

- In contrast with the top-down approach—where we have to carve up matter on the nanometer-length scale—here, we start from constituents—atoms smaller than the nanometer—and we introduce them to interact with one another such that, from the bottom up, they form new materials.

- One exciting class of new materials at the heart of nanotechnology today is quantum dots. These are semiconductor particles a few nanometers in size that invent what's called quantum size effects. Through quantum size effects, the size of the particle changes its resonance.

- When we shrink materials down to the nanometer-length scale, we also gain the capability to fit a huge amount of surface area into a finite volume. This capability is useful whenever we need a lot of surface, such as to drive chemical reactions at surfaces.
  o The catalytic converter in your car leverages having a huge surface area to convert noxious emissions into more environmentally acceptable ones.

  o Engineering materials on the nanometer-length scale gives us even greater capability to refine and control materials and chemical reactions.

- Nanoscience also gives us the ability to engineer new composite materials that have a number of properties in combination. They can be incredibly lightweight, firm, strong, or flexible.

Nanotechnology and Medicine
- If we think about the biology that underlies physiology and the anatomy of humans, we realize that we have to focus on the nanoscale. Leeuwenhoek used a simple microscope to observe red blood cells for the first time in 1684. We now know that our bodies are made up of trillions of cells, and each of these cells is about 10,000 nanometers across. Inside a cell, many structures are measured in hundreds of nanometers.

- The molecules that do all the work in our cells truly reach the nanoscale. For example, the pumps that move molecules in and out of our cells are about 10 or 20 nanometers. The proteins that keep our cells going are typically around 10 nanometers, and the DNA molecules that program our genetics measure only 2 nanometers across.

- Nanotechnology is particularly relevant to medicine because the drugs we use to treat disease are all targeted at proteins or DNA molecules. Understanding what's happening at the nanoscale allows us to make smarter drugs, such as those that can be delivered to specific sites within the body by carbon nanohorns, or nanosized drug capsules.

- The ability to work on the nanoscale means that we can see molecules more readily, which enables us to diagnose disease early, when it's most treatable. Nanoparticles can be made to act as very sensitive and specific detectors of bacteria and other cell types and can be used for this type of diagnosis. Further, nanoparticles can be activated to selectively destroy harmful cells.

- Nanomaterials can also be used to generate new types of surgical tools. Nanotweezers, for example, are able to grip particles that are close to the size of cells, enabling precise surgery to be performed.

- Another exciting area of nanomedicine research is work being done on the growth of artificial tissues and organs.
  o Scientists can engineer hard and soft materials at the nanoscale, using such techniques as lithography or self-assembly, and these nanomaterials can be used to teach cells to grow in set patterns the way they do in natural tissues.

  o It's also possible to interface these nano-trained artificial tissues with a blood supply so that they can receive oxygen and nutrients.

- Being able to work with matter at the nanoscale is a powerful way to advance a variety of important medical applications, but the distinctive properties of nanomaterials are important, as well.
    o For example, gold nanoparticles represent a promising material for disease diagnosis and treatment, both because of their small size and because of their electronic properties, which are directly tied to being at the nanoscale.

    o Regular gold, as you know, reflects yellow light. But nanoscale gold particles actually appear purple in solution—they absorb much longer wavelengths of light. This feature of gold nanoparticles arises because of a change in the electronics of gold that occurs at the nanoscale.

    o How do gold nanoparticles seek and destroy cancer cells? They can be made in a form that absorbs infrared light and converts it into cell-killing heat.

Themes of the Course
- Biology, information technology, and energy may seem to be disparate fields, but as we proceed through the course, you'll notice that a few common themes emerge.

- For example, the huge surface areas that are so important in the field of catalysis and energy have an analog in such structures as mitochondria in cells.

- Another theme that cuts across these different fields of application is commensurability. For example, with quantum dots, the sizes of electrons are matched up with the size of the "box" that will contain them, which has a powerful influence on their properties.

- These themes arise from our capacity to engineer matter, our capacity to use control and dexterity at the nanometer-length scale to build materials having designer properties that don't occur naturally.

- What's the fundamental underpinning that leads to this commonality of themes cutting across different fields of application? The answer is, essentially, a common alphabet and a common grammar.
  - Our common alphabet in nanotechnology is made up of atoms, the elements in the periodic table. The way in which these atoms assemble and form structures and the way they interact is our grammar.

  - In the next lecture, we'll spend a bit more time on this alphabet and grammar. We'll learn the common scientific principles that underpin all advances in the field of nanotechnology.

Suggested Reading

Aldersey-Williams, Hall, Sargent, and Antonelli, "Design and the Elastic Mind."

Alivisatos, "Less Is More in Medicine."

Frankel and Whitesides, *No Small Matter*.

Sargent, *The Dance of Molecules*.

Questions to Consider

1. Why do we view physics, chemistry, and biology as distinct fields of science? How could we instead view these three fields as a hierarchical stack of disciplines, each building on the others? Which would be the most fundamental, and which would be built on top of this field?

2. What are examples of devices around us—computers, mobile phones, and so on—that were enabled by key advances in science? What were the seminal conceptual advances that enabled the resulting inventions?

The Crossroads of 21st-Century Science
Lecture 1—Transcript

Ted Sargent: Hello. Welcome to Nanoscience and the applications of nanoscience that we call nanotechnology. My name is Ted Sargent. I'm a Professor of Electrical and Computer Engineering at the University of Toronto and with my colleague Professor Shana Kelley, also from U of T. We will explore together the world of nanoscience and its applications.

What does nano mean? Nano is referring to the nanometer so it's a unit of measure and it's incredibly small. How small is it? Let's start with something that we can picture, something we can visualize. A grain of sand is about a millimeter. It's about a thousandth of a meter. What about things that are much smaller than that, things that we may not be able to see unaided, something we'd need a microscope for? Well, the particles that constitute clay are about a thousand times smaller than the familiar grain of sand. Very hard to see these as particles on our own; typically we'd need an optical microscope. The same thing with the cells that are in our body or with bacteria; they're also about a millionth of a meter, a micrometer.

The nanometer is a thousand times smaller than that. In fact, optical microscopes don't allow us to visualize nanoparticles. We're limited in our ability to resolve images by the wavelength of the light or other particles that we're using to look at something, to image something, and so with an optical microscope we're limited to the wavelength of the light that we use. Well that too has a measure of length, that wavelength; it's a bit smaller than a micrometer. Light's actually measured in the 500 nanometer kind of length scale. As a result, we can't typically resolve things that are smaller than that. So, we need to turn to other methods to be able to visualize the world on the scale of the nanometer.

Take a look at these images, which actually show individually resolved atoms. This is a cross-section of a semiconductor device used in one of the integrated circuits that's inside your computer, that's inside your cell phone and it's showing that we're able to use what's called transmission electron microscopy, TEM, to see a slice of material and to visualize its individual atoms. Some of the layers that we're looking at here are just a few nanometers thick. The number of atoms that constitutes their thickness in the vertical direction is countable. It can be five or ten. Atoms tend to be spaced out in solid matter on the scale of maybe half the nanometer. So, by venturing into the world of nanoscience, we're venturing down to the length scale of atoms and also of molecules.

What's so remarkable, I think you would necessarily expect this, but what's so remarkable is that it is an incredibly visual world. It's something we can't visualize with our own eyes, it's something we can't visualize with a microscope, but it's something that we can visualize with the aid of very special microscopes, whose design or purpose is to allow us to see at this length scale. In fact, there are other tools that we have our disposal as well. The scanning tunneling microscope, such as the one that took this image, allows even finer resolution. We can skate across a surface, we can see individual bumps, we can feel the bumps with the tip of a microscope that traces across the surface, and we can see the egg carton like shapes that atoms packed into a perfectly ordered array make up. In fact, we can even see, we can even feel the way in which their electrons waves are shaped.

So our ability to see using what we now call nanoscience, the field in which we seek to understand at a deep level, the constituents of matter on the atomic, on the nanometer length scale, we can visualize matter at this scale today. In fact, when you think of the scanning tunneling microscope and the transmission electron microscope it's an interesting convergence, these two inventions are very far apart in time. The transmission electron microscope was invented around 1937 and the scanning tunneling microscope around 1980, and yet the inventors of these very different types of imaging shared the 1986 Nobel Prize in Physics together. This must be one of the Nobel Prizes in Physics shared by people separated most in time in the periods of their inventions.

It was Ernst Ruska who won the prize for the TEM and it also illustrates another interesting point about nanoscience, which is we think of it as kind of a revolution that's unfolding today, something new, and it is a very lively field, huge numbers of scientists and engineers are passionate about it, are engaged in it, but the foundations, our ability to visualize matter at the nanometer length scale, the foundations necessarily go back many, many decades. It's the scientific discoveries that were made before we started using terms like nanotechnology. In fact, even the first initial use of the word nanometer was around 1960. Well it was well before that, before we were speaking in nanometers that we were doing the foundational basic science that enabled us to visualize and to have dexterity at the nanometer length scale. In fact another example of some early important work in nanotechnology, before the word was even utilized popularly, was Richard Feynman.

Richard Feynman, a very distinguished professor at Caltech also a Nobel Prize winner in Physics, who in 1959 proclaimed there's plenty of room at the bottom. There's plenty of capability for us to increase our dexterity in manipulating matter on smaller and smaller length scales. He thought of miniaturization, he thought of packing more and more information. He talked about writing the entire contents of the Encyclopedia Britannica on the head of a pin. His ability to visualize how much we could do if we could become dexterous on this new length scale was remarkable. It foresees a lot of what's important about nanotechnology.

Take a look of this picture of an integrated circuit. These are inside your computer; they're in your mobile phone; they're in calculators. These integrated circuits based on silicon, they have on them now billions of individual transistors. So, each of these transistors is now defined on the scale of the nanometer, tens of nanometers, describe the spaces between the various electrodes that make these transistors operate properly. It's only because we have these tools. It's only because we have this capability to understand the materials making up the transistor and cross-section. It's only because we can engineer those materials on the right length scales. It's only because we understand the atoms that make up those materials and how the atoms making up those materials give rise to the electrical properties, insulators, semiconductors, metals, it's only because of that understanding and that scientific context that we have been able to engineer the computing revolution.

In fact, it's because of our dexterity of that length scale that we can do more than simply compute, but we can sense our world. So if you think of your smartphone and the fact that it's got an image sensor in it, it's got a GPS, it's got temperature sensors, it's got proximity sensors, all these are connected to multiple integrated circuits. The integrated circuits are talking to the rest of the world. They're talking to the internet through extremely high frequency communications channel, through wireless communications. All of these capabilities are directly traceable to our ability to engineer matter towards a specific purpose.

What we've succeeded in doing, and a smartphone is a great example of it, is we've taken such a vast array of semiconductor technology, such a vast array of building block materials and combined them rationally in order to make devices that implement so many and integrate so many functions. In fact, the batteries that are inside your cell phone increasingly they have achieved dense storage, so dense in terms of a lot of energy per mass and also dense in terms of a lot of energy per volume to make things spin into a very compact form factor. All of these are coming through our increased ability to engineer materials at this very, very short length scale.

In fact, the fact that there's something for your cell phone to communicate with, the fact that there is an internet is also enabled by some very important advances also on this length scale coming though in this case from light, coming from the field of fiber optics. Today, we're able to send trillions of bits per second of information over a single glass optical fiber cable. A crucial piece of that was our discovery of how to make glass so pure and so perfect, so lacking in defects, that we're able to ensure that light is launched into one of these fiber optic cables and that it can bounce down and that it can travel over thousands of kilometers without the loss of power and thus without the power of information.

The sources of this light, they have to be incredibly pure, they have to provide a single frequency that's extremely powerful, that's very focused, that we can couple into one of these optical fibers and so it's the laser, in particular the semiconductor laser, that gives us this capability. With these lasers we're able to make very, very pure, even coherent beams of photons, coherent beams of light, that we can launch down an optical fiber with which we're able to propagate information over these vast distances. You know, some of this may sound exotic; some of it may sound difficult to do, difficult to engineer. In the first instances before we knew how to do it, it certainly was, but what's so striking is that with many of these innovations, such as integrated circuits or fiber optic communications, what it's actually done is it has reduced cost. It's meant that the price of a long distance call has fallen by an order of magnitude over the last decade or two. It's meant that we're getting an increasing computational complexity and sophistication, but, in fact, at lower and lower cost per unit of computing.

The advances that have described this field of integrated circuit engineering, computers, mobility, lasers, the internet, communications, you can think of them as one branch of nanotechnology that I'll call top down. By that I mean, we set ourselves upon a design of a device, a design of a material, and we then make an imprint, we convey that imprint using a technique called lithography, which is analogous to screen printing, the way we make T-shirts, we use this on a massive scale and on a very, very small length scale to generate these billions of identical transistors and connect them together. But in fact, one of the most exciting things that's going on today in the field of nanotechnology comes at it from exactly the other side. It comes at it, it's what we call bottom up nanotechnology, and it comes at engineering materials from the point of view of saying through chemistry we understand atoms, we understand their proclivities, we understand the propensity of one atom's style to like to bend to another style of atom, from one element to interact with another element.

Through that understanding, we're able to engineer materials that self-assemble. In contrast with the top down where we do have to define matter, carve up matter on the nanometer length scale, here we start from constituents, atoms smaller than the nanometer, and we introduce them to each other. We introduce them to interact with one another such that from the bottom up they form new materials. One very exciting class of new materials that is very much at the heart of nanotechnology today is quantum dots, such as those shown here. These are semiconductor particles a few nanometers in size, that invent some very special properties.

They're called quantum dots because they invent what we call quantum size effects and through the quantum size effect, the size of the particle changes its resonance. What happens is that electron waves, because when we get down to the scale of the nanometer we have to think in the rules of physics, the quantum world of physics, not just the classical, is electron waves get condensed or compressed down and just like when you change the size or the tension on timpani drum and you change its frequency, well we change the frequencies, the resonances, and therefore the colors that these quantum materials emit. In fact, a similar idea of resonance is at play in the field of plasmonics. This is the area such as with metal nanoparticles that make stained glass have different colors. These different size effects lead to resonances, in that case, with light to resonant interactions between the wavelength of light and the characteristic length scales at play within these plasmonic structures.

There's another really interesting and important way in which getting down to the nanometer length scale ends up being really important in influencing the properties of matter. When we shrink materials down to these incredibly small length scales, we have the capability of fitting a huge amount of surface area into a finite volume. That ends up being powerful whenever we need a lot of surface. We often drive chemical reactions at surfaces. That is the field of catalysis, and in fact catalysis is just something that's already widely utilized and something very familiar in your own automobile, the catalytic converter, something that leverages having huge surface areas in order to convert noxious emissions into more environmental acceptable ones. It's taking advantage of this huge surface area. Well going down to engineering materials on the nanometer length scale gives us even greater access to the capability to refine and control materials and chemical reactions on these scales.

Let me suggest one other interesting example of the power of nanomaterials in nanotechnology and of nanoscience, our ability to understand these structures. It comes from our ability to engineer new composite materials that have a number of properties on combination. They can be incredibly light in weight, they can be very, very firm, they can be very strong, or we can engineer them to be flexible. You know, ultimately what the field of nanotechnology comes down to for me is making the connection between the form and the function of the material. As a scientist, it's to understand the connection between nanoscale form and then behavior. And as an engineer, obviously we're incredibly driven to try to take advantage of those insights, take advantage of that understanding, and then build designer materials tailored toward specific applications.

Shana Kelley: Now that you've been introduced to the nanoworld and a few of the technologies that nanoscience enables in computing and communications, we'll switch gears and we'll talk for a few minutes about how thinking about biology at the nanoscale can lead to similar advances in medicine.

I'm Shana Kelley and I am a professor of Biochemistry and Pharmaceutical Sciences at the University of Toronto. My background is in the chemical sciences, and I run an interdisciplinary research group at U of T that works on a variety of nanotechnology projects. In this course I'll be the one to take you through the aspects of nanotechnology that relate to biology and medicine. This is a very exciting field that is moving at a really fast pace and producing incredible advances in medical care.

Now Ted Sargent just gave you a great overview of the unique aspects of science and technology that come from taking the size scale of materials to the nanometer regime. For biology and medicine, going to the nanoscale also has a set of unique advantages. If we think about the biology that underlies physiology and the anatomy of humans, we realize that we have to focus in on the nanoscale to truly understand it. Cells are the most basic unit in living organisms; Ted already touched on the fact that the sizes of these units approach the nanoscale. Our bodies are made up of trillions of human cells, each of which is about 10,000 nanometers across. But, cells can be smaller. Bacteria, for example (and we have lots of friendly bacteria in our bodies), are much smaller—about 1000 nanometers. Some types—Mycoplasma, for example—can be only 300 nanometers. So cells, our basic building block, are almost nanoscale.

If we look inside of a human cell we find that there are many structures and compartments, like the mitochondria that produce our energy, and these compartments are hundreds of nanometers. But what are truly nanoscale are the molecules that do all of the work in our cells. The pumps that move molecules in and out of our cells are tens of nanometers. The proteins that do all of the work to keep our cells going are typically 5 nanometers in diameter, and the DNA molecules that program our genetics measure about 2 nanometers across. So the fundamental building blocks of life are molecules, and those molecules are nanoscale.

The study of biology and biochemistry has changed so much over the last 50 to 60 years, and it has focused on the nanoscale more and more. Over the last several decades, we have developed really powerful tools to study life all the way down to its fundamental building blocks: the structure of proteins became known beginning in the 1940s; then the structure of DNA was identified in the 1950s; enzymes that allow us to recombine DNA in new ways were developed in the 1970s; then the human genome was sequenced in the 1990s. So with every decade that passes, we have new ways to get more and more information about biology.

So as you see, biology really operates at the nanoscale and this means that nanotechnology is particularly relevant to medicine because in order to cure or diagnose disease we need to know what is going on at this level. The drugs that we use to treat disease are all targeted at proteins or DNA molecules, and so to understand how drugs work and in order to make better drugs, we need to understand what's happening at the nano level.

Understanding the nanoscience of biology has already been proven to allow us to deliver drugs more effectively. Using nanomaterials that can be programmed to be much more specific than the macroscale materials we have used for drug delivery in the past, we can deliver a drug to where it is needed within the body rather than just letting it distribute randomly. Here's an example of a structure used for drug delivery. What you are looking at is an image of a carbon nanohorn: This is a carbon-based structure that is just a few nanometers across. Nanohorns are relatively easy to make; if you produce soot from burning organic matter there will usually be some carbon nanohorns in the mixture that results. And the shape of carbon nanohorns really seems compatible with using them as containers. This nanohorn can actually serve as a nanosized drug capsule. It can be filled with an anticancer drug, injected, and then it only releases the drug once it has reached a tumor. This type of nano-packaged drug has been shown to be 100 times more effective than one formulated using existing methods, which instead use different types of solvents or chemicals to disperse a drug in solution.

Of course, the ability to work on the nanoscale—or the molecular scale—means that we can see molecules more readily, and that's a huge advantage. If we want to diagnose disease earlier—when it's more treatable—we need to be able to detect the first few molecules that signal the presence of disease rather than waiting for symptoms to develop—which typically means that there are many molecules are present. So to look for something as small as a molecule and do it with the sensitivity needed for early diagnosis, we obviously need really small detectors. There are a variety of nanomaterials that we now have at hand that are really good at giving off signals and providing high sensitivity to diagnostic tests.

For example, gold nanoparticles are a very promising material for disease diagnosis and treatment, both because of their small size and because of their electronic properties, which are directly tied to being nanoscale. Regular gold, as you know, reflects yellow light, but nanoscale gold particles actually appear purple in solution—they absorb much longer wavelengths of light. In a few lectures, we'll spend quite a bit of time talking about this feature, which arises because of a change in the electronics of gold that happens at the nanoscale. What we'll learn is that this electronic feature can be harnessed to readout very small changes in the sequence of a DNA molecule—a capability that allows the diagnosis of genetic disease.

Gold nanoparticles have many other important applications in nanomedicine. Recently, we've been able to engineer them to seek and destroy cancer cells. How does this work? Well, gold nanoparticles can absorb light and can convert that light into cell-killing heat. And they can be made in a form that absorbs infrared light—and this is quite important. Unlike visible light that is absorbed by skin and tissue, we can actually get infrared light into a tissue, so we are able to get the signal into the gold nanoparticles even if they are under layers of tissue and skin. This is very important for targeting tumors that almost always are under these types of structures.

And these gold nanoparticles are really versatile; they can also be used to combat infectious disease. You are looking at gold nanoparticles that have found a dangerous type of bacteria. The nanoparticles, that can be made to act as very sensitive and specific detectors of bacteria and other cell types for disease diagnosis, have an added benefit: They can be activated and made to selectively destroy cells that are harmful. This is something that is difficult or even impossible to achieve with materials that are not nanoscale. And you can see that because of the small size of the nanoparticles, a group of them can actually gang up on a bacterium and attack it. This allows nanotherapies to deliver a stronger punch.

Nanomaterials can also be used to generate new types of surgical tools. You are looking at two carbon nanotubes that have been attached to a stem to form a set of nanotweezers. Amazingly enough, we can bring the nanotube tips together so that they are touching and they are able to grip particles that are close to the size of cells. So if we want to perform more precise surgeries that are less damaging to healthy tissues, we'll need this type of nanotool that can take out one cell at a time.

Another very exciting area of nanomedicine research is the work being done on the growth of artificial tissues and organs. Scientists can engineer hard and soft materials at the nanoscale using techniques like lithography or self-assembly, and these materials can be used to teach cells to grow in set patterns the way they do in natural tissues. We have also figured out how to interface these nano-trained artificial tissues with a blood supply—which is great, given that tissues need to be in contact with the blood supply in order to get oxygen and important nutrients. Working at the nanoscale to manipulate cells and build up tissues is how we finally made the breakthroughs required get this to happen; otherwise we just couldn't get fine enough control to grow artificial tissues that are functional.

In all of the systems I just told you about, we can visualize the nano-size scale of biology and the nanomaterials we can use to manipulate biology with the imaging tools that Ted mentioned. Using these powerful types of microscopy is really one of the most satisfying aspects of working with nanomaterials. Despite the fact that nanomaterials and the basic building blocks of life are really small, things like electron microscopy are easily able to provide pictures. So we don't have to use our imagination or do any guesswork; there are always pictures to look at. When I was a graduate student, I studied lots of different types of spectroscopy, and I made molecules and characterized them using spectroscopy. There, you never really get a picture of your molecule, but rather you get a pattern of signals that needed to be interpreted.

My dad, who is a civil engineer, would always ask me how I knew what kind of molecules I was making, and how could I trust a pattern of lines on a sheet of paper? I always told him that I just trusted my spectroscopic tools 100%; but now to be honest, I am much happier with the pictures I'm able to look at that tell me exactly what a nanomaterial looks like!

Throughout this course, you'll be able to look at lots of different nanomaterials and nanosystems. I will rejoin you for a collection of lectures that will land right in the middle of the course where we'll look at biology and the range of ways that nanotechnology is enabling cutting edge advances in medicine. I think you'll find this material and the promise of nanomedicine to be really exciting.

But for now, I'll turn things back over to Ted, who will give you some thoughts on common themes uniting nanomedicine and nanotechnology, and then he'll lead you through the first main section of the course.

Ted Sargent: It might seem like Shana and I have been talking about pretty disparate things—biology information technology energy—and yet you'll notice that quite a few themes converge. They span what we're discussing. Let's think of a couple of examples. Well I talked about huge surface areas being so important in the field of catalysis, really important area underpinning energy. When you think of the biological entities that Shana's been telling us about, they often have structures like the mitochondria in cells that are folded over one another the way our intestines are folded up. They maximize surface area too. In the case of mitochondria, they do it for the purpose of maximizing opportunities for chemical reactions.

Another theme that cuts across these different fields of application is the theme of commensurability, the fact that in these quantum dots I was matching up the sizes of electrons with the size of the box that I was going to put them in and that had a powerful influence on their properties. The fact that in the field of plasmonics we see a field of commensurability, a similarity in length scales between the light waves that we will manipulate on the scale of hundreds of nanometers and the size of the metal particles that we can contain them in. There are applications of these that go well beyond information technology of course and information technology are currency as electrons, but in biology often we use photons as reporters of phenomena that are occurring within cellular systems. These themes of commensurability what they really come down to is our capacity to engineer matter, our capacity to utilize control and dexterity of the nanometer length scale in order to build materials having designer properties that don't occur naturally.

Well why is it then? What's the fundamental underpinning that leads to this commonality of themes that cuts across these different fields of application? Well ultimately, it's that whatever Shana and I talk about, we're talking about using a common alphabet. Our building blocks within nanotechnology are the atoms, the elements that make up the periodic table. Further, we're utilizing a common grammar: The way in which these atoms assemble and form structures, the way they interact with each other, which ones can be juxtaposed and which ones will always remain apart, that is our grammar, that is the physics, that is the chemistry of the nanometer length scale. In the next lecture what we'll do is we'll spend a bit more time on that alphabet and on that grammar. We'll understand what the common scientific principles are that underpin, really, all advances in the field of nanotechnology. That will put us all in a position together to think about a vast swath of exciting and important applications. It will allow us all to dream together in this incredibly creative space to use this palate of materials, palate of rules towards our objectives.

Then throughout the rest of this course what we'll do is we'll explore these implications and these applications together. I'll get to talk about the world of nanotechnology and information and communications technologies, how it's revolutionizing our ability to communicate information, compute, sense the world around us. Shana will take us through a fascinating voyage of discovery in the worlds of medicine and biology, and how nanomaterials and nanostructures and their commensurabilities, their surface areas, are allowing us new abilities to interact with organisms and really provide some solutions to our most important health problems.

Then I'll get to talk about another really important societal problem and how we have some solutions to it through nanotechnology; this is the field of energy. We're all so concerned about our climate; we're concerned about what we're doing to our environment. Nanotechnology is giving us some opportunities to harvest the Sun's abundant energy, to store the energy that we capture, and to replay it efficiently. I'm looking forward to this journey together.

The Fundamental Importance of Being Nano
Lecture 2

This second lecture is our opportunity to venture into the physical principles that govern the world of the nanoscale. It's also our chance to get reacquainted with the building blocks of the nanoworld—atoms and molecules—as well as photons. We'll look at how the properties of these materials influence our experience of them and how some of the specific rules of the game are changed at the nanometer-length scale.

The Building Blocks of the Nanoworld

- We often picture an atom like a planet with electrons orbiting it. The planet is the nucleus of the atom, and it consists of a combination of protons, having positive charge, and neutrons, which are neutral.

- For nanotechnologists, the electrons are the building blocks, but the focus is on the electric and magnetic fields—the forces—rather than on the subatomic or subnuclear behaviors that are the concern of particle physics.

- What matters to nanotechnologists is the fact that the core of the nucleus has a positive charge that is attractive to electrons, which have a negative charge.

The Periodic Table

- The way in which the periodic table is formed maps to a description of shells. We think of electrons that orbit the nucleus as being able to occupy one of a number of gradually increasing energy levels. How full each of those "shells" is determines which column of the periodic table an atom resides in. The column of the periodic table, in turn, determines the personality of the atom.

- Elements in the same column often have quite similar chemical behaviors. For example, in the first column, sodium and lithium have a single electron in their outermost shells. The valance electrons that populate that outermost shell are the key ones that relate to chemical reactivity.

o   Atoms that have 1 electron available to participate in bonding represent an opportunity from the point of view of atoms having shells that are almost complete. Sodium chloride, for example, consists of sodium, with 1 valance electron, and chlorine, with 7 valance electrons.

o   In this example of bonding between elements on the far left and right of the periodic table, note that the relationship is symmetric; it involves polarity. This preference for the movement of electrons in one direction or the other is called ionic bonding.

- Another kind of bonding that is much stronger is based on sharing. The kinds of atoms or elements that are most prone to this covalent bonding are those toward the middle of the periodic table, such as silicon or carbon.

o   Carbon is in group 4, which means that it has 4 electrons available to participate in bonding, and it has 4 missing in order to form a complete shell.

o   Materials in this group are sort of halfway through; they're going to form symmetric relationships with each other. For example, silicon and carbon lattices form materials that are extremely stable based on this strong covalent force.

o   The bonding of atoms with one another is one of the central tenets from which we build up materials.

- So far, in talking about these elements, we've visualized almost infinite arrays of atoms, exhibiting a systematic behavior that's common throughout the entire solid. But they're not infinite materials; eventually, a piece of silicon will have an end. At that point, we become concerned with its interface and the management of that interface.

The Classic Picture of Light

- The classic wave picture of photons of electromagnetic radiation (light) has an oscillation of an electric field and a magnetic field. If we think of a single pure color—monochromatic light—the electric field oscillates with a defined period in space and in time. That period in space is referred to as the wavelength.

- Visible light has wavelengths in the range of 400 to about 650 or 700 nanometers. It's measured in nanometers, but it's getting close to the micrometer-length scale.
  - That property of visible light is important because it turns out that a wave is difficult to condense down to a length scale that's smaller than its own wavelength.

  - Thus, the wavelength of an electromagnetic wave will determine how well it can be focused down. We can use a traditional optical microscope to see biological cells that are 10 micrometers in size, but it's much more difficult to see a virus, which can be as small as 100 nanometers in size.

  - If we're using light as a tool to carve matter or to investigate structure, such as through a microscope, we use images projected with ultraviolet light rather than visible light.

The Photoelectric Effect

- Instead of a wave picture of light, Einstein invoked a particle-like quality to light to explain the photoelectric effect. Here, light is a packet of energy.

- The photoelectric effect was observed in an experiment that involved illuminating a metal with different colors of the electromagnetic spectrum.
  - For longer wavelengths, there was essentially no emission of electrons from the metal upon photo excitation; thus, there was no photoelectric effect.

- o Short wavelengths, however, produced a large number of electrons, and the intensity of that collection of electrons was in proportion with the light intensity.

- Einstein's explanation was that electrons needed to be elevated to a certain energy to escape from the metal, and that only those photons of a short enough wavelength contained sufficient individual energy.

- Einstein thought of the photons as quanta, or packets of energy, and saw a direct, inverted relationship between their wavelength and their energy.

Material Properties
- The connection between materials and light is important because many of our discussions in this course will relate to how we can shape nanomaterials in such a way as to emit light, reflect light, or convert light into an electrical form or vice versa.

- The macroscopic properties of materials, including their optical and their mechanical properties, are a manifestation of what goes on at the nanometer-length scale.
  - o One way to understand this concept is to think about materials that are compositionally the same, but when you look at them in the periodic table, they have vastly different properties as a result of different confirmations, or ways in which they bind together.

  - o A good example of this is carbon, the basis for diamond. As we said, carbon can bind in a covalent manner, a way in which every carbon is satisfied. Diamond, of course, is an extremely hard material, and its hardness is symmetric in all directions because this binding occurs with a kind of spherical symmetry. Thus, there's no particular plane of vulnerability for diamond.

  - o Graphite is also made out of carbon, yet unlike diamond, it's soft and opaque. The explanation comes down to the nanoscale

Both graphite and diamond are carbon based; the differences in their properties can be explained by the nanoscale structure of each material—the way in which the carbon atoms are arranged.

structure, the way in which the carbon atoms are arrayed, that is, in planar sheets stacked on top of one another.

The Quantum World

- One of the exciting regimes in nanotechnology is the exploration of how we can use nanostructured materials and the quantum effects that emerge on these length scales to control the behavior of matter and, thus, create materials having custom or designer properties.

- In this field, there's an interesting class of materials called quantum dots that take advantage of the wavelike nature of atoms. To understand this wavelike behavior, we need to look at how an electron configures itself.

- In the quantum world, we no longer think of electrons as points, the way we looked at them in the beginning of this lecture. Just as we began thinking of photons as waves but then had to consider their quantum behavior, it's also true that we're inclined to think of electrons as particles, but they also have a spatial extent, on the scale of a couple of nanometers.

- An electron wave can be sort of a parabolic shape that's very smooth, but electrons can actually take on resonances with the materials they exist in and exhibit very complex, wavy structures.

- The visible photons we interact with as waves are measured in the hundreds of nanometers, but with electrons, we think of them as waves once we get down to the scale of a few nanometers. Quantum dots take advantage of the wavelike properties of matter.

- Consider a group of beakers filled with semiconductor particles all of the same underlying composition but glowing in different colors. The reason they exhibit different colors is that the particles are all of different sizes.
  o In the very small particles, the electron wave, which would like to be free, is confined; essentially, it's trapped in a very small box. As a result, its energy levels are elevated.

  o In the beakers that have larger nanoparticles, the electron wave is squeezed less and is able to occupy a lower energy level.

- The unavoidable wavelike nature of the electron leads to the idea of localization and the fact that we can tune material. It also leads to a curious phenomenon known as quantum tunneling.
  o To understand this phenomenon, consider how an electron would behave if it was thought of only as a particle. If an electron encountered a barrier and that barrier was of an energetic height that the electron could not climb over, then it would simply reflect back.

  o But in the world of waves, the electron isn't just a discrete particle; it has a spatial extent. Thus, when that electron arrives at the barrier, even if it doesn't have sufficient energy to overcome it, there's some probability that the electron will find itself on the far side of that structure.

- Conceiving of electrons as waves also gives us possibilities for different kinds of interactions with materials, such as partial transmission of a wave through a material and partial reflection of it.

- Quantum dots are actually another manifestation of our periodic table concept but another layer up. They allow nanotechnologists to build up a kind of periodic super-table, a new set of atom-like materials that go beyond the properties of their constituent atoms.

Suggested Reading

Callister and Rethwisch, *Materials Science and Engineering.*

Green, *Physics: Why Matter Matters!*

Nobelprize.org, "The Nobel Prize in Physics 1986."

Robinson, "Electron Microscope Inventors Share Nobel Physics Prize."

Questions to Consider

1. How is the world the same—just scaled down—when we enter the realm of the nanometer? How, on the other hand, are the rules of physics entirely transformed? What are the consequences of this new rulebook?

2. Are the colors as we see them—red, green, and blue—fundamentally distinctive from a physical standpoint, or is our definition of color a narrow and specific consequence of the particular way in which the human eye evolved? What forces prompted the human eye to evolve in this way?

The Fundamental Importance of Being Nano
Lecture 2—Transcript

Ted Sargent: This second lecture is our opportunity to venture into the laws, the rules that govern the world of the nanoscale, the physical principles, and the chemistry. It's also our chance to get reacquainted with the particles, the building blocks of the nanoworld, atoms and molecules that make materials, photons, light that conveys energy. It's our chance to think about how the properties of these materials—the way in which they bind, their shape, their structure influences how we experience them—how the nanoscopic translates into the macroscopic. Finally, it's our opportunity to think about some of the specific rules of the game are changed at the nanometer length scale, how quantum effects start to become important. They start to become something we can actually engineer with.

Let's start in on the materials and their constituents. Here's how we visualize an atom. It's an approximate picture and we'll go into more detail about the approximations and how to make this more precise. But to start with, we often just picture it like a planet with electrons orbiting it. The planet itself is the core, it's the nucleus of the atom, and it consists of a combination of protons having positive charge and neutrons which are neutral.

As nanotechnologists we often think of electrons as our building block. We think of atoms surrounded by electrons as the next layer up and we tend to focus on the electric fields and the magnetic fields that behave and so we're focused on these particular forces rather than what people refer to as the subatomic or subnuclear behaviors that reside in the field of particle physics. So we distill the behavior of electrons in this way, we distill the behavior of atoms in this fashion. What ends up mattering to us principally is the fact that the core of the nucleus has its positive charge that is attractive to the electrons having their negative charge.

Now the way in which the periodic table is formed maps on to this description of shells. We think of these satellites, these electrons that orbit the nucleus as being able to occupy one of a number of gradually increasing energy levels. They're able to fill up these regions where the electrons are allowed to orbit and depending on how full each of those shells is that will determine which column of the periodic table an atom resides in and the column of the periodic table that resides in, in turn determines the personality of that atom. Atoms or elements in the same column have quite similar chemical behaviors often. So for example in the first column, we have things like sodium and lithium that have a single electron in their outermost shell. That outermost shell, these valance electrons that populate this outermost shell, they're the key ones that relate to chemical reactivity so we pay most heed to them when we're thinking about materials being built up from such elements or atoms.

In the case of this first column, because atoms love to have their shells completed, those atoms that go around with one electron available to participate in bonding they represent an opportunity from the point of view of those atoms having a shell that's almost complete. So, table salt, sodium chloride consists of sodium having a single valance electron, chlorine having seven valance electrons. When they form a complete shell together, eight being complete, they're satisfied. Chemical bonding has occurred in a fashion that achieves stability.

Now the other thing to note about this example of bonding between something far on the left of the periodic table and something far on the right is that it's a very symmetric relationship. It's one that involves polarity. There's a preference for the movement of electrons in one direction or the other. It's called ionic bonding. There's another kind of bonding that is crucial and, in fact, is much stronger. It's a kind that occurs based on sharing. The kinds of atoms or elements that are most prone to this sharing or covalent bonding are those more in the middle of the periodic table. Here is where there are some very important materials that we'll see many times throughout this course, silicon is a great example, carbon is also in the middle of the periodic table in group four. Group four means that it has four electrons available to participate in bonding and it has got four missing in order to form a complete shell.

These materials that are sort of halfway through, they're going to form symmetric relationships with each other. For example, a silicon and a carbon lattice forms materials based on this very strong covalent force and based on sharing, and they form the shells that are extremely stable. If you look at the diamond lattice, every carbon atom will be participating in bonding with four nearest neighbors. Through that sharing with four nearest neighbors every one of them will feel complete; it will feel that it has its shell completed.

We'll invoke these ideas from the periodic table relating to the feeling of completeness by atoms, the propensities they have to pair with one another throughout this course. The bonding of atoms with one another is obviously one of the central tenets from which we build up materials. So far though when we talk about things like diamond or silicon, that crucially important electronic semiconductor material, we're thinking of almost infinite arrays of atoms, periodically arrayed forming a very systematic behavior that's common throughout the entire solid. When we think about those materials as well, we will eventually arrive at an interface. They're not infinite materials; eventually a piece of silicon will have an end to it. It will have an interface, and there we'll become very concerned with the management of that interface.

Another way to say that is that these materials that rely on this long distance periodicity and coherence when we do reach an interface we have to manage the interface. They're not a self-contained material. In contrast with that, molecules are combinations of atoms where the binding amongst the atoms is completely satisfying to that structure. It's a self-contained structure. There's of course many famous molecules that we're very well acquainted with, water, H_2O is one of them, oxygen in the air we breathe is in fact molecular oxygen, O_2 where the two oxygen's can satisfy one another in a nice strongly bound pair. Some of the next larger molecules that we'll discuss throughout this course—things like DNA and proteins, the sugars that make up our bodies, the sugars that are generated as a consequence of the process of photosynthesis—these are all the molecules that achieve these relatively stable confirmations. Things like Buckyballs and Buckytubes are also these structures that are satisfied with their bindings within themselves.

Now we've spoken about the building blocks of matter. We've spoken about things that have appreciable mass. What about energy, how is it conveyed? We'll start in on this discussion of energy, color, and spectrum from a wave perspective, from a point of view of electromagnetic radiation as a picture for light. But then we'll also realize that there's more to the picture of light than just this classical picture, this wave picture and then we also need to start thinking within the vocabulary of photons, particles of light.

Well let's start and just see what we can get out of this wave picture. The wave picture of photons of electromagnetic radiation has an oscillation of an electric field and of a magnetic field. In fact, if we think of a single, pure color, I'll call that monochromatic light and the electric shield oscillates with the defined period in space and in time. That period in space is referred to as the wavelength. So let's take a couple of examples. The visible light that we can see with our own eyes, this has wavelengths characteristically in the range of 400 to about 650 or 700 nanometers. So it's measured in the nanometers, but it's getting close to the micrometer length scale.

That property of visible light ends up being very important because it turns out that a wave is difficult to condense or shrink down to a length scale that's smaller than its own wavelength. We're able to maybe tie the two ends of a string down at a spacing of a wavelength or a half a wavelength, but we're not able to do much better than that. So the wavelength of an electromagnetic wave will determine how well you can focus it down and so if you think of using a traditional optical microscope to try to look at something well you can see cells with it, biological cells that are 10 micrometers in size. You can even see bacteria that are perhaps a few micrometers in size. It's much more difficult to see a virus that can be as small as 100 nanometers in size. That's really starting to get to the limits of what you can see using visible wavelength light.

But the word visible wavelength isn't a comment on a fundamental quality of light itself. It's actually about the colors that we are particularly attuned to see. Because the Sun is at a very elevated temperature, it has a very strong emission in the visible wavelength range and our eyes are adapted to make very good use of those wavelengths. But it runs out that one can go very, very far to longer wavelengths or much farther to shorter wavelengths is incredibly broad electromagnetic spectrum. So for example we call visible light visible light but to a snake the light that many pythons can see is actually infrared lights. It corresponds to much longer wavelengths than what you and I sense and that's actually very useful to them because infrared radiation is more of a signature of heat and so snakes are able to sense vulnerable regions of their prey based on their infrared or thermal signatures.

We can go far in the other directions towards shorter wavelengths as we go to shorter wavelengths. Now if we're using light as a tool to carve matter or if we're using it as a tool to investigate structure such as through a microscope well in that case we're able to see with much finer spatial resolution For example, with ultraviolet light we're able to define structures using images projected using ultraviolet light much better, much more finely using UV rays than we are able to do with visible light and that gets even more true as we go into the regime of X-rays.

Now we've spoken about light as a wave and that is a very useful concept as well, but Einstein is famous for many discoveries and many insights, but one of them is his ability to explain a simple, but hither to mysterious experiment called the photoelectric effect. An explanation that Einstein provided that invoked a particle-like quality to light, something where it was a packet, a unit of energy and this photoelectric effect that Einstein was trying to explain, it was based on experiments that had been done prior to his coming along and thinking about their interpretation. The experiment was the following. It involved having a metal, one could use various different types of metal, and illuminating it with different colors of electromagnetic spectrum and what had been observed in the photoelectric effect is that for longer wavelengths there was essentially no emission of electrons from this metal upon photo excitation so there was no photoelectric effect.

Once one went to short enough wavelengths and the exact wavelength depended on the metal, but once one went to a short enough wavelength one produced the generation or the emission of a large number of electrons and the intensity of that collection of electrons that photo current went in proportion with the light intensity when one was above this threshold, when one was at a short enough wavelength, but for the longer wavelengths it really didn't matter how hard you hit the material with light. It essentially didn't emit at all and Einstein was able to provide a simple and elegant explanation that has very much stood the test of time since he proposed this in 1905 and won his Noble Prize for it in 1921.

In the explanation was that there was a certain energy that that electron needed to be elevated by to escape from the metal, and that only those photons of a short enough wavelength contained sufficient individual energy. He started to think of the photons as quanta or as packets of energy and there was a direct relationship, an inverted relationship, between their wavelength and their energy so the long wavelength ones had insufficient quantized energy available to induce the emission of an electron from this metal whereas those of the short wavelengths had a greater quantum of energy that was able to kick that electron out of the metal.

This then brings us to this additional dimension or this additional property of photons that we need to pay careful heed to. When we use thermal imaging or when the snake sees in the dark, we're actually dealing with very low energy photons. That's consistent with the fact that instead of being produced by the very hot Sun which produces higher energy photons in the visible, we when we're doing thermal imaging when we're say looking at a warm person against a colder background, we're actually looking at much lower energy photons corresponding to those that are realistically emitted by somebody who's just a little bit above room temperature, just a little bit above the temperature of their background.

Moving to a slightly higher energy are the visible photons, the visible wavelengths, and then just beyond that the ultraviolet. Ultraviolet rays are familiar to us because they're arriving on Earth, they're emitted by the Sun, and we're concerned about their effects on us, their correlation with skin cancer. Well the reason why ultraviolet rays are much more prone to promote skin cancer than visible wavelength rays are is because of their added energy. They're more likely to interact with DNA or proteins, various potentially reactive species in our bodies and result in the excitation of an electron that can lead to a new reaction. It can lead to a confirmation change or a chemical change inside one of our cells. Here to the energy aspect of light becomes very important and is central to explaining why ultraviolet rays are really qualitatively different from the way visible ones are.

Then if we move further still to higher energies, we get into the X-ray regime, familiar of course in medical imaging. In the case of X-rays, these are considerably more energetic. They can have a thousand times the energy for X-ray photon compared to what we see in the visible or even more than that. One of the consequences is that X-ray detectors that are used now especially in digital X-ray, digital mammography, are able to collect thousands of electrons worth of current for every photon incident upon them. This is just a testament to the huge amount of energy contained in the X-rays and the good news about that is that you can therefore get away with using a relatively small dose or a small abundance of X-rays when we perform medical imaging.

I'd like to spend a moment now to think about the connection between materials and light, because much of our discussions in this course will relate to how we can shape the nanomaterials in such a way as to emit light, reflect light, convert light into an electrical form, or vice versa. It's interesting to note that some of the earliest nanotechnologists were simply making stained glass, long before one thought in terms of nanotechnology. Thousands of years ago, people—artisans—were mixing a paste together and forming red versus yellow stained glass where the red versus yellow was determined as a consequence of different metal particles of different sizes that were included in the stained glass. These different sizes of particles were able to support different resonances on them. Today, we call this effect plasmonics. It refers to the idea that waves related to electromagnetic waves can be supported resonantly on a structure that fits that wavelength nicely whereas if there's a lack of a resonance there will be no particularly strong interaction between the metal particle and the wave. So, stained glass is one of these early manifestations of the interaction between material and electromagnetic waves and resonances that occur at the nanoscale.

It's important, as we were discussing earlier, to think about how materials macroscopic properties beyond just their visible, their optical properties, but also their mechanical properties are a manifestation of what goes on at the nanometer length scale. One way to get at this concept is to think about materials that actually are compositionally the same when you look at them in the periodic table that have vastly different properties as a result of different confirmations or ways in which they bind together. A really good example of this is carbon. Carbon, group 4, remember the periodic table the basis for diamond, can bind in this covalent manner that we were describing earlier, in which every carbon is satisfied. It has got a bond up and three down in symmetric tetrahedral form. Diamond, of course, is an extremely hard material and its hardness is symmetric in all directions so because this binding occurs kind of with a spherical symmetry, there's no particular plane of vulnerability for diamond. It's strong essentially in all directions.

Now graphite is also made out of carbon. Graphite is what's misnamed pencil lead, but it's the basis for how we write with pencils. It's also carbon based, and constitutionally it's built up of the same elements as diamond—and yet it's so incredibly different. It's so soft and it's opaque instead of being clear; we can't see through. How can that be? Well the effect does come down to the nanoscale structure the way in which the carbon atoms are arrayed. In the case of graphite the carbon atoms bond together in the plane. They form little hexagonal regions. They have three nearest neighbors instead of four within the plane. Then these planar sheets stack up on top of each other and the interactive forces amongst the sheets are much weaker in the stacked or vertical direction than they are within the plane.

It's very easy whereas internally these graphene sheets are quite robust. They can slide past each other. There's nothing really keeping them from translating relative to each other. Essentially we have a sloughing off, a flaking off of these graphene sheets that occurs in graphite so now the material properties are very directional and that arises from the very different behavior, a very different confirmation, of these materials in the plane compared to out of the plane. In fact, graphene is a nice example; carbon's a nice example as well, for many of the building blocks of nanomaterials. Bucky balls, which are little soccer balls of carbon bonded together. Bucky tubes, which are these nanotubes, are in graphene itself, the planar sheet but now at a single layer, they're all materials of great interest in nanotechnology that we'll spend quite a bit of time on in this course.

Another thing to think about in graphene is that its electronic and optical properties are so different from diamond. Diamond is this transparent material, which is related to the fact that its bonding is so strong. There are very few low energy transitions available to it so it doesn't absorb low energy or even medium energy photons like visible ones. We need to go well into the ultraviolet to excite a transition within diamond and therefore to have optical absorption. Whereas in graphite, graphene, and related materials, these are in fact essentially conductors and they have an abundance of electrons available to participate in the process of electronic flow and also to participate in the process of optical absorption at a wide range of wavelengths.

We've alluded to the fact that quantum effects play a major role in the behavior of nanomaterials and that there is something that we need to understand. In fact, one of the exciting regimes within nanotechnology is to explore how we can use nano-structured materials and the quantum effects that emerge on these length scales in order to control the behavior of matter, to create materials having new custom or designer properties. Here there's an interesting class of materials called quantum dots that take advantage of these properties of the wavelike nature of atoms. But to spend a moment just to understand this wavelike behavior, we should just take some time to look at how an electron actually configures itself.

In the quantum world, we no longer can think of electrons just as points the way we were trying to depict them in this cartoon at the beginning of this lecture. We're trying to think of them as very small point satellites orbiting their nucleus. But, in fact, quantum mechanics and in general the concept of wave particle duality tells us that just as we began thinking of photons as waves, but then we had to consider their quantum behavior. It's also true for electrons which we're inclined to think of as points, we're inclined to think of as particles, well they also have a spatial extent and that spatial extent is on the scale of a couple of nanometers.

Take a look at this picture of the distribution of electron wave. It can be a very simple one. It can just be sort of a parabolic shape that's very smooth, but electrons can actually take on resonances with the materials that they exist in, they can take on very complex wavy structures. The thing to remember about electrons is that whereas with photons it's their wavelength, say for the visible ones in the hundreds of nanometers that we're interacting with where we have to really think of them as waves, with electrons we need to think of them as waves once we get down to the scale of a few nanometers. Quantum dots are an example of some particles in a class of semiconductor materials that we'll definitely see a few times throughout this course that are leveraging, are taking advantage of the wavelike properties of matter.

You see here a bunch of beakers filled with semiconductor particles all of the same underlying composition. They all have the same elements inside them, but you can see that they're all glowing different colors. The reason for that is that these particles are all of different sizes. The ones on the left are 2 nanometers in diameter. The ones on the right are 5 nanometers in diameter and the ones in between are sizes in between. What happens in the very small particles is that we've confined this electron wave which would like to be free. It would like to be delocalized. It would like to expand its territory within the semiconductor, but we've confined it by making a very small particle, essentially a box into which we've trapped the electron. As a result, we've pushed up its energy levels.

On the right-most beaker, we have these nanoparticles that are considerably larger. We're squeezing our electron wave less and it's able to occupy a lower energy level as a result of that. Using these quantum effects, leveraging the wavelike properties of matter, we've found a way to engineer or make a tunable semiconductor. These quantum properties of materials, the unavoidable wavelike nature of the electron, it leads to this idea of localization and the fact that we can tune the material in this fashion. It also leads to a very curious phenomenon that's known as quantum tunneling.

Quantum tunneling can be described first by saying how would an electron behave if it was only to be thought of as a particle. Well if an electron were coming along and it were just a particle and it would see a wall or a barrier, and that barrier was of an energetic height that the electron could not climb over, then it would simply reflect back. Now, in the world of waves though, this electron isn't just a discrete particle, it has a spatial extent and when that electron arrives at this boundary even if it doesn't have sufficient energy to overcome it, there's some probability that the electron will find itself on the far side of that structure. It would be more like electromagnetic wave seeing say a piece of glass at a particular angle and having some chance of making it through, some being reflected, but some of it making it through. So, the same wavelike phenomena start to occur for electrons and so we have these confinement ideas, like the plasmonics for photons we have electron confinement inside a quantum dot.

We also have these possibilities of different kinds of interactions with materials. Partial transmission of a wave through a material and partial reflection of it and these are things that we see when we get down to the quantum length scale. They're properties of electrons that we only need to heed, we only need to pay attention to, once we get down to this scale. You know, the other really intriguing thing about these quantum dots is that they actually are another manifestation of our periodic table concept, but now another layer up. It's not the atoms themselves that now in these quantum dots is periodic table like, but once we put them together we make the semiconductor having a single set of fundamental properties, but then we change the size. It's like scanning across or down the periodic table where we change the energies we change the amount of pull that the electrons see keeping them confined. Just the way when we change the number of protons in the nucleus of a given atom or element we change the potential that it sees and as a consequence of this people refer to quantum dots as artificial atoms. They're an analogy with the periodic table. What they allow nanotechnologists to do is to build up a kind of periodic super-table—a new set of atom-like materials that go beyond the properties of their constituent atoms and that add another layer of complexity, another layer of tailoring or engineering.

To finish this lecture, we'll just review some of the concepts that we'll use throughout this course—also, some of the ideas that we'll use. One of the central tenets, really, is that the behavior of the macroscopic world around us, even if it's not typically nanometer-scale in which we think of ourselves as interacting with the world—objects are hard, they're heavy, they have certain colors—that in fact, their properties do emerge from the nanoscale. Their morphology, the ways in which atoms are arrayed at the nanoscale, the bonding amongst these atoms, whether there's a directional nature to that bonding, an alignment, whether these materials have shape—these underlying nanoscale properties all influence the macroscopic behaviors.

In addition, there are nano-specific concepts that we need to pay attention to when we're engineering within the quantum world. In fact, this is where a great deal of the opportunity for nanoscale engineering lays. Concepts like: the confinement of electron waves, the fact that electron waves can tunnel through a structure, which classically it would not be able to do; the fact that electrons are delocalized in semiconductors; the fact that they form waves that can propagate, convey electrical information, electrical energy; and then also the fact that in nanostructured materials we have an abundance of surfaces. These are all concepts and they're all tools that we'll be using to engineer at the nanoscale.

From Micro to Nano—Scaling in a Digital World
Lecture 3

This lecture looks at nanotechnology through the lens of the computer revolution. We've talked from a basic point of view about electrons flowing and controlling one another. Here, we'll see that electronics and computers are really about electrons controlling other electrons and, of course, our capacity to design integrated circuits that control, program, and take advantage of that behavior. We'll also see the top-down progression of developments in electronics, from the macroscopic scale, to the microscale, to the nanoscale.

ENIAC: The First General-Purpose Computer

- The Electronic Numerical Integrator and Computer (ENIAC) was designed in World War II to enable the U.S. Army to perform rapid calculations for launching artillery. It was the first general-purpose electronic computer, meaning that it could be reprogrammed to perform other functions besides calculation.

- The way the ENIAC was programmed wasn't the way we think of programming today. It wasn't with software but with specific plugs and electrical connections.

- One feature that's common to the ENIAC and computers today is the fact that they both work via electronics, that is, electrons controlling other electrons. In fact, the basis for digital computing (which uses 1s and 0s to represent information) is this: a current flowing between 2 electrodes and a 3rd electrode, either a current or a voltage, to steer the current around—to turn it on and off.

- If you can control that current flow not just with 0s and 1s—not just either on or off—but to intermediate phases, then you have the basis for analog computing, a kind of continuous electronics that allows variation. With analog electronics, if you can change the control signal just a bit and get a large change in the current, then you have amplification.

Vacuum Tubes

- A vacuum tube looks like a light bulb, and it has something in common with a light bulb: Inside it is a vacuum. The vacuum is necessary to allow the free flow of electrons without interference from air molecules.

- If we heat up 1 of the electrodes in a vacuum tube, enough energy becomes available to result in the emission of an electron. This phenomenon is called thermionic emission. Then, with the aid of an electrical field, electrons can flow freely through the vacuum. But this is just establishing the current; we don't have electrons controlling electrons yet.

The vacuum tube, the basis for early computers, offers the perfect environment for the free flow of electrons.

- Where the control comes in is with the 3rd electrode, which can control independently whether or not the current flows. Think of it as being in the perpendicular direction. Conceivably, we can turn on or off the flow of current using this 3rd electrode without having to invest much electrical current. That's the key to amplification: to have just a touch of a modulation on the control side that has a big impact on the flow of current.

- Of course, we can easily imagine the problems of running a computer based on something similar to a light bulb: They frequently burn out.

Transistors

- The field of transistor electronics was born of the desire to take advantage of the best properties of the vacuum tube—the free flow of electrons and control over that flow—but get beyond this reliability issue and a size issue. In the first transistors, the electronic current didn't flow through a vacuum but within a semiconductor.

- Think about a crystal of silicon. It is a perfect array of atoms, completely ordered and completely periodic. Now, think about an electron as a wave. A semiconductor uses the idea of commensurability, meaning that the wave of the electron can follow perfectly the wave of silicon atoms. The electron wave can be delocalized and ubiquitous.

- Now, without having to establish a perfect vacuum and use large tubes that have reliability issues, we are able—through the structure of semiconductors, through their crystallinity—to achieve an "everywhereness" in the electrons. That's the key element that was taken from the vacuum tube and translated into the solid state.

- From a chemical standpoint, unless we take special steps to manage the interface, silicon is not perfect at the surface of the interface. But silicon has a special property, which is that it will form what's called the native oxide (SiO_2—glass) when oxygen or water is introduced on top of it. This oxide forms a very clean interface on the surface of the silicon.

The Breadboard versus Integrated Circuits

- Of course, a single transistor is not a basis for computing. It must be connected to other transistors on a breadboard. Unfortunately, with a breadboard, you often get wires in the wrong places, which means you have to debug the circuits. This technology is also not conveniently or cost-effectively scalable. This is where the integrated circuit comes in.

- The term "monolithic integration" makes sense in this context because the innovation involves carving many transistors into the same "rock," the crystalline piece of silicon. Typically, the transistors are just copies of one another that are connected with wiring on the 2-dimensional chip.

- The process for connecting transistors on a chip involves using a shadow mask, but this technology doesn't even get us down to the micrometer-length scale.
  - To do this, we use photolithography. Here, the mask is optically transparent in certain regions and opaque in other regions. Light projected through a lens interacts with photoresist on the wafer and forms a template for wiring or for selectively altering the properties of the silicon.

  - This lithography process enables the manufacture of incredibly scalable integrated circuits.

- One of the inevitable needs of the electronic sector is to make integrated circuits that are faster, use less power, and are more sophisticated and complex. To meet these needs and keep size under control, it's necessary to make smaller and smaller transistors.

- Of course, photolithography uses photons, which are waves, and as we said, it's impossible to confine light onto something smaller than about its own wavelength. The march forward of lithography is also the march to shorter and shorter wavelengths, from invisible, to ultraviolet, to X-ray.

- How do we ensure reliability of these circuits? As you may know, they are built in clean rooms, which minimizes the possibility that dust or particles will contaminate the transistors.
  - Today, to build a clean room costs $3 or $4 billion. For this reason, the foundry model has emerged, which allows outside organizations to pay for the use of clean room facilities to build custom circuits.

  - The foundry model is also called the fabulous model because it allows the leveraging of existing fabrication facilities.

Moore's Law

- The trend toward the smaller and smaller—what Feynman called the race to the bottom—has been described by Moore's law, an observation made by Gordon Moore, one of the founders of Intel.

- Moore said that between 1958 and 1965, there had been a doubling of what could be put onto an integrated circuit of a given size. An integrated circuit that could accommodate twice as many transistors enabled a circuit, a computer, that was twice as sophisticated and complex every 2 years.

- Moore's law can be used to describe how the integrated circuit revolution took place: We've gone from discrete elements, where we put tens of transistors onto a breadboard, to being able to put billions of transistors onto a chip. Further, it's possible to do this for costs that are measured in just a few dollars per chip.

- What we've discussed in this lecture is the precursor to the nanorevolution, but in fact, through Moore's law, we are now right up against the nanometer. We now have the capacity to use shorter wavelengths of light, through photolithography, to make transistors smaller and smaller. Inevitably, this puts us at the cusp of the nanoscale.

- In our next lecture, we'll look at what happens when we start to build transistors on the scale of the nanometer. As we continue this tremendous legacy of Moore's law, we'll find that we are doing so in a new physical regime, a regime where we encounter quantum effects.

Suggested Reading

Brock, ed., *Understanding Moore's Law.*

Ceruzzi, *A History of Modern Computing.*

Wikipedia, "History of Computing Hardware."

1. Moore's law refers to the remarkable forward march of integrated circuit/microprocessor speed, complexity, power, and cost-effectiveness over time. Can you think of examples of other fields in which a 40-year exponential growth curve has been sustained? Why is the field of the integrated circuit so distinctive in its ability to sustain such dramatic improvements over so many cycles of innovation?

2. What are the similarities and differences between vacuum tube and semiconductor transistors? Why was one down-scalable and integrable and the other not?

From Micro to Nano—Scaling in a Digital World
Lecture 3—Transcript

Ted Sargent: Let's talk about nanotechnology through the lens of the electronics revolution, of the computer revolution. Why is that a sensible thing to do? Why does that make sense? Well we've talked from a really basic point of view about electrons flowing and controlling one another. I'll make the case that electronics and computers are really about electrons controlling other electrons and of course our capacity to design integrated circuits, chips, that control program and take advantage of that. I'll also show in this first of two lectures on electronics and computers that the march forward for electronics since its advent in the 1950s and '60s has been taking us from kind of the macroscopic to the micrometer, to the millionth of the meter. Then in the second lecture, I'll show that the march that electronics is marching along is now well into the nanometer.

When you talk about electronics today, you're talking about nanotechnology. There's nanotechnology inside your computer and in your cell phone and in your digital camera. The final point is that the technologies that have enabled us to get down to this nanoscale; they were the ones that took us first to the microscale. They were the basis for carving matter on the scale first of the micrometer and then the nanometer. These are platform technologies for what we call top down nanotechnology. They are the basis for our ability to manipulate matter the way we need to for nanotechnology.

First, in this lecture, we'll speak about going from the macroworld around us to the scale of the micrometer and how that relates to building computers. First though, let's just look back at some old pictures that I think many of us have seen about computers like the ENIAC, which stood for the electronic numerical integrator and computer. ENIAC was the first general purpose electronic computer. What does that mean general purpose? Well it meant that it could be reprogrammed so it wasn't something that was only a calculator, only did a specific set of arithmetic operations. You could use it to solve a whole bunch of different problems.

Now, it was actually designed for a fairly specific purpose so it was in World War II and the United States Army needed to be able to rapidly calculate how to launch artillery. This was for its ballistic research laboratory and so in 1943 in a secret agreement it started off with the University of Pennsylvania's electrical engineering school on building this general purpose computer, building this ENIAC, if you adjust the dollar figure to today's values costs about $6 million dollars. I think impressively it came going in continuous operation from 1947 to 1955, so getting on for ten years. How many computers do you have that you have continuously used for eight or ten years without them going obsolete and you upgrading to another one? I think that's impressive that the ENIAC had such a long useful life.

I mentioned this idea of general purpose computer, but the way the ENIAC was programmed wasn't the way we think of programming today. It wasn't with software. It was actually with specific plugs and electrical connections and wires connecting with each other. That idea of a reprogrammable via a stored program which is software idea actually was exploited a little bit after ENIAC and I think that's kind of interesting to think back to there was a day, there was a time when we didn't think of the world of computing as having hardware on top of which software ran, but that itself was a new idea.

How do computer like ENIAC work? How did the original ones work? Well the founding feature that's common to ENIAC and is common to what's in your computer and your cell phone today is as I was saying what we call electronics, which really is electrons controlling other electrons. Why is that a basis for computation or analysis or computing or arithmetic? Well, if you think of one simple component and I'll start with the vacuum tube than we'll move on to transistors, start with the vacuum tube, if you have a current that can flow between two points, between two electrodes, and if you can use a third, either a current or a voltage, but some kind of other electrode to steer that current around, to turn it on and off, well then you have the basis for digital computing where the world is filled with 1s and 0s and with 1s and 0s we can accurately represent information over huge swaths of dynamic range.

If you can control that current flow not just with 0s and 1s—not just a complete on and off—but if you can control it to intermediate phases, then you have the basis for what we called analog, a kind of continuous electronics where you can vary these different levels. Well that second phenomena, the analog electronics, if I can change the control signal just a bit and I can get a large change in the current well then I have amplification. The history of computing is really intimately tied to the original discoveries like Lee De Forest's work, which allowed electronic amplification because then you take a radio signal as was done then and you can amplify it so you can pick weak link signals just out of the air and then turn them into an audio signal, in this case, that you can listen to. This field of the analog and the field of the digital, at least, are the two primordial bases of electronics, but in a way they're sort of using the same building blocks, these vacuum tubes initially which then evolved into the transistors, which we'll talk about in a second, one of them uses them in this sort of continuously varying mode and then the other is the on and the off.

Okay so let's go to the vacuum tubes. I think these pictures of vacuum tubes are familiar. When we were looking ENIAC we saw all of these sort of panels with periodic arrangements of things and those were the vacuum tubes. It kind of looks like a light bulb and it has something in common with the light bulb, which is that inside it is a vacuum. Now for this controlling of the flow of electrons why do we need a vacuum? Well the answer is that if we didn't have a vacuum, if we had air, then electrons trying to flow in the form of a current would basically run into the molecules that make up the air. They'd collide and so we'd lose our current. We'd need to apply vastly more voltage than otherwise in order to get a sufficient current to flow.

Inside the vacuum tube we have the perfect environment for the free flow of electrons. We just heat up in a vacuum tube one of the electrodes and enough energy is now available from thermal energy to result in the emission of an electron. The phenomenon is called thermionic emission, the "therm" being the temperature, the thermal. Then with the aid of an electrical field these electrons can really scream through this vacuum without any impediment because of a lack of anything else present. Now that's just a start; that's not something that has electrons controlling electrons yet, that's just establishing the current.

Where the control comes in is with this third electrode, which can control independently whether that current flows. Think of it as being kind of in the perpendicular direction. I will turn on or off the flow of that current using a third electrode conceivably without having to really invest much electrical current or very much electrical power at all. That's the key to amplification is to have just a touch of a modulation on the control side have a big impact on the flow of current.

We talked about how the vacuum was necessary. It led to the free flow of electrons. But, you can easily picture and you already know the problems with the computer based on kind of a bunch of light bulbs. I mean they're all going to be burning out and if there's thousands of light bulbs or thousands of vacuum tubes making up the computer, at any given time the things going to be down as a result of one of the vacuum tubes has gone off and that's exactly what happened and that was exactly one of the problems.

Really the field of transistor electronics, of semiconductor electronics, was born of the desire to take advantage of the best properties of the vacuum tube, which is this free flow of electrons and its enablement of control over that flow, but get beyond this reliability issue, get beyond the size issue, scale things down. This picture is showing one of the very first transistors and here the electronic current didn't flow through a vacuum, it flowed within the semiconductor, and that's the first function of the semiconductor. Let's think about a crystal of silicon. It's this perfect, a perfect pure array of atoms, they're completely ordered, they're completely periodic.

Now think of the electron. We spoke about how it's actually a wave. We don't usually think of it that way. We picture sometimes as a pointer, as a particle, but it's actually a wave. Within a semiconductor, we can have an idea of what's called commensurability and this means that the wave of the electron can follow perfectly the wave of silicon atoms. You can have a silicon atom, a silicon atom, and there's another silicon atom and you can have commensurable flow of this electron wave. It can be delocalized as we were speaking about with ways it can be ubiquitous. It can be everywhere and so now without having to establish this perfect vacuum and make this large tube that has these reliability issues, we're able through the perfection, through the order, through the structure of semiconductors, through their purity, through their crystallinity, we're able to achieve the same "everywhereness" in the electrons.

That's this key element that we took, the learning from the vacuum tube filled and that we managed to translate into the solid state so when we talk about solid state electronics we're talking about going from this evacuated phase, the vacuum, and we're talking about translating the good stuff from that into a solid state device that we can then also start to make many of and we can make them a lot smaller. Before we talk about making them a lot smaller, there's something crucial and it was a crucial discovery in the field of electronics and it was only when we figured out how to manage the interfaces of these materials so the connection between say a piece of silicon or a piece of germanium as a lot of the early work was done in, the connection between that and the outside world, which of course we refer to as the surface of the interface, here not all the silicon atoms are happy right. They talked about how in diamond or in silicon the carbon or the silicon atoms respectively see four nearest neighbors. Well that's perfectly true right inside the bulk of this semiconductor, but at the interface one of these silicon atoms could see nothingness above it.

From a chemical standpoint, unless we take special steps to manage the interface, silicon is not perfect right at its interface; nor is any semiconductor. Now, silicon it turns out has this very special property, which is that when you take a interface of silicon with the rest of the world and you just let it oxidize, you let it form SiO_2, which is glass, and you do it at the right temperatures and you do it in the right humidity, you can form this oxide, we call it the native oxide because it's exactly what silicon forms when you introduce oxygen or water on top of it. You can form this oxide that forms a very clean interface and so now these silicon atoms that are mostly satisfied in the bottoms, but they have this one bond hanging up, that bond can be satisfied through the formation of this native oxide. That's also really easy to make. That's very convenient because of oxidation and we just need to put things in the right environment and we grow this native oxide on the surface of the silicon.

What we've talked about here and what's in this picture is a single transistor. Of course, that's not a basis for computing this discrete transistor. We need to connect it together at least with some other transistors. There's going to be wiring involved, right. There's going to be points of connection involved. Well okay let's connect together a couple of transistors. Here's what an undergrad electrical engineer still builds today, it's called a bread board and it's got a bunch of these individual transistors, each one of these blue things and black things is a transistor typically with three terminals and this bread board allows for a relatively convenient connection and you can put resistors in it as well. Every electrical engineer and I'm an undergraduate electrical engineer, I remember suffering through this in third year in our electronics course and we build these circuits by actually jabbing these little discrete transistor elements into this board and then putting wires and resistors and connecting them all together.

About how many of these can you put together until you go crazy, 10, 20, 30, maybe 40 if you're lucky. Most of the time you've got a wire in the wrong place and it doesn't work and you've got to debug your circuit and so it's what we now would say with the insights of the integrated circuit revolution. It's what we would now call not a scalable solution. It's not something where if you come up with a good idea to make a circuit based on the manageable 30 transistors and then the next day you say wow if I could take two of those circuits and combine them or four or 16 of them and combine them, I could make a parallel computer that could do 16 times more computations. It's 16 times more work and so it's not conveniently or in a cost-effective way scalable technology and so that's where the integrated circuit comes in.

We use the word monolithic integration and the monolithic makes sense. It's one rock where we're making one piece of semiconductor now and people found out in the '50s and the '60s how they could carve many transistors into the same rock. The rock is a crystalline piece of silicon; it's a large piece of silicon. It's a large substrate and what we needed was as well as the ability to make many of these transistors, typically they're actually essentially all the same as each other. We're just making many copies, many repeats of the same thing. It's like you're taking a potato carving image out of it and then just repeating it many times. We then also have to connect them and so what we needed was a path to build many transistors and then systematically connect them and of course reliably connect them with each other.

That wiring on a 2-dimensional substrate that's fairly readily done once we first define how we put these transistors down and where we locate them relative to each other then we'll connect them with a bunch of wires, say for example and we do this all the time. You can imagine having a mask that we call a shadow mask where you cut holes in it and you allow a metal, you heat a metal up, and you allow it to evaporate and it only penetrates through the holes and it doesn't penetrate where it's obscured and so you can form interconnect, you can form layers of connectivity. You can make wires on your 2-dimensional chip and your wires can now connect together all of your transistors.

Let's take a little bit of look here at how we do this. That shadow mass technology, it's a start and actually do it in my own lab at University when we're trying to do course connections and many of them, it's a great way to do things and you can go and carve out that mask yourself, but it's not going to get you down even to the micrometer length scale. The technology that we use to get down to the micrometer and somewhat beyond is called photolithography and in photolithography instead of just taking that mask and sticking it right up against your wafer you have a mask whose purpose is to be optically transparent in certain regions and to be opaque in the other regions. Then you project light through a lens and you project it down onto the wafer, onto the substrate, the silicon that you're going to go build your transistors on.

You essentially just put an image of your mask onto that wafer. Now, what does that light have to do with anything? Well on that wafer, at every stage is something we call the photo resist and it's really just like photographic film. It's something where you expose this material and if it sees light than when you put it later in a developer's solution like what fashioned pre-digital photography, it washes away. But, if it wasn't exposed to light it goes in the same developer, but it doesn't develop. It hasn't had this photocatalytic reaction occur, it will stay intact. Now what you've done is you've formed a template on your silicon wafer that allows you to do quite a number of different possible things. One of the things you can do if you want to make wires is you evaporate that metal on here and then you subsequently wash away the remaining photoresist and where the metal made direct contact with a semiconductor it sticks and where it was just sitting on this soluble, removable photoresist you lift it off.

What if you wanted to build a transistor? Well the building blocks of transistor construction involve taking the silicon crystals and putting controlled levels of impurity, very low concentrations of impurities in there. You can use this mask that you've made and you can introduce impurities onto the surface of your silicon and if they're in direct contact with the silicon surface they'll diffuse in through that surface into the silicon and where you have a mask that blocks their contact, their interaction with the interface, they don't and so you can selectively alter the properties of your silicon from on top. This lithography process that is done using photons today, using light, is the basis for being able to make incredibly scalable integrated circuits.

One of the inevitable needs of the electronic sector is we're hungry as consumers, as soon as we get something we want something even better and so there's this desire to scale, to make things more integrated, to make integrated circuits that are faster, that use less power, that are more sophisticated, more complex that can process a huge image, a huge and complex image and can process it so fast that you can't even tell when you're interacting with your computer that billions of operations had to happen. Well how do we do that and keep size under control? It involves making the transistors smaller and smaller with every generation. To make them smaller and smaller, you can see where this is going. If we're using photons, which are waves, which have extent then eventually we're going to sort of run out of steam there because as we said before we're not going to be able to confine that focal point of light onto something smaller than about the wavelength of the light that we're working with.

The march forward of lithography is also the march to shorter and shorter wavelengths. It's gone from being invisible to in the ultraviolet, to deeper into the ultraviolet, and there's even work on X-ray lithography today. Here our understanding of waves and wavelengths and the ability to focus them is key to understanding the technological march of photolithography as we move to shorter and shorter wavelengths to more and more energetic particles as we do so.

How do we build these circuits in a way that's reliable? I mean let's think about the number of transistors that we have to put down. Today, it's in the billions in one these integrated circuits. Well perhaps you've seen a picture of somebody working in a clean room as they're called. Obviously the purpose here is to minimize dust and particles because a little piece of dust that lands on one of our transistors in one region of this big wafer containing many integrated circuits and all of a sudden that integrated circuit has a chance of not working.

In clean rooms, the pictures you will have seen have people wearing what we call bunny suits, technical term, and they're covered head to toe. You can't see who it is or if it's a man or a woman. They have little slippers on that are disposable slippers and these allow all the little bits of dust, little bacterial, little viral particles, people are very dirty. They allow us to minimize the extent to which these particles get released into the room and potentially onto your wafer. In fact, the latest generations of clean room technologies try to just minimize the extent to which there's people in there at all, try to do everything as much by robotic operation of moving these wafers around where everything can be just kept in this completely pure and clean environment.

You know, for my own Ph.D. I used to go into a clean room at Cornell. It was called Cornell Nanofabrication Facility and there and at every clean room, if you wanted to write your notes or write in the lab you'd have a special lab book or a special notebook, a kind of paper that doesn't slough of little bits of dust, but that's allowed for use in a clean room because it's essentially dust free paper. That's how sensitive we are to these kinds of issues.

Given this complexity, given that we're talking about these rooms with incredible environmental control with control over temperatures, with control over humidity, these are very costly things to build. In fact, today to build a clean room in which we can build the latest generations of integrated circuits costs $3–4 billion dollars. The number of these places where we build integrated circuits is actually very small now and what has emerged in the last couple of decades is what people call the foundry model. There are companies that make all their own branded integrated circuits, but there are also places where anybody can come in and for a price (typically charged per wafer) you can build using an established set of technologies. Using these kinds of photolithography you can choose your metal layers, you can choose how you diffuse, put this into a semiconductor, you can build using these available recipes and you can send them your circuit designs and they can actually build your circuits for you so you don't end up spending the $3 or $4 billion dollars as a company or as a startup company in order to build your circuits, but instead you just pay for the use of that facility.

People call this model the fabulous model and by that they don't mean that it's not fabulous, they mean that you don't have to have your own fabrication facility, but instead you can leverage existing infrastructure. Where are these integrated circuits? I mean we know that they're inside our computers; that's kind of the canonical example, but these integrated circuits are in all sorts of places. For example, the digital camera that you use; it has an integrated circuit. Now the silicon is being used to absorb the light. There are processors these days that are devoted entirely to the processing of graphics. In fact, the processors these days have become so complex and so sophisticated that the amount of heat being generated, energy being generated on them so large that they're now starting to become segmented where instead of having a single processor there are what are called multiple cores where there are different regions of processors that talk to one another to some degree, but most of the time they're often parallel working on different computational problems and then kind of sharing the information.

You know, there's other sort of more surprising or more unusual things that you do with integrated circuits. Your cell phone transmitter is now made with an integrated circuit. That's more on the analog side of the world where just like in the first radios you're trying to transmit electromagnetic waves or receive and then amplify very sensitively electromagnetic waves.

This whole trend, this whole incredible race to the bottom as Richard Feynman called it, this race towards the smaller and smaller; it was described in what has become known as Moore's law and some people object to the use of the word law to describe Moore's law; the law here is that it's an empirical law. It's an observation; it's a description that Gordon Moore made, Gordon, one of the founder's of Intel made in about 1965 and he described that from 1958 to 1965 that about every two years there had been a doubling of what you could put onto an integrated circuit of a given size. You could put twice as many transistors, you could make a circuit, a computer, that was twice as sophisticated, twice as complex every two years and typically you could do it for about the same price.

This is a great recipe and it's that doubling every two years, an exponential growth law, that can be used to describe how the integrated circuit revolution has happened and we've gone from those discrete elements where thinking about putting tens of transistors onto a bread board is already difficult to being able to put billions of transistors onto a chip becomes possible and it's possible to do it for costs that are either measured in the few dollars or measured in the tens of dollars per chip. It all is directly traceable to this scalability of integrated circuit technologies.

To summarize really what we've discussed in today's lecture, it's kind of the precursor to the nano-revolution, but in fact we really through Moore's law, we face right up against the nanometer now because we do have the capacity to use shorter and shorter wavelengths of light through photolithography to make our transistors smaller and smaller, to pack so many of them on that we are invariable, inevitably at the cusp of the nanoscale. In fact, the integrated circuit you have in your computer today consists of transistors that are made using technologies that can access below 100 nanometers so they're well into the nanometer length scale.

The big question for the remaining half of this discussion of electronics in the next lecture will be the following. What happens when we start to build our transistors on the scale of the nanometer? I argued in the discussion of the physics of the nanoscale that exciting things happened that this was an opportunity to engineer phenomena—like quantum mechanic phenomena. On the other hand, when you think about Gordon Moore's observation, even if it's just an empirical law there is an impression of continuity of that. There's the sense that we will be able to scale, we'll be able to gradually transition to smaller and smaller geometries, build greater and greater complexity and there's no brick wall there. There isn't a change in the rules, but they were extrapolating on the existing rules.

In the next lecture what we'll talk about is this tension. On the one hand, the fact that to extrapolate to smaller and smaller geometries to continue this tremendous legacy of Moore's law that we're going to be doing so within a new physical regime, a regime where we hit up against quantum effects. At the same time there will be opportunity; there will be these new physical effects, things like electron tunneling, things like really seeing the size of electronic waves, not being able to ignore their ways anymore, and there are people who are working at the nanometer scale in nanoelectronics to try to leverage those phenomena for new paradigms in computing.

Leveraging the Nanometer in Computing
Lecture 4

W e've seen how the success of Moore's law has allowed us to make smaller transistors and more complex integrated circuits, taking us into the nanoworld, where the rules are different. In this lecture, we'll explore how these rules become manifest, how we can manage them, and what exciting phenomena become available to us in the nanoworld. What new classes of electronic devices can we make once we gain dexterity on the scale of a nanometer?

The Workings of a Semiconductor Transistor

- A cross-section of a transistor shows 2 electrodes through which current can flow. This is called the channel, and it's exactly what it sounds like. An electron current flows through this channel, just as water might flow through a channel.

- On top is the control, referred to as the gate. The gate is used to open and close the channel through a specific mechanism. Through the application of voltage on the gate, we either attract a sea of electrons into the channel, enabling the flow of current, or repel electrons, disabling the current flow.

- The gate electrode is separated from the channel by a layer called the gate oxide. The oxide is an excellent insulator, preventing the flow of current from the gate into the channel. This means that the control requires us to expend very little current.

- In the case of silicon electronics, this oxide is the native oxide, silicon dioxide. The process by which it is grown is a natural one; the silicon wafer is simply put into a furnace. Introducing the right temperature and the right ingredients in terms of water and oxygen allows us to grow this oxide on the nanoscale.

- The native oxide is inherently disposed to passivate, or terminate, the states of the silicon that are sticking out of the substrate, the wafer. Thus, we have a natural strategy using silicon's own native oxide for passivation—for termination of these sites chemically—and for the formation of an oxide of essentially whatever thickness we desire. We just increase the temperature a bit in order to grow a more complete oxide.

Scalability

- We've spoken about scalability, a component of which is the ability to put many, many transistors on 1 integrated circuit. But in the course of scaling, we've also shrunk the transistors in the lateral dimensions in order to fit more into the same region of an integrated circuit.

- This lateral shrinking forces us to scale vertically, as well. The gate oxide must be made thinner, because it can't be too far away from where the channel is located to induce the channel. As transistors get smaller, the gate oxide must get closer to the channel.

- What happens when the gate oxide is only a couple of nanometers thick? It means we have to envision electrons as waves and think quantum mechanically.
  - If the electron is a wave and the oxide is thin on the scale of the electron's own wavelength, then that wave can be on both the left and right sides of the barrier.

  - Through the probabilities of quantum mechanics, the electron can be simultaneously on the gate electrode, where we want it, or it has some probability of ending up in the channel.

- Recall that a major advantage of the transistor model was that essentially no current flowed into the channel. Almost no current was required to switch a very large current. Through quantum tunneling, that advantage is compromised.

Nanotechnology to the Rescue

- Materials science and nanotechnology have come to the rescue on this important issue.

- Experts in these fields have discovered how to put down an insulator between the gate and the silicon that can be thicker yet can still induce the channel just as effectively. As a result, we've postponed the onset of the tunneling problem. These high-k dielectrics, these new insulating materials, are very exciting.

- Of course, in adding this insulator, we've given up the ability to simply grow the native oxide, which would then passivate everywhere across the silicon.

- There have been some interesting advances recently in putting nanometer-thin films of materials other than silicon on top of silicon. The technique is called atomic layer deposition, and it allows us to build up, layer by layer at the atomic scale, materials that we are able to interface perfectly with the silicon beneath.

- This is a great example of where by scaling down, we confronted the rules of quantum mechanics, but through innovation, we have been able to gain more runway. The longevity of the continued direct extrapolation of Moore's law has surprised a great many people.

The Advent of 3-Dimensional Devices

- Another challenge that emerges as we make transistors smaller is that some current can flow through the very short channel in what should be the off state. One solution here has been to wrap the gate electrode; the technique for making this nanoscale wrapper is atomic layer deposition.

- Wrapping a gate around the channel involves etching into the silicon. When we do that, there's the possibility of creating damage below the 2-dimensional structure. That means we are starting to build silicon structures that have aspect ratios—that are tall.

- The advent of 3-dimensional devices has been viewed as very challenging, but it's starting to show some success, and it will enable us to continue to extend Moore's law, using new materials and new deposition strategies, especially at the scale of a few nanometers in length.

Carbon Nanotubes

- Carbon nanotubes are one of two fascinating materials that are showing great progress for extending the run of Moore's law. A carbon nanotube is a rolled-up piece of graphene.

- In the early 1990s, the Nobel Prize was awarded for the discovery that it was possible to make long tubes of a single atomic layer of carbon, forming a hexagonal lattice, and that these could be synthesized and purified.

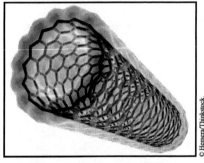

© Hemera/Thinkstock.

Carbon nanotubes are formed from a single atomic layer of carbon; the properties of these materials may differ depending on how they are rolled.

- Unlike a sheet of paper, which can be rolled in any direction, a sheet of graphene, with its hexagonal structure, presents fewer options for rolling. In connecting a carbon atom at the rolled end with another carbon atom, we're limited to a large but finite set of options.

- Interestingly, the properties of carbon nanotubes are different depending on the angle at which they are rolled up. For example, one can be a semiconductor and another can be a metal. This gives us a diverse material that can serve many different functions.

- Purifying carbon nanotubes—ensuring that they behave in the same way—becomes important when we try to use them to build a transistor. One way to do this is to find a technique for querying each nanotube to identify whether it has certain properties. Research was recently published that accomplished this using DNA that would selectively stick to nanotubes differently depending on their roll-up.

- It may also be that going forward, we have to develop a new conceptual paradigm for building computers. We may have to think of ways to build computers where not every building block is absolutely identical and we don't have complete control.

- When we do that, we can start to use nanoparticles and nanomaterials that are similar but perhaps not absolutely identical. We will then need to figure out new ways of architecting integrated circuits and programming those circuits in a way that embraces the variability that occurs at the nanoscale.

Graphene

- Graphene itself, before being rolled into a carbon nanotube, has actually been a more recent star of the show in nanotechnology. The discovery and understanding of the properties of graphene was the basis for a recent Nobel Prize in Physics.

- Graphene has a rich energy landscape above it that has surprising properties for transporting electrons. In this planar structure that is only a single atomic layer thick, electrons can propagate as waves.

- The challenge here is: How do you integrate graphene, this sheet that's 0.5 nanometer thick, with a circuit, perhaps a silicon circuit? In recent years, researchers have found that they could lay down a single perfect layer of graphene onto a substrate and, thereby, start to control it.

- The rapid propagation of electrons—the fact that they just skim along at incredible velocities over this energy landscape—could be the basis for a considerable extension of Moore's law.

- Temperature presents another challenge inherent in extending Moore's law. As we crowd all these transistors together into smaller areas, we seek to reduce the power each one uses, but nevertheless, the power density grows. Thus, there's a need for excellent thermal conductors, and graphene has shown great promise here, as well.

Revolutionary Computer Architectures

- The nanoworld presents us with properties that have not been used in digital computing. Revolutionary ways of architecting our computers may be able to exploit capabilities offered to us from the nanometer-length scale.

- A resonant tunneling diode takes advantage of current flow in the vertical direction, leveraging the flow of electrons from a top layer through to a bottom layer. This new class of devices turns to our advantage the tunneling phenomenon that was the bane of our existence in extending Moore's law to thinner gate dielectrics.

- The idea behind the resonant tunneling diode is this: We can set up an electron in a particular state on the left side of a barrier and create a state—an opportunity—for that electron to go to the right side by ensuring that there is strong coupling between the left and right only if the electron takes on a particular energy, the resonant tunneling energy.

- A resonant tunneling diode enables voltage to be applied to induce different transfer states in electrons and stable regions within them. This, in turn, allows us to create multiple-level logic in electronics. The potentials in currents are no longer just 0s and 1s but 0s, 1s, 2s, and 3s. Instead of being limited to binary logic, we can give ourselves many more options within every transistor.

- In this way, we can scale not just by making the building block smaller but by enriching the amount of information that can be stored and processed within every building block.

Suggested Reading

Bohr, Chau, Ghani, and Mistry, "The High-k Solution."

Dragoman and Dragoman, *Nanoelectronics*.

Perry, "Gordon Moore's Next Act."

Nobelprize.org, "The Nobel Prize in Physics 2010" (see "Popular Information" and "Advanced Information").

Questions to Consider

1. Could a digital computer ever be successfully built that relied on the transaction of a single electron for every computation?

2. What is the cost per transistor in one of today's billion-transistor integrated circuits? What was it in the ENIAC?

Leveraging the Nanometer in Computing
Lecture 4—Transcript

Ted Sargent: We've spoken about how the success of Moore's law, the success of scaling, the incredible scalability of lithography has allowed us to make these smaller and smaller transistors, these more and more complex integrated circuits, but that's taken us over the precipice well into the nanoworld where we've also said the rules are changing. In this lecture, I'd like to speak about how what happens, how the rules of the nanoworld become manifest and both how we can manage them. That's kind of one approach, how we can try to continue to scale and there's lots of success in continuing to scale by managing these effects of the nanoscale and then the other approach which we can pursue in parallel and which does get pursued in parallel by researchers around the world is to try to see what exciting phenomena are available to us. What's new in our tool kit? What kinds of new classes of electronic devices can we make once we gain dexterity on the scale of a nanometer?

Let me start with this first topic of why is it a challenge, how does the world change when we get down to the nanoscale specifically in electronics. To do that, I need to take just a bit of time to describe a little more detail how one of these semiconductor transistors works. This picture is showing a transistor in a cross-section and laterally disposed are two electrodes through which current can flow. This is called the channel and it's exactly as it sounds just like water would flow through the channel, here electron's current is flowing through a channel.

Now on top is the control. It's referred to as the gate and this gate is used to open and close the channel, but this specific mechanism by which it opens and closes the channel is as follows. Through the application of the voltage on the gate we either attract a sea of electrons into the channel enabling flow. We fill it up with water, our channel, or if we put on a bias and electrical potential of the opposite polarity, we repel electrons away. Our channel becomes depleted; current flow is no longer possible. Now you'll see in this image that the gate electrode is separated from the channel, it's distinct. This is referred to as the gate oxide and this is one of the things that we love about silicon. It's one of the things we love about transistors.

This oxide is an excellent insulator. It prevents current from flowing from the gate into the channel. That's a good thing. Our control now requires us to expend very, very little current. Essentially no current flows from the gate into that channel, but through the application of this potential we modulate the flow. We fill or empty our channel, but it doesn't cost us any electrons; it just costs us the application of quite a small voltage. Now the other thing that just makes us love silicon so much is that this oxide is in the case of silicon electronics it's the native oxide, silicon dioxide. That's great for a couple of reasons.

It means that the process by which we grow it is a very natural one. We simply introduce our silicon wafer into a furnace. We introduce the right temperature, the right ingredients in terms of water and oxygen, and we can grow an oxide and we can grow it on the nanoscale. We can grow it to be a couple of nanometers thick. The other thing we love about it is that that oxide is just inherently disposed to passivate or terminate the states of the silicon that is sticking out of the substrate, sticking out of the wafer. We have a natural strategy using silicon's own native oxide for passivation, for termination of these sites chemically and for the formation of an oxide of essentially whatever thickness we want to grow it to. We just take a bit longer; we just increase the temperature a bit in order to grow a more complete oxide.

Now, here's where things start to get challenging. We spoke about scalability and a component of our scalability was our ability to make many, many transistors on one integrated circuit. But in the course of scaling, we've also shrunk it. We've shrunk in the lateral dimensions of our transistors to fit more into the same region of an integrated circuit. In so doing, we're forced to scale vertically as well. We're required to make this gate oxide thinner and thinner. Why? This gate has to induce this channel. It can't be too far away from where the channel is located. It has to have that influence for a finite, for a modest amount of voltage. To induce this very conductive channel, we need to be very close to the channel and we have to get closer and closer as our transistors get smaller and smaller. This is a scaling challenge now that we have.

Well what happens when we made this gate—our oxide—a couple of nanometers thin? Well now we have to think about electrons as waves. Now we have to think quantum mechanically. If the electron is a wave as is depicted in this image then through a very, very thin oxide—thin on the scale of the electron's own wavelength—that wave can be both on the left and the right side of this barrier. It is simultaneously through the probabilities of quantum mechanics, it can be on the gate electrode where we want it, or this electron has some probability of ending up in the channel. Now, the thing that we love so much about this transistor model in which essentially no current flowed into our channel: We got a huge leverage in our switching. It cost almost no current to switch a very large current; now that advantage is compromised through tunneling.

This is an example of where quantum mechanics—if we don't change our paradigm, if we don't change our approach—starts to imperil the advantages of silicon electronics. Now, material science and nanotechnology to the rescue here. They have been able to come to the rescue on this particularly important issue. On the left is a transmission electron micrograph of a standard silicon gate. The SiO_2, that's the glass. That's the native oxide that's been grown. These TMs, by the way, are pretty incredible. The structure that you're seeing in these images, these are individual atoms. With our transmission electron microscope, we're able to image individual atoms. In fact, this is another illustration of our concept from earlier lectures on how small you can confine waves. We're able using electrons to see things as small as electrons, to see things on the scale of about a nanometer. There's no way you could take pictures like this using visible wavelength photons, which are so much larger.

This is showing a gate oxide that's a couple of nanometers thick. It needs to get so thin again so that we can control through the gate, we can control the formation of the channel beneath. We can't have our gate electrode be too remote from our channel in order to effectively control it.

Now on the right, you'll see what's called a high-k solution and the high-k is referring to putting down a different material with different properties. Folks have discovered how to put down an insulator that resides between the gate and the silicon that can be thicker. You can get away with making it thicker, but it can still induce just as effectively this channel, this inversion region, inside the transistor. It's able more effectively to transfer the impetus of the gate. It's able to modulate the current flowing even though it's thicker and as a result of being thicker we've postponed the onset of our tunneling problem. We are able to make this gate oxide thicker and still have the same strength and modulation, but we do so without the cost of having this large current. These high-k dielectrics, these new materials, are very exciting and are very attractive.

You recognize though what we've done is we've given up one of the things we absolutely love about working with the native oxides so it can dioxide. We love the fact that we could simply grow it and that it could passivate everywhere across our silicon. We could grow it in such a way that it formed itself everywhere across the entire wafer at the same time. As long as there wasn't any dust or anything, there were no pinholes; a pinhole would be an opportunity for current to start tunneling through so it would be very bad.

On the right-hand side of this image that somehow we've discovered how to put a new material onto silicon that's not the native oxide of silicon and it has to have all of those good properties. Well this is where there's been some very exciting advances recently in how to put very, very thin, nanometer thin films of different materials other than silicon on top of silicon. The technique is called atomic layer deposition and it's incredibly clever so the materials that constitute these new dielectrics, an example of it is hafnium oxide and so it's a two-component material, hafnium is one of the elements in it and oxide is the other. Folks have figured out through this atomic layer deposition process how to be down exactly one first layer of the hafnium, which then is very prone to react with oxygen and then to waft over it a little bit of water or another oxygen precursor and react that first half layer to form a full layer of hafnium oxide and then to start again.

We are truly building up layer by layer at the atomic scale these perfect materials. In so doing, we're also able to interface them perfectly with the silicon beneath. When we bring in our hafnium it sees this structure, it sees this texture of the silicon surface, and the hafnium atoms go where they go in response to this landscape of silicon atoms that are exposed.

This kind of control is what becomes necessary in order to manage these interfaces because a silicon atom with its unpassivated, unsatisfied electron sitting up is very unhappy and we have to passivate each one of these atoms individually and extremely well. This is a great example of where by scaling down, by getting to smaller and smaller length scales, we confronted straight on the rules of quantum mechanics, the fact that the ground is shifting beneath us, the fact that our foundations are physical, our physical foundations are starting to change and where Moore's law cannot simply be extrapolated based on the existing material set, but through innovation, through the development of new tools, like the atomic layer deposition technique, we're able to give more runway.

You can see that as we go to further and further generations we're going to start running into more and more problems, but this is a great example of where a while ago people called for the end of Moore's law. People said that inevitably we'll have to run out, the question is when, but there were people predicting 20 years ago that it would run out within ten years and yet these extrapolations have been able to continue till now. They've managed to surprise people. The longevity of the continued straightforward direct— challenging but direct—extrapolation of Moore's law has surprised a great number of people. In fact, it's interesting to note that when Gordon Moore made his observation in 1965 that from 1958 until 1965 there had been this doubling every year.

He did make a bit of prediction and his prediction was that Moore's law could be sustained potentially for another decade until 1975. Well, he's viewed as a very brilliant man for a number of reasons. But, the fact that it was sustained for so much longer and the challenges that folks had to overcome now at the atomic, at the nanometer length scale, are remarkable and many, many people have been surprised by this longevity of Moore's law.

There's another challenge that starts to exist in these transistors when we make them smaller and smaller and smaller. This comes from the fact that current can now leak in what we call the off state and so when we try to turn the channel off, as we make this transistor smaller and smaller and smaller we can still get in what's normally the off state we can get some flow of current through this very, very short channel. One of the solutions has been to try to wrap, to no longer really think of this as just a planar device, it's not just flat anymore, but instead to start to think about how we can wrap a gate, a gate electrode around the sides, around the edges, of one of these devices.

Now here ALD, atomic layer deposition is very much our friend, because if we're going to try to wrap things we can't just have a process of depositing an oxide that's directional, that will only grow vertically, we need a wrapper. We need a nanoscale wrapper and atomic layer deposition provides a technique where because we're working with the chemical reactivity of surfaces, because the hafnium element atoms will stick to the sides as well as the top. We have a technique that's very prone to creating a nice compact continuous consistent wrapper all the way around the edges of one of these transistors.

There is another challenge that comes here, which is we thought we were doing planar lithography, right. We thought that we were just building kind of a 2-dimensional circuit. We were kind of working in the flat landscape and then we were just putting materials here and there and there. But to wrap a gate around the channel involves etching into the silicon. It involves digging down into a little trench. When we do that there's the possibility of making damage where we're no longer dealing with something that's just a sort of straightforward flat structure. We're starting to build in 3 dimensions. We're starting to build almost skyscrapers. We're starting to build silicon structures that have aspect ratios that are tall; I mean they're very, very small that from an aspect ratio, from a kind of architectural standpoint they're starting to get tall on us.

This advent of 3-dimensional devices; there's also 3-dimensional circuits coming, but this advent of 3-dimensional devices is something that people have been waiting for because they knew that it had to happen, but it has been viewed as very challenging. Now this is starting to show its value. It's starting to show that it can be done and it's starting to show that we are able to continue to extend Moore's law by using these techniques, these new material strategies, new materials deposition strategies especially at the few nanometer length scale.

I'd like to go on and I'd like to talk about how we can do more than just try to sort of extend the paradigm using essentially the same architectures of circuits and that new nanomaterials can be our friends in trying to extend the run of Moore's law; and here not extend it by a generation or two, but maybe extend it by many generations into the future. Let me talk about two very beautiful and fascinating materials that are seeing great progress and that are showing real promise for extending the run of Moore's law. The first one of these is called the carbon nanotube and you can see a picture of it here. It's actually a rolled up piece of graphene. In fact, this was the basis for a Nobel Prize in the early '90s for the discovery that it was possible to make these long tubes of a single atomic layer of carbon forming this hexagonal lattice and that these could be synthesized so we could build them and they could also be purified.

Their purification turns out to be incredibly important and let me explain why. You can imagine a sheet of paper. Let's take and 8-1/2 by 11 that you could roll up from the tall side, you could roll this way, of course you could roll along the height of the piece of paper or you could go to any arbitrary angle and you could roll up in many directions. Well now let's layout a sheet of graphene with it hexagonal, its honeycomb structure, I could roll it any way, but in fact, there's a few fewer options. If I'm going to connect a carbon atom at the end of my rolling with another carbon atom then I'm limited to a large, but finite set of operations so there's many different species of carbon nanotubes that can exist. They can have different diameters; they can bond; they can terminate one another once we finish rolling in different fashions.

Well the fascinating thing about these carbon nanotubes is that depending on how you roll them up, exactly what angle you roll them up at, their properties are completely different. They can be, for example, one can be a semiconductor and another can be a metal. Now that's incredibly powerful; now we have a diverse material set that can serve many different functions. We're just starting from the same building block, this graphene sheet, and we can make it into any number of different things so that's a great opportunity and it's a fascinating property of these nanoscale materials. But, when you think about electronics, I mean I've been using words like control, I've been using words like one in a billion doesn't work we're in trouble if a piece of dust lands. Well the same logic will apply here then. If we're going to try to find a way to build a transistor using carbon nanotubes, and there's much progress in doing that, then we're going to have to find ways to make sure that all of our carbon nanotubes are behaving the same as one another and so hence the need for great purity and great purification.

There's been some very neat work on both finding ways to make all carbon nanotubes the same and then also very interesting ways of purifying them. The smartest way to try to purify these nanotubes is to try to purify them based on their properties so to ask them to find some kind of technique for querying each one and seeing whether it's got the right properties and there were some beautiful results published a couple of years ago in which people actually used DNA which selectively would stick to these nanotubes differently. Depending on the sequence of the DNA and depending on the rollup of the carbon nanotube and so they were able to use that specificity to do some sorting. It does also imply that when you're talking about one in a billion kinds of perfection that we may also have to think about a different architectural or conceptual paradigm for building computers going forward. We may have to think of ways to build computers where not every building block is absolutely identical, where we don't have complete control. When we do that we can start to utilize nanoparticles and nanomaterials, carbon nanotubes that are similar, but maybe not absolutely identical and then we need to figure out new ways of architecting integrated circuits and programming those integrated circuits in a way that embraces the variability that occurs at the nanoscale.

Now graphene itself before you roll it up into a carbon nanotube has actually been a more recent star of the show in nanotechnology. It was the basis, the discovery and the understanding in the properties of graphene was the subject of a very recent Nobel Prize in physics and graphene is this very beautiful material; it's got this energy landscape above it that's also very rich and that has surprising properties for the transport of electrons. Electrons behave in weird ways within this 2-dimensional, within this planar structure something that's only a single atom, a single atomic layer thick, where electrons can propagate as waves through this landscape. The challenge of course is if you have a sheet of something that's half a nanometer thick, how do you lay your blanket down on something? How do you integrate graphene with a circuit, like perhaps a silicon circuit? Well there've been a number of advances just in recent years where people have understood how they could put down a single perfect layer of graphene onto a substrate and thereby they could start to control it.

The rapid propagation of electrons, the fact that electrons are even more perfectly delocalized in graphene, the fact that they just skim along at incredible velocities over this energy landscape, this is something that people are now exploiting more and more and that many people are very excited could be the basis for really a considerable extension in Moore's law. One of the other ways of looking at the challenges inherent in extending Moore's law and in building integrated circuits that consistently work well and continue to scale, one of the ways of looking at the problem is that it's actually a problem to do with temperature, the reason why is the following. When you crowd all of these little transistors together into smaller and smaller areas scaling seeks to reduce the power each one utilizes, but nevertheless the power density, the intensity of generation of heat locally on this integrated circuit it grows and it grows. We're always looking for ways to avoid these leakage currents that we talked about, to minimize the voltages that we need to apply.

There's also a real need for techniques that allow us to whisk away thermal energy with excellent thermal conductors, conductors of heat and here graphene has shown great interest and great promise as well. Now, there's some very exciting work on using graphene to connect vertically down to the substrate to whisk away the heat laterally within the substrate. Graphene it turns out also has these extremely good thermal conduction properties and so that quality of graphene, not for electron transport, but for heat transport, is starting to be exploited as well.

I'd like to finish this lecture with talking about approaches that aren't direct extrapolations of Moore's law or ambitious and challenging longer run extensions of Moore's law, but where instead we say this nanoworld, this quantum world, it's weird; surely it affords us properties, behaviors that we have not used in digital computing until now. Surely there are new ways, revolutionary ways of architecting our computers that can take advantage of this new facility that is offered to us from the nanometer length scale. Here in this image I present an example of what's called a resonant tunneling diode.

Here we're actually going to take advantage of a current flow in the vertical direction. We're going to leverage the flow of electrons from a top layer through to a bottom layer. We're actually going to use this same tunneling phenomenon that was the bane of our existence in extending Moore's law to thinner and thinner gate dielectrics, but we're going to use this tunneling to our advantage to make a new class of devices.

Let's take a look at how it works. You can see in this image now a representation with on the horizontal axis, space in angstroms (1 angstrom is 10 nanometers), and on the vertical axis is energy. What this is showing is a calculated solution, a model-based prediction, for how electron waves are distributed on the left and on the right. Now the resonant tunneling diode is ingenious. What it does is it recognizes that we can setup an electron in a particular state on the left of a barrier and we can create a state, really an opportunity for that electron to go to on the right-hand side in that we can insure that there is strong coupling between the left and the right only if the electron takes on that particular energy, the resonant tunneling energy.

What we do in a resonant tunneling diode is we apply a voltage—applying a voltage is just giving an electron a bit of energy—so we can raise it up in energy, but until it sees this resonant transmission, this tunneling phenomenon, it's not going to go over to the right with any reasonable probability, and so we raise our voltage a bit and essentially no current flows. We raise it a little bit more and all of a sudden we become aligned with this resonant state and huge current tunnels over to the far side of our transistor. Now here's the thing that happens next that is not done within contemporary electronics. We raise the voltage even more and we become off resonance; we lose the capacity to tunnel resonantly; our current goes down again.

This kind of behavior instead of looking like what we call a mono-tonic characteristic where for more voltage the current just keeps going up, this kind of behavior where it goes up and then it goes down again, this is the shape of a curve, the shape of what we call a transfer curve that is not currently exploited in electronics. And yet what you can do with that is you can create multiple level logic, it's called. You can have many bumps that you engineer through many transfer states and you can have stable regions within them and so you can have potentials in currents that aren't just 0s and 1s, but you can have 0s and 1s and 2s and 3s. In principle, if we can figure out a good way to do computation based on this we can embed more information inside every transistor. Instead of being limited to binary logic only, 0s and 1s, two options, we can give ourselves many more options within every transistor.

Now our scaling paradigm instead of being fixed at one pair of states, a binary option 0, 1 for transistor, we can scale not purely by just making that entity smaller. But, we can scale by enriching the amount of information that can be conveyed or can be stored or can be processed within every building block. That in turn hands over from this exciting concept, that hands over to the computer designers how do you make an integrated circuit on this and there's certainly progress and there's certainly work, but it remains the case that today the integrated circuits that are used in your computer continue to rely on binary logic.

In today's lecture, we've started from the perspective that electronics and its evolution over time is really one way to get at the nanoworld that initially in the 1950s and '60s this opportunity to integrate more and more transistors in this very scalable way onto a single material, to do it monolithically; that this than drove the emergence of aggressive scaling or the emergence of Moore's law and we scaled down and down and down. Then we developed technologies, techniques, methods of fabrication, cleaner clean rooms to allow us to build things smaller and smaller and then inevitably we got to the nanoscale. That is challenging and that is exciting. It's challenging because the rules do change on us. We can't avoid it anymore.

As we scale more and more, we start to see these phenomena emerging and nanotechnology and nanomaterials help us manage those challenges and continue to drive forth within this paradigm. However, no matter how far we go there will be limits and this field of electronics and of computing is looking for the next breakthrough. It's looking to nanotechnology, to the new types of behavior that occur not just as the problem, as in the first part of today's lecture, but also as the solution that allows us to embrace the behavior at the nanoscale and leverage it towards new paradigms in computation.

Leveraging the Nanometer in Communications
Lecture 5

In the last two lectures, we talked about how electronics has enabled computing—the processing of information at vast speeds and low cost. But these days, our computers are connected to every other computer in the world, so in this lecture, we'll look at the communications side of the computer story—the Internet. Here, we'll see how information is sent and received with high fidelity and at a very low cost per bit.

The Optical Internet

- The information-carrying backbone that resides behind our mobile communication devices is the "optical internet." This term refers to our capacity to send vast quantities of information down what we can think of as pipes—pipes that carry light.

- Light is conveyed independently through each fiber in a fiber optic bundle and modulated—turned on and off. Through that modulation and a synchronous measurement at the receiving end, we're able to convey information. The key to sending a lot of information per second is to modulate the light many times per second.

- In a cross-section of one of these "pipes," we see a light ray bouncing back and forth. This idea of bouncing is important because light tends to diffuse. If we're going to communicate information over long distances using just one of these small glass pipes, we must confine the light.
  - Optical fibers are called single-mode fibers because they have only 1 angle at which the light can bounce. The glass core and the cladding that wraps around the core are designed such that light propagates with only 1 bounce angle and, consequently, with a single velocity over very long distances.

  - That quality is engineered by creating an optical environment in which light has only two options: It can either propagate, or it can be lost. In sending light into one of these optical fibers, only the mode in which it can propagate at a single, well-defined speed is excited.

o   If the light in the optical fiber had more than one option, it would disperse, resulting in a loss of signal integrity.

The Absorption of Light
*   There are a variety of mechanisms by which light can be absorbed in any medium, one of which is "band-to-band absorption." This term refers to the idea that the available electronic state, say, in a semiconductor, cannot be successfully breached by light.
    o   If a photon can come in, shine on a material, take an electron, and excite it to a higher energy, the result will be absorption.

    o   Clearly, that's not what we want if we're sending information over thousands of kilometers. Optical fibers are designed to have essentially no electronic transitions available at the energies that are used to send information.

*   Another way to lose light is through scattering, the phenomenon we see in clouds or fog.
    o   Here, light doesn't actually transfer its energy into the particles of water that make up a cloud or fog, but having this medium that is a bit different from the air environment—a droplet of water suspended in the air—leads light to see a discontinuity, and it ends up, with some probability, being scattered in another direction.

    o   You can't see through clouds or fog as a result of that scattering, and it doesn't enhance the visibility of light going down an optical fiber either.

    o   The key here is smoothness. If we have an optical fiber that creates a path that isn't smooth, then we have a reason that light can scatter out of its propagating mode, rather than staying confined down the pipe.

- A certain range of wavelengths of light is particularly conducive to propagating down optical fibers without loss or scattering. At an optimal wavelength, light can propagate for more than a kilometer with almost no loss or scattering.

Properties of Light for the Optical Internet
- The light that is sent down these optical fibers must have some specific properties. First of all, it must be capable of being coupled into an optical fiber, which is only about 10 micrometers in diameter.
  - Lasers provide a beam of light having a single direction and, thus, allow coupling into the precise direction that the light will be propagating down in the optical fiber.

The key to the realization of very low cost per bit in sending and receiving information is fiber optic communication.

  - In fact, laser beams can be tailored such that the range of acceptance angles of the optical fiber can be matched by the output of emission angles from the laser.

  - This directionality is one sense in which light from a laser is very pure and perfect.

- Another sense in which laser light is very pure is the spectral sense. Returning to our wave picture of light, we would say that it has a single wavelength, a single periodic oscillation in time and space. In the quantum picture of light, we would say that its colors have a single, well-defined energy.

Semiconductor Lasers
- How do we go about generating light with these properties? Semiconductor lasers have been developed that are extremely small

and use the semiconductor itself as the means of transferring energy from the electronic domain into the optical domain.

- These lasers rely essentially on two phenomena occurring simultaneously. The first is amplification, which refers to growing the intensity of signal—giving it more power—but retaining the underlying form of that signal. In lasers, the amplification we're referring to is amplification of light.

- The second phenomenon is resonance, which we can think of as feedback.
  o In the simplest terms, the front and back of a laser are both slightly less-than-perfect mirrors. The light generated between these mirrors is mostly trapped, but occasionally, it can escape out the front facet.

  o A photon generated in this laser cavity can be amplified into many photons, building up to a crescendo of light as they are reflected back and forth within the cavity.

  o Eventually, such an intensity of photons is built up within the laser cavity that the amount of energy being pumped in electrically to create this gain cannot amplify further; thus, we reach a steady state, an average expectation of a density of photons inside the laser cavity.

- Although they are very small, the intensities locally in the most powerful of these semiconductor lasers are amazing. Within this very small device, we've built up an incredibly high-power density using the combination of amplification and feedback.

Quantum Wells
- Inside a normal semiconductor, the energies of photons that can be produced are determined by the structure of the semiconductor, but that can be quite limiting.

- There are only certain colors that are available from a given composition of semiconductor. As we saw in discussing fiber optics, there is a very specific wavelength that is the perfect compromise to allow light to propagate for more than a kilometer with almost no loss or scattering. But it's difficult to find a semiconductor that matches that wavelength precisely.

- In quantum wells, however, we take advantage of the fact that the electron wave has a physical extent.
  - If it's a cloud, and we compress it down to 1 dimension to make a confined structure, that boosts up the energy of the electrons. We can then tune the resonance energies that this electron wave experiences, the same way one would tune a guitar.

  - By pushing these energy levels up, we're able to achieve stimulated emission, the process of gain inside the laser at exactly the wavelength that is needed.

- Through this quantum engineering—and only because of it—we're able to perfectly match the colors of light that are generated from a semiconductor with those that we desire to achieve, resulting in extremely efficient, low-energy, low-cost-per-bit communications.

- The semiconductors used here are made of such materials as gallium arsenide or indium gallium arsenide.
  - These compound semiconductors combine elements from different groups in the periodic table to achieve strong covalent bonding.

  - Introducing a third or a fourth element into the compound allows more degrees of freedom, more room to engineer the band gap of the semiconductor.

  - As a result, we're able to make materials that are much more agile, much more conducive to enabling us to choose just the right wavelength for the emission of light.

Silicon as an Optical Material

- Compound semiconductors work well in engineering discrete components, but the materials used in them are typically much more expensive than silicon. Many researchers feel strongly that if we could engineer optical materials and devices using silicon, we would be able to make the use of light in communications and, potentially, in computing much more widespread.

- As we saw during our discussions of the field of electronics, as chips are made smaller and smaller, more energy density is put into a given region of the chip. The goal is to whisk that energy away quickly so that the chip doesn't heat up, melt, or start to lose performance.

- One of the most energy-consuming factors in the operation of a chip today isn't the computing but the communications. And one of the reasons to be so interested in seeing whether electronics silicon can be integrated with optics is that we may be able to lower the energy consumption of the communications function by building it on top of a silicon chip.

- One of the elements of this work is to be able to guide light around a silicon chip in such a manner that it's not lost. Researchers have realized that silicon is actually an extremely good guide for light and can be made into highly efficient wave guides for integrated circuits.

- Another field that has attracted great excitement is plasmonics. Here, researchers are making metal particles that are spaced a defined distance from each other and allow electromagnetic waves to hop from one particle to the next. Where this is ultimately leading is the ability to convey light around a silicon integrated circuit.

- Until about 5 years ago, silicon wasn't thought of as being an active optoelectronic material; that is, it could pass light through itself, but that was about it.
  - Very recently, however, researchers have found that they can make lasers on silicon, as well as modulators that turn on and off optical signals.

      o   These laser and modulator technologies are now fast enough to be useful in lowering the power burden in silicon integrated circuits, but the thrust of the field now is to scale them down.

Suggested Reading

Agrawal, *Fiber-Optic Communication Systems*.

Jalali, "Silicon Photonics."

Nobelprize.org, "The Nobel Prize in Physics 2009" (see "Popular Information" and "Advanced Information, Scientific Background").

Questions to Consider

1. What properties do photons—the currency of fiber optic communications—and electrons—the currency of computing—have in common? How do they differ? Why is it important at the moment to be able to interconvert information between the electronic and the photonic domains?

2. Thinking of the price of your computer and the price of your cell phone: Which costs more, 1 unit (1 bit-flip) of computing or 1 unit (1 bit-send) of wireless communications?

Leveraging the Nanometer in Communications
Lecture 5—Transcript

Ted Sargent: Do you remember there was a day not too long ago when there were computers and there was communications, but they were distinct from each other? You would actually go and you'd sit down at a computer and you'd do some work, but you had no expectation that it was connected to every other computer in the world. Maybe you had a personal digital assistant that you carried around with you in the palm of your hand, but it wasn't tethered to every other PDA, every other computer to an internet.

What is it that happened in the last decade or so that made it possible that information was everywhere? In the previous lecture, pair of lectures, we talked about how electronics has enabled computing, the processing of information at vast speeds and at low cost. Well the internet is the communications side of that story. It comes down to our ability to send information and receive it with high fidelity and at very low cost per bit.

How low is the cost? Well back in 1971 if you wanted to send a terabyte of information (a terabyte is about a thousand movies—it would be a couple of hard drives today), if you wanted to send that data over the network rather than sending your hard drive from Boston to California, it would've cost about $150,000 dollars to do so. Today, it costs about 12 cents. In 1930, if you wanted to pick up the phone and have a three minute call between New York and London it would've cost you about $300 in today's dollars. Today, that costs us about 20 cents.

The key that we'll talk about today to realizing this incredibly low cost per piece of information, per unit, per bit, per binary digit, the key has been fiber optic communications combined with wireless communications. Now we spoke during the previous two lectures really about the basis for wireless communications. This was our ability to make silicon circuits that were very low in cost, that got smaller and smaller, and that got faster and faster and more and more efficient in their utilization of electrical power. It's that success of electronics to microelectronics to nanoelectronics that's the basis for our untethered communications.

There's a backbone, an information carrying backbone that resides behind the mobile devices that we are all able to carry around with us and achieve continuous communication with. That backbone I'll call the optical internet. That refers to our capacity to send vast quantities of information down what you can think of as pipes, pipes for information, and the pipes carry light. Let's talk about these pipes. Let's talk about the optical internet.

Here's a picture, a very familiar one, of a bunch of optical fibers. These are pieces of glass and through each one is independently conveyed a stream of light and the light is modulated. It's turned on and off and through that on and off and through a synchronous measurement at the other end with a detector we're able to convey information. Now the key to sending a lot of information per second is to modulate that light many times per second. We've seen these familiar pictures before, these glass fibers. I'd like to talk about how they work. What are their properties that are so important? What does that have to do with the materials, the atoms, the molecules that underlie them?

But first, on to the structure itself. What does the pipe look like? Well here's one of these pipes in cross-section. You can see a light ray, which is the red line, bouncing back and forth and back and forth down this optical fiber. This idea of bouncing ends up being very important. Light is prone to diffuse. It's prone to disperse. When you think of a spotlight you have to work hard to try to focus it, but the further away you are from the spotlight realistically the more that beam is going to be spread out. If we're going to communicate information from Boston to California using just one of these small glass pipes we're going to have to confine the light. This is one of the first properties of optical fibers.

In fact, we call optical fibers, based on this glass cladding and also a glass core; we call them single mode fibers because there's only one angle at which the light can bounce. We design the shape of this core, which is cylindrical and we design the optical properties of the cladding that wraps around that core such that light propagates with only one bounce angle and consequently with a single speed, with a single velocity over these very long distances. How do we engineer that quality? Well, this is really all about creating an optical environment in which light has two options. It can either propagate or it can be lost. It can escape.

Then our job in creating the source of light and shining a beam of light into one of these optical fibers is to excite only this one mode, only the light mode, where light can just race down this fiber without impediment and at a single well-defined speed. Imagine what would happen if light had a couple of options. Imagine if it could bounce at different angles and therefore make it a different race. Our signal would disperse in time; it would spread out. That phenomenon is known as dispersion. If we're going to try to get as much information packed in as possible we want to modulate our optical sources as rapidly as possible. We can't afford any spreading. Spreading in time would be a loss of signal integrity. We would smudge our signal. We would no longer be able to resolve it. The design of fiber optic cables that achieve this very low dispersion is one of the central tenets of successful fiber optic communications.

There's another really crucial aspect to the ways in which optical fibers have been designed and have been constructed and that relates to loss. Clearly to insure that our signals go as long as possible without losing information, without losing power, we're required to make this glass as transparent as possible. There's a variety of mechanisms by which light can be absorbed really in any medium so our first one is what we call band-to-band absorption. By that we simply mean that the available electronic state, let's say in a semiconductor, those states cannot be successfully breached by light coming in, by a photon having a particular energy. If a photon can come in, shine on a material, take an electron and excite it successfully to a higher energy, if there's a shelf it can elevate that electron to, a higher-up energy level, then we will have absorption.

Clearly that's not what we want if we're going to send information over thousands of kilometers. Optical fibers are designed to have essentially no optical transitions or no electronic transitions available at the energies that we'll be using to send the information with. There's another way to lose light though that's not absorption, it's called scattering. This is the phenomenon that we see in clouds or in fog where light doesn't actually transfer its energy into the particles of water that make up a cloud or fog. But having this medium which is a bit different from the air environment, having this little bubble, this little droplet of water suspended in the air leads light to see a discontinuity and it ends up with some probability being scattered in another direction. Well that doesn't make seeing very easy. You can't see through clouds and you can't see fog as a result of the scattering and it doesn't enhance the visibility of light going down an optical fiber either.

This is all about smoothness. This is just like with the clouds. If we were to have an optical fiber that created a path that wasn't smooth, a bit like having a well-paved roadway, then we would have a reason why light could scatter out of its propagating mode rather than stay confined down the pipe. Making these interfaces in these glass fibers very, very smooth and perfect and well-controlled and very homogenous, making the core material out of a single type of glass, making the cladding material out of a single type of glass, that is another one of the key steps in the development of optical fiber growth that was so crucial in allowing information to propagate such vast distances.

Now there's a particular wavelength of light or range of wavelengths of light that are particularly conducive to propagating down optical fibers without loss or without scattering. It really comes from a compromise. On the one hand, if you go to too short a wavelength, too high a photon energy, you're prone to participate in certain scattering and absorption processes and if you go to too long a wavelength, you're prone to participate in other absorption processes; processes that are more like thermal processes, lower energies, but that can become very abundant once you get down to these very small energies and so that drives us to kind of a compromised wavelength or compromised photon energy. At this wavelength, light can propagate for over a kilometer with almost no loss or scattering loss at all. It's pretty incredible. Imagine if you were to take say a window on your home, is it maybe a centimeter, two centimeters thick, well imagine taking that window and instead of it being a centimeter or two thick it being a kilometer, almost a mile thick and being able to see perfectly through it. That's what optical fiber technology has achieved for us.

This incredible transparence is the basis for being able to convey information over such incredibly long distances. Now we ask ourselves, we have our window, we have our basis for confinement, we have our basis for sending information over these very long distances, well where will we get the light from. This light needs to have some very specific properties. First of all, it needs to be something that we can couple into an optical fiber. These optical fibers, in order to achieve their single mode properties, in order to insure there's only one available bounce angle, only one velocity for light, these optical fibers are quite small. They're about 10 micrometers in diameter so they're not of the nanoscale; they're more on the optical length scale. But, in order to couple into these, we need to make a beam of light that's similarly small. Imagine taking a light bulb that puts light everywhere. It would be very, very hard to focus much of that light inside. Even with a light emitting diode, it would be very difficult to couple most of the light into this very small aperture. Lasers, on the other hand, are famous for having exactly the properties that we're looking for. Lasers provide a beam of light having a single direction and so they provide us with the opportunity to couple right into this direction that the light will be propagating down in the optical fiber. In fact, these beams can be tailored such that the range of acceptance angles of the optical fiber can be matched by the output of emission angles from the laser. Now that's one sense in which light from a laser is sort of very pure, very perfect. It's the sense in which it's very directional.

There's another sense in which laser light is very pure and that's in the spectral sense. When we're thinking in our wave picture of electromagnetic, we would say that it's got a single wavelength. It's got a single periodic oscillation in time and in space. It's very pure and in spectral content. It would be like singing a single operatic note without any vibrato, a very pure note, a very clean note. In our photon picture, in our quantum picture of light, we would say that these colors of light have a single well-defined energy and that ends up being very important as well because as I describe the low loss of the optical fiber derives in part from having selected a color of light that's very not prone to be absorbed. It's very unlikely to be absorbed and so that point about photon energy is extremely important as well.

This is what we desire. These are the properties of light that we're looking for, but how do we go about generating it. How do we go about building one of these lasers? In fact, if you were to picture a laser that perhaps you've read about or seen on TV, perhaps you've seen pictures of the early lasers that were developed in the 1960s using gasses as the medium, which transferred energy from the electrical domain into the optical domain. Or perhaps you've seen pictures of lasers that are going to be used to shoot down missiles, incredibly powerful, large lasers; you'd think this doesn't match with the size scale we're talking about. You'd think, you know, these optical fibers have this aperture that's 10 micrometers in size that I need to couple into, how am I going to match that with the laser?

Well it turns out that semiconductors, including semiconductors using quantum effects, that have components of them that are nanometer sized, semiconductor lasers have been developed that are extremely small; they're extremely compact, they look a lot like very small chips, very small integrated circuits and they use the semiconductor itself as the means of transferring energy from the electronic domain where we're able to pass a current through one of these lasers into the optical domain. This is how one of these lasers works. The lasers rely essentially on two phenomena occurring simultaneously. The first one is amplification. Amplification is familiar to us. For example, obviously your stereo speakers participate in amplification. They take a very weak signal, a little modulation in the electrical domain and they turn it into first a much stronger electronic signal and then that in turn is transduced into an acoustical signal.

Amplification, of course, then refers to growing the intensity of signal, giving it more power, but retaining the underlying form of that signal just amping it up, bumping up the intensity of that signal. In lasers, the amplification that we're talking about is amplification of light. We're talking about taking a weak optical signal and a weak optical signal can emerge anywhere at any time within the laser. It's called spontaneous emission wherein light is always being absorbed and emitted. There are always little bits of light around. One of the key components of a laser is to take some of these little stray bits of light that are always coming and going in the real world at room temperature and gain them up, provide them of amplification. We call this optical gain. That's the first ingredient in a laser.

The second ingredient is a resonance. You can also think of this as feedback. In the simplest terms, the front and the back of a laser are both mirrors. They're not perfect mirrors. If they were perfect mirrors than light generated between those two mirrors would always remain trapped. But, if they're just slightly less than perfect mirrors light is mostly trapped and then occasionally it can escape out the front facet. It can be transmitted through the front mirror that has a less than unity reflectance and so within this laser cavity we have a photon occasionally being generated through a spontaneous process. Amplification of that photon where its intensity grows, in fact, it turns into many photons as it propagates through, substantial reflection and then back and forth and back and forth as we build up and we build up and we build up this crescendo of light within our laser cavity.

Now eventually, we build up such a crescendo, such an intensity of photons within our laser cavity that the amount of energy we're pumping in electrically to create this gain cannot amplify further and so we reach what we call a stead state. We reach an average expectation of a number of photons of a density of photons inside this laser cavity. While these lasers are very small—the length of their cavities are perhaps a millimeter and their lateral dimensions are on the order of microns—the intensities locally within the most powerful of these semiconductor lasers are amazing. They're about the intensities of light inside the Sun. Within this very small device, we've built up an incredibly high power density using the combination of amplification or gain and feedback or resonance.

Inside this laser, there're some crucial nano-engineered components. In fact, this is the field that brought me into the field of nanotechnology. I was just an undergraduate student at the time. I was studying engineering physics or applied physics and I loved my physics courses, I loved studying quantum mechanics, solving problems, solving equations, but I found it got so much more interesting if I could actually see the manifestations of these very exciting, sometimes weird, sometimes unusual concepts that we've talked about together, if I could see them manifest in some kind of device and where they weren't just present, but they were what we were using, they were what we were taking advantage of. Well quantum wells, which are the heart of most semiconductor lasers today, are examples of quantum engineering in order to make a better laser. Let's talk about how they work.

Inside a normal semiconductor, the energies that are available, the photons, the energies of photons that can be produced these energies are determined by the structure of the semiconductor, but that can be quite limiting.

There're only certain colors that are available from a given composition of semiconductor. Now as I described in fiber optics, there's a very specific wavelength that is our perfect compromise that makes our glass window completely transparent over a kilometer's distance. We need to match that wavelength very, very well and it's very difficult to find a semiconductor that matches it just right. In quantum wells, we take advantage of the fact that the electron wave has a physical extent. If it's a cloud as we've discussed, and we compress it down just in the plane, just in one dimension to make a confined structure, which boosts up the energy of these electrons, we tune it the way one would tune a guitar. We tune the resonance energies that this electron wave experiences. By tuning them just right, by pushing these energy levels up, we're able to achieve stimulated emission, the process of gain inside our laser at exactly the wavelength that we need.

Through this quantum engineering, and only because of it, we're able to perfectly match the colors of light that are generated from a semiconductor with those that we desire to achieve extremely efficient low energy, low cost per bit communications. It's also just worth mentioning that the semiconductors that we use here, they're semiconductors the way silicon is, but they're not silicon. They're materials such as gallium arsenide or indium gallium arsenide. Instead of residing in Group 4 of the periodic table where the elemental semiconductors, such as silicon or germanium reside, these are called elemental because only one element, pure silicon, pure germanium is required to make materials this way, they're in what are called the compound semiconductors.

With the compound semiconductors like gallium arsenide, we combine an element from Group 3 and another from Group 5, gallium from Group 3, arsenic from Group 5, and we combine them together in equal stoichiometry. Thinking back to our periodic table we've achieved a good match. Group 3 and Group 5, they together will satisfy a full electronic orbital the way silicon 4 + 4 will satisfy a full electronic orbital. They also rely on covalent bonding so they're very, very strong. They're very robust materials, but by introducing another element, by having a pair of elements or, in fact, we can introduce a third or a fourth element from Group 3 or from Group 5. We have more degrees of freedom. We have more room to engineer the band gap of our semiconductor. As a result of that, we're able to make materials that are much more agile, they're much more prone to enable us to choose just the right wavelength for the emission of light.

That point about which semiconductor we use in optoelectronics brings us back to a really attractive and exciting opportunity for the field of photonics, the engineering using light, which is researchers have made considerable advances in the last couple of years in figuring out how we could use silicon as an optical material and that would be very, very attractive. These compound semiconductors that have been the basis for lasers and fiber optics, they work well when you're thinking of engineering discrete components. It's a bit like when we were talking in our electronics lecture about the original transistors where even in the 1950s and '60s people were starting to make very competent transistors that could switch, but they had a really hard time connecting them together.

Well the problem with these compound semiconductors is that typically their cost is much, much higher than that of silicon. A component of that is the actual materials themselves and their availability. But, another is that silicon, because of the electronics industry, has scaled so much that there's now many, many ways, many different foundries in which to make silicon. There's a community of researchers and now companies that feel very strongly that if we could engineer optical materials and devices using silicon we would be able to make the use of light and communications and potentially even in computing much more wide spread. Well why is this almost an inevitable trend an important thing to do?

We talked during our discussions of the field of electronics about how as we make our chips smaller and smaller we put more and more energy density into a given region of that chip. In fact, it's amazing, if you look at the evolution of the energy density of integrated circuits we're only a few doubling factors away from having the same energy generation density in the very most active part of an integrated circuit as the energy density inside a nuclear reactor. We're starting as we shrink and shrink and shrink in the field of electronics we're moving towards the denser and denser generation of energy. Now on our chips, of course, our goals is to whisk that energy away and to transport it away as quickly as possible so that our chip doesn't heat up, melt, or start to lose performance.

One of the most energy consuming factors in the operation of a chip today isn't the computing, though that consumes energy too, but it's the communications. One of the reasons to be so interested in seeing whether we can integrate electronics silicon with optics is that we may be able to make the communications function much lower in its energy consumption by building it on top of a silicon chip. There's a lot of exciting work going on in exactly this area and there's a couple of pieces to it. One of them is to be able to guide light around a silicon chip in a manner where it's not lost; it's just like in the fiber optic case.

In order to do this, researchers have recently discovered how to use existing electronics processing—things like photolithography and etching, which are always utilized to make electronic circuits. Well they figured out how to make good wave guides out of silicon and once they figured that out they actually realized that silicon was an extremely good guide for light. It's almost more like a wire, a tightly confining wire for light, than a fiber optic cable is. Silicon has a very high refractive index. In fact, this is a place where silicon has something in common with diamond. The appearance of diamond, the fact that it's got this beautiful ability to reflect light in many directions when you hit it and yet it's transparent, that comes from its having what we call a very high refractive index. It's got a high optical density. Silicon does as well and what that means is that if you can get light into it, which is the hard part with something with high refractive index, but if you can get light into it then the light doesn't want to escape. It's tightly confined. It gets trapped inside and it's that trapping and the multiple bounces that make the diamond have its characteristic flash of appearance.

In the case of silicon what this means is that we can make wave guides that can meander across an integrated circuit, can take multiple bends, can go around loops, can go around tight turns, and they can do that very efficiently. Silicon is proving itself out to be an extremely good mode of conveying light on integrated circuits. That's looking very promising.

Another problem though is with this high refractive index, it was hard to get light into the silicon wave guides. There have been recent advances in the design of the regions where we couple light from the outside world into these wave guides, called adiabatic coupling, where we kind of go continuously from the size and character of light in the air and we funnel it down and it really does look just like a funnel. We funnel it down into the silicon wave guide for convenient conveyance across the integrated circuit.

There's another field that's attracted great excitement these days that doesn't even use an optical medium at one of these high refractive index media for the conveyance of light. The field is called plasmonics. Here researchers are making metal particles that are spaced a defined distance from each other where electromagnetic waves can hop from one particle to the next particle to the next particle. It's a bit like crossing a stream and having a bunch of evenly spaced rocks that you can use as steps along your way. This has yet to be fully proven out as a practical technology, but it's very much a nanotechnology because the steps, because of light's characteristics size, the steps themselves are measured in the kind of 50 to 100 nanometer range. These are actually the same particles that I was describing earlier when we were talking about stained glass.

These particles that were, without even knowing that early artisans were introducing plasmonic particles into stained glass they were doing so and they were shaping the color that the glass appeared to have. These same kinds of phenomena are now being used to provide a means of carrying light systematically around an integrated circuit. Where this is ultimately leading to is being able to convey light around a silicon integrated circuit, but the other piece of this is just like in our fiber optic communications, the ideal thing would be to generate light and to turn it on and off right on the chip. Until about five years ago, we hadn't thought of silicon as being an active optical, or an active optoelectronic material. It was one that could pass light through itself, but that was about it.

In the last half decade, researchers have found that they can now using new phenomena make lasers on silicon and they can make modulators which turn on and off optical signals. One of the missing pieces in this field of active silicon electronics is that at the moment these components are a little bit big so they end up taking up a fair amount of the real estate of the space on one of these silicon integrated circuits. The thrust of this field now is to figure out how we can take these laser technologies and modulator technologies, which are now fast enough to be extremely useful in lowering the power burden in silicon integrated circuits, how we can take these new building blocks and condense them even further in order to scale down. Just the way Moore's law enabled us to scale down the electronics we need to proceed with scaling down the optics as well on silicon.

In this field of optical communications, it moves so fast. We talked about Moore's law on the context of electronics where there was this doubling every year, well in optics, the fiber optic communications, there was a doubling in efficiency or a number of bits that could be sent per second over a given fiber cable. Every 18 months, there was an even faster generation turnover and at one point when people realized they could put many colors, they could put a rainbow of colors down an optical fiber there was just a sudden increase of a factor of 10 essentially over night with the advent of wavelength division multiplexing.

It's these kinds of leaps and bounds advances that led to an optical internet where bits were nearly free. This field of optical communications, building the optical internet, connecting it to the wireless world, it's got a rich set of fascinating physics at the nanoscale. It involves light as a wave propagating down fibers and it also looks closely at light as a particle, something where we generate in a fundamentally quantum device, the laser, a light that is not absorbed in the fiber and can travel many, many kilometers, in fact hundreds even thousands of kilometers, very, very long distances without losing its energy. This has also given us a chance to feature two of the stars of the show in nanotechnology, electrons that are the basis of computation because they love to interact with one another and photons, which can propagate freely. Many of the devices that enable this are at the junction between the two. They're the ones that allow us to transduce between the electronic domain of the world of information and computing and the optical domain, the domain of communications.

Sensing the World through Nanoengineering
Lecture 6

In the last lecture, we talked about generating light—converting electronic information and power into the photonic domain. In this lecture, we're interested in the reverse process—how we transduce information about the world around us into the electronic domain for subsequent processing and communication. Light provides an incredibly rich source of information about the physical world, and here, we'll learn the role of image sensors in converting that light into the language of the digital.

Digital Cameras

- The optical module inside a cell phone has a lens that must be a certain distance from the image-sensor integrated circuit so that the image is focused onto that image sensor. There is then essentially an array of millions of pixels of photodetectors—light sensors—that are read out using this integrated circuit.

- The sensors are called CMOS integrated circuits. The use of the acronym communicates the fact that the image sensors are built using existing processes for making silicon electronics, in which there is normally no light involved. That's great news for the ability to manufacture very low-cost cameras.
  - It also puts the image sensor onto the Moore's law track. There is constant pressure to shrink the dimensions of the components of these integrated circuits and the circuits themselves.

  - Again, that's great news for fitting more megapixels into a given area, but there are some compromises that must be made when pixels are shrunk. The bottom line is that we end up having fewer photons impinge on each pixel.

The Challenges of Using Silicon

- The brilliant electronic properties of silicon have driven the emergence of the electronics industry based on it, but silicon is not a particularly strong absorber of light. That's one of the first challenges in existing image sensor approaches that use only silicon to achieve their functions.

- Another challenge comes in reading out what our pixels have "seen" in the electronic domain. For this, we need wires, but those wires get in the way of the light detector on the sensor. This problem, known as the fill factor problem, has led to deteriorating images as the size of the pixels is shrunk.

- Recently, however, light detectors have been built that can function the way silicon does, in a sense, as light absorbers that transduce photonic information into electronic currents.
  - We're able to build these detectors using a new material set, not necessarily even silicon based, involving colloidal quantum dots. These semiconductor particles are synthesized in solution so that they're just like a paint, and they can be coated onto the very top of a silicon wafer.

  - In this way, the light no longer has to pass through layers of wire to be absorbed in the silicon beneath. Instead, the sensor is brought closer to where the light impinges from.

  - Quantum dots can also be engineered to be extremely strong light absorbers. Using them is almost like putting photographic film on top of a CMOS image sensor, enabling the capture of the image on top and the reading of it using the silicon electronics below.

  - This is a return to using silicon for what it was originally intended for and what it's so effective for: the electronic function. We've built a second story on top of the silicon using nanomaterials, and this second story now reaches out and senses the light to be read by the silicon beneath.

Wavelengths beyond the Visible

- Quantum dots can be synthesized to have different sizes and, thus, different colors—different ranges of wavelengths in which they absorb or emit light.
    - The mechanism by which that occurs is the quantum size effect, wherein if we compress an electron wave down to a size even smaller than its wavelength, we push up its energy levels and turn it into a blue emitter.

    - If we make the particle of a larger size that doesn't compress the electron as much, we allow it to take on a lower energy and, as a consequence, be an absorber of lower-energy photons.

- In looking at an image of a forest fire taken with a traditional visible image sensor, we see mostly smoke. If we look at the same image taken in the infrared wavelengths, we're able to see through the smoke as a result of the interactions of different wavelengths with the particles that reside in the smoke. In other words, we're able to get more information about the scene by going to different spectral regimes in the electromagnetic spectrum.

- Quantum dot nanoparticles are not limited to only tuning over the visible spectral range. In fact, they can extend all the way to these other wavelengths that have traditionally not been the purview of low-cost silicon-based cameras.

- The infrared image of the forest fire was produced with technology using the compound semiconductors we talked about earlier, but these aren't the basis for low-cost silicon electronics. Quantum dots are now enabling the augmentation of low-cost, consumer-appropriate technology to make it capable of seeing colors that exotic semiconductors have seen in the past.

- We can also image a scene with a bullet whizzing through the air, capturing its thermal signature with an infrared camera.

Seeing Color with Digital Image Sensors

- How do we see color at all in today's digital image sensors? At the moment, the answer can be found in the arrays of optical filters that are put on top of a chip.

    o Picture a color wheel with red, green, and blue filters that can transmit those corresponding colors of light from behind a white light source. Those color wheels seek to map onto our eyes' sensitivity, where color sensing is also based on sensors that are differently attuned to red, green, and blue.

The megapixel digital cameras in use today are incredible, but their capabilities only just scratch the surface of the information that can be garnered about the physical world using light.

    o To make a digital camera that can take color images, we overlay an array of pixels on the silicon with a matrix of red, green, and blue filters.

- This technology works, but in using it, we are throwing away quite a bit of light. Using a filter means that we are letting only certain photons through a sieve. When we do that, we're reducing the number of photons that are impinging on each of the pixels in the image sensors.

- Through their wide spectral tuning and the sharpness of their cutoffs, quantum dots and nanomaterials enable a new strategy called stacked pixels. Here, instead of using filters that throw away light, followed by sensors that sense all colors, the top sensor in a stacked pixel both detects the shorter wavelengths and filters them, passing down the green. Then, a green light–sensing layer detects

101

green photons and passes the red, and another layer beneath absorbs and senses the red.

Multiexciton Generation

- Nanomaterials have recently enabled researchers to see how we can use the concept of "multiexciton generation" to make more sensitive image detectors.

- To understand this term, it's important to know that normally, we expect photon detection to occur in a 1-for-1 way: 1 photon comes in, and the best case scenario is that we see 1 electron worth of information.

- In today's image sensors, we may be interested in getting down to the range where we're seeing only a few photons, a few particles of light impinging on every pixel. In that case, when we have only a few electrons, it becomes challenging to read out the information conveyed by those few electrons. We need very sensitive, low-noise circuits to do so. What if we could impart multiple electrons worth of information for every photon that comes in and, thereby, ease the burden on the circuit?

- In the phenomenon of multiexciton generation, every photon that comes in generates not 1 electron but many electrons inside the material.
  o Initially, light comes in and generates 1 excited electron, but then there's an amplification cascade. You might think of it as a billiard ball knocking into a couple of other billiard balls and generating a number of excited electrons.

  o We need a good bit of energy in this primary photon that leads to this primary excited electron generating a cascade of lower-energy electrons, but the ultimate outcome is that we have achieved multiplication from 1 photon into multiple electrons.

- In 2009, researchers found that they could make a photodetector that took advantage of this technology; as a result, they were able to see (and measure) multiple electrons worth of signal collected in a macroscopic current.

The Terahertz Spectral Regime

- One spectral regime that has been hard to access until now is the terahertz. The megahertz range is familiar to us from tuning the radios in our cars, and the gigahertz is familiar as the basis for cell phone communications. As we go to much higher frequencies than that, we get into the optical frequencies, the infrared, the visible, and beyond.

- In between the gigahertz and the optical is the terahertz regime. Until recently, the reason we had little information in the terahertz regime is that we weren't able to make efficient sources of terahertz radiation.

- However, a new class of lasers, light sources, and photodetectors has been realized based on quantum phenomena that allow the creation of terahertz photons.

- Terahertz imaging is now being used in security applications because it allows us to see through fabric and even get information on the chemical composition of material that may be concealed.

Standoff Imaging

- The field of imaging at a standoff takes advantage of the fact that we can shine a beam of light over miles and image from a distance; we can also use spectral signatures to see chemical compositional information from a distance. But sometimes, the kinds of molecules we're looking for are too subtle, too complex; there are spectral signatures that can't be discerned from miles away.

- The field of biodetection at a standoff has thus emerged, in which researchers look for very specific and subtle differences between two organisms, perhaps anthrax and something posing as anthrax.

- Scientists have come up with new ways to launch an aerosol into the region of a positive threat and have binding occur between nanoparticles (themselves containing a distinctive fingerprint) and the subject of interest; if the nanoparticles stick to the subject, they change color, and this change can be detected from long distances.

Suggested Reading

Federici, Gary, Barat, and Michalopoulou, "T-Rays vs. Terrorists."

Konstantatos and Sargent, "Nanostructured Materials for Photon Detection."

Ohta, *Smart CMOS Image Sensors and Applications*.

Questions to Consider

1. How does the resolution of photographic film compare with that of a digital camera? What limits the resolution of an imaging system, the materials on which the image is imprinted or the properties of light?

2. If we were to record information about the location of every object in the room in which you are sitting, how much memory would it take up? What if we were to record the location of every atom?

Sensing the World through Nanoengineering
Lecture 6—Transcript

Ted Sargent: We've been talking a lot about processing information, using electronics and nanoelectronics and about conveying information with the aid of lasers, lasers based on nanomaterials like quantum wells. How do we gather this information? Where does this information about our world come from? Light provides an incredibly rich source of information about our physical world. Obviously our eyes are our most rich, most information expressive sense. To convey that, to convert that into the language of the digital, to feed it into our image processors inside our computers, to feed it into our fiber optic pipes, we need something analogous to our eyes and that is the world of image sensors.

Whereas we've been speaking in the previous lecture about generating light, converting electronic information and power into the photonic domain, we're interested now in the reverse process. We're interested in how we transduce information about the world around us, into the electronic domain for subsequent processing and communication. It's pretty incredible what we can do already with our megapixel digital cameras, the ones in our phones, the ones in our larger, more formal photographic cameras, our professional cameras. But, in fact, I'll make the case in this lecture that that just scratches the surface of the information that we can garner about our physical world using light.

In fact, in wavelengths where you and I can't see without own eyes, there's additional information to be harvested. You know, you can think of any material, and chemical compound, as having a color or having kind of a fingerprint in the spectral domain. We are able to tell what's coming out of a smokestack that's a kilometer or two away by looking at the colors that that absorbs or that it reflects or that it emits when we stimulate it with light. We're able to look off in the distance at a safe standoff and potentially identify whether something emitted into the air is some innocent spore or whether it's anthrax.

We're able to use colors in the ultraviolet to start looking for the early signs of skin cancer. These are all wavelengths; that I just mentioned, that your and my eyes don't see, and so here we have the chance to use advances in materials and specifically in nanomaterials to perform spectroscopies or to image in wavelength ranges that on our own we aren't able to access. In a sense, we're able to augment our senses using the capacity of imaging and imaging materials.

Let's start with what's so ubiquitous now. Let's start with our digital cameras. It's interesting to just step back for a moment and think about film-based cameras, which of course were so widespread and so used even though now we've converted over to digital and even in film-based cameras there was nanotechnology even though it wasn't deliberately included. The way in which these silver-based films worked was that there were sort of 50 to 100 nanometer sized particles each independent of the others in which a photocatalytic reaction occurred. When a photon came in, there would be many knock on effects where one of these silver-based salts became soluble and so the resolution, the spatial resolution, of these photographic films was tremendous and that often comes across in the beautiful images that we're able to generate with film-based cameras.

With silicon based cameras, we're also very focused on resolution, being able to heighten the number of pixels of information that we're able to read out. It's remarkable how we go around now with this camera. It's so small, it's just something that we take with us everywhere because it's embedded inside our mobile handset and a lot of its advantages, convenience, relates to its small size, also relates to the fact that it's got a direct interface to information processing: the processor, the integrated circuit inside our cell phone, many integrated circuits in our cell phone, in fact, and it's also directly linked to the internet.

It consists of a lens. The lens has to be a certain distance from the image sensor integrated circuit that the images focused using the lens onto that image sensor, and essentially there's just an array of millions of pixels of photodetectors, of light sensors, which are then read out using this integrated circuit. One of the challenges in making these optical modules more and more appropriate for use in cell phone cameras going forward is the fact the need to make our cell phones slimmer and slimmer. One of the key driving forces for mobile devices is that they should be more compact, and more convenient. So there's great interest in being able to make the module slimmer because today it often limits the thickness of a cell phone.

We'll talk in a moment about how using nanomaterials we're able to make image sensors that allow us to build optical modules that are slimmer, more compatible with the mobile form factor. Let's take a look at this picture of one of these image sensors. This is actually rather a large one by comparison in your large professional digital camera. They can be an inch on side, which is actually quite large for an integrated circuit and leads to higher cost. These sensors are called CMOS integrated circuits. The CMOS is an acronym for the kind of baseline process that we use throughout silicon electronics. What it really communicates is the fact that the image sensor industry has been able to take the available processes used to make silicon electronics, normally no light involved, no photons involved in what your typical processor does inside a computer, but it's been able to leverage that capability those set of boundaries invested in making silicon and it's been able to use that existing resource to build our image sensors. That's been great news for achieving very, very low cost cameras.

What it also does is it puts the image sensor role onto the Moore's law track. It means that there's this constant pressure to be able to shrink the dimensions of the components of these integrated circuits and the integrated circuits themselves to become smaller and smaller, more and more compact. That is great news for fitting more megapixels into a given area. But, there are some compromises that we'll talk about in a second when you shrink pixels down further and further. The bottom line one is that you end up having fewer and fewer photons impinge on each pixel. If you've taken a picture with your cell phone camera and haven't always been satisfied, maybe especially if it's in low light, that's a consequence of this shrink down in the number of photons that impinge on each pixel as a result of shrinking the pixel.

Let's zoom in one of these pixels and take a look at it in a little bit more detail. The last image is representing the conventional silicon image sensor approach. At the bottom of a well is the silicon based light sensor. Now, silicon is not a particularly strong absorber of light and you can't blame silicon for this. Silicon was not selected as the material because of its optical properties. It's its brilliant electronic properties that has driven the emergence of the electronics industry all based around silicon. But, silicon does also have optical absorption; it's just a little bit on the weak side. That's one of the first challenges in existing image sensor approaches that use silicon and only silicon to achieve their functions.

The other challenge you can also see by looking at this image; if you look at what's above the silicon you'll see various layers of materials and those are called the interconnect stack. To make an integrated circuit and including an image sensor, we need those wires that we were talking about in our lectures on microelectronics and nanoelectronics. We need to connect together our transistors. In the case of image sensors, we need to reach in and see our pixels electronically. We need to read out what our pixels have seen in the electronic domain. We need wires. But now, because we build those wires on top of silicon and silicon functions as our substrate, we end up putting wires in the way of the light detector itself.

This problem, which is known as the fill factor problem wherein the area of a pixel is taken up quite a bit by wiring that obscures illumination. This is a problem that has led to deteriorating images as we shrink the size of our pixels. Now here's where nanotechnology comes in. Recent research has shown that we're able to build light detectors that can function in a sense the way silicon does as light absorbers that transduce photonic information into electronic currents. We're able to build these using a new material set, not necessarily even silicon based, involving quantum dots, what are called colloidal quantum dots. These particles—they're semiconductor particles; they're synthesized in solution. They're dispersed in a solution so they're just like a paint and you can coat them onto a silicon wafer and you can coat them on the very top.

As shown with this film at the top level of this nano-enabled integrated circuit, we're able to absorb the light closer to where the light is coming from. The light's no longer responsible for passing through these layers of wire, for passing through an optical aperture, and then being absorbed in the silicon beneath. Instead, we bring our sensor closer to where the light impinges from. So this is the first advantage, this use of nanomaterials overcomes the fill factor problem. The other challenge that it overcomes is that whereas silicon was not engineered in the first place for light absorption we're able to engineer these quantum dots to be extremely strong light absorbers. Now we're able to make a very, very thin film. It's almost like putting photographic film on top of a CMOS image sensor and we're able to capture the image up top and then read it using the silicon electronics below.

This now is a return to using silicon for what it was originally intended for and is so effective for, which is the electronic function. We've built a second story on top of the silicon using nanomaterials and this second story now reaches out and senses the light to be read by the silicon beneath. This is also a great illustration of where some of the greatest opportunities in nanotechnology reside. It's not just in making revolutionary products that are so disruptive that they have nothing to do with previous generations, but instead in overcoming some of the limitations of existing micro-based technologies and augmenting them, but not throwing the baby out with the bath water and continuing to utilize that very attractive properties of silicon and silicon electronics, but augmenting them with the distinctive properties of nanomaterials.

There's another particularly useful property of these quantum dots that bears directly on imaging and that's depicted in this array of colors that we can see here. These quantum dots can be synthesized to have different sizes and when we synthesize them to have these different sizes they can have different colors, different ranges of wavelengths in which they absorb or emit light. In this set of beakers of quantum dots, you're actually seeing a set of semiconductor particles that are compositionally identical. The atoms, the elements that are making up these particles are in all cases the same, but their colors of absorption and emission are very much different spanning the entire visible spectrum depending on the beaker we're looking at here.

The mechanism by which that occurs is the quantum size effect that we've already discussed wherein if we compress an electron wave down to even smaller than its wavelength, we really squeeze it, well in that case we push up its energy levels through the quantum size effect and we turn it into a blue emitter. In the alternative, if we make a somewhat more accommodating quantum dot, if we make our particle of a larger size that doesn't compress or condense the electronic as much, we no longer push its energy as much up above the bottom of the box. We allow it to take on a lower energy and as a consequence be an absorber of lower energy photons.

This concept is useful in a number of ways. I was explaining how we're so good with our own eyes at seeing visible light and to a large extent that's what our digital cameras see today as well because silicon's wavelength, silicon's band gap, the regions in which it's most prone to strongly absorb light, are substantially confined to the visible wavelength region. Let's look at some examples of where we're able to do new things and see in ways we haven't seen before if we're able to look at wavelengths that go beyond the visible.

This image is illustrating the case of a forest fire and on the right you see what you can see if you just use your own eyes or a traditional visible image sensor, which is you see a whole lot of smoke. It doesn't tell you much about where the fire is actually emanating from. It doesn't give people trying to extinguish the fire the detailed information they want to enable them to go straight to the source. On the left, you can see what happens when you're able to take an image in the infrared wavelengths. As a result of the different interactions of these different wavelengths with the particles that reside within the smoke, we're able to see through the smoke all the way to the fire. We're able to get more information about the scene, more information about our physical universe by going to different spectral regimes in the electromagnetic spectrum.

Here's another example, this one not to do with fire, but to do with fog. This is taking a picture of the Bay Bridge and then across to Oakland in the San Francisco Bay area. On the left, you see the usual view on a foggy day where there's not much to see, but on the right, where instead of using a visible camera we use an infrared camera, for similar reasons to the case of the smoke we're able to see beyond the absorption and the scattering of the fog and we're able to see things that with our own eyes we're not capable of seeing. The connection to the quantum dots is the following; these quantum dot nanoparticles are not limited to only tuning over the visible spectral range like we showed in the beakers. In fact, they can extend all the way to these other wavelengths that have traditionally not been the purview of low-cost silicon based cameras. Instead, the images that you saw in the previous slides were taken with a much more costly technology. These used the compound semiconductors; things like the gallium arsenide that we talked about in the context of lasers.

They use these kind of compound semiconductor technologies that are able to see out to these wavelengths, but that aren't the basis for very low cost silicon electronics. What these quantum dots are now doing is taking this very low cost, high volume consumer appropriate, consumer technology appropriate building block, which is silicon, and augmenting it and making it capable of seeing colors that exotic semiconductors have seen in the past, but that now we can with just the top layer of nanomaterials coated on top. Here's another image making another point about the properties of materials and how they're distinguishable from one another based on spectral information.

On the left, you see our subject taken with a visible camera. Nothing too suspicious. But on the right, you can see which parts of his facial hair are his own and which parts are synthetic. We're able to distinguish between biological materials and synthetic materials using the spectral reflective properties of these different classes of materials.

Here's another example, something that we can do when we can see beyond the colors that you and I can see which is we can create bullet tracer technologies. We can image a scene and because the bullet whizzing through the air is so hot it has a signature. It's actually a thermal signature that we can resolve with an infrared camera, but that's not available to us using a visible only camera. As a consequence, we're able to image a scene and not only see where the bullet ends up, but exactly where it came from. We're able to trace it back to its point of origin and this is very useful in military applications and also in law enforcement applications.

Now you may have been wondering a bit about how we see color at all in today's digital image sensors. The answer is that at the moment we put little arrays of filters on top, optical filters, you can probably picture a color wheel in which we have a red and a green and a blue filter that can transmit those corresponding colors of light from behind a white light source. Those color wheels seek to map onto our own eyes sensitivity where we have our color sensing also based on different sensors in our eyes that are differently attuned to the red and the green and the blue. To make a digital camera that can take color images, what we do is we take this array of pixels that we've made on the silicon and then we overlay that with a little matrix of red and green and blue filters.

That works, it's effective. But in doing that, we are throwing away quite a bit of light. When I say a filter, I really mean that we're only letting through our sieve a certain photon, say just the green photons, and we're catching within our sieve the red and the blue ones. When we do that we're further reducing the number of photons that end up impinging on each of the pixels within our image sensors. This is what we call loci color. It's an approach to seeing in color that does so by throwing away information and when we're light starved, when we're trying to take an image in very low light, that's a regrettable thing to be doing.

What quantum dots and nanomaterials enable through their wide spectral tuning and the sharpness of their cutoffs is they enable a new strategy called stacked pixels wherein instead of using filters that first throwaway light followed by sensors that sense all colors, they enable the realization of a stacked pixel in which a first top sensor senses the shorter wavelengths, the higher energy photons, and it detects them there. It doesn't just filter them. It detects them, but it also filters them passing the green and then a green light sensing layer detects green photons and then passes the red and then a further layer beneath absorbs and senses the red. You can think of this as kind of a perfect pixel because rather than sacrificing photons, sacrificing information to the cause of sensing color, it makes the best use of every available and precious photon.

Nanomaterials have recently enabled a very exciting phenomenon that has been the purview until now really of chemists and physicists. They've enabled researchers to see how we can use this new concept called multiexciton generation to make better image sensors more sensitive detectors. Let me start by explaining what this multiple exciton concept is and then how we've managed to use it in order to achieve more sensitive detectors.

Multiexciton generation refers to the fact that normally the way we expect photon detection to occur is in a one-for-one way. One photon comes in and the best case scenario is that we see one electron worth of information. Now in today's image sensors, we're often trying to see very, very weakly lit scenes. In fact, we can be interested in getting down to the range where we're only seeing a few photons, a few particles of light impinging on every pixel. In that case, when we only have a few electrons it starts to become very challenging to read out the information conveyed by those few electrons. We need very, very sensitive low noise circuits to do so. What if instead we could for every photon that comes in, what if we could impart multiple electrons worth of information and thereby ease the burden on our circuit.

Physicists have been studying in these colloidal quantum dots a phenomenon known as multiexciton generation wherein every photon comes in and generates now one, but many electrons inside the material. In fact, it's a multistage process. Initially light comes in and does just generate one excited electron, but then there's a little amplification cascade. You might even think of it as kind of a billiard ball knocking into a couple of other billiard balls and generating a number of excited electrons. Energy is still conserved, we need a lot of energy in this primary photon that leads to this primary excited electron that generates this cascade, that generates a couple of lowering energy electrons, but the ultimate outcome is that we have achieved gain, we have achieved multiplication from one photon into multiple electrons.

Until a couple of years ago, researchers had studied this as a fascinating phenomenon, something that occurred with higher efficiency inside confined structures like quantum dots. We were able to enhance the probability of interactions, essentially make more billiard ball collisions occur by putting our electrons into a small box, but they hadn't actually made a device with it. Then in 2009, researchers found that they could make a photodetector that took advantage of this technology and as a result they were able to see multiple electrons worth of signal collected in a macroscopic current and something that you could measure. Using an instrument, an electronic instrument, they were able to see the benefits of this, see the benefits of this amplification and prospectively we should be able to take advantage of it in making either more sensitive image sensors. This is particularly prone to being useful in the ultraviolet because this is where we have an abundance of photons already and an abundance of very energetic photons. The ultraviolet is a wavelength range that's prone to excite multiple excitons inside these materials.

Now X-ray detectors are another example of another spectral regime for photons as well, but this one into the very, very high energy range and where new insights into new materials have led to extremely promising sensors. One of the key challenges and opportunities for the field of X-rays for the medical applications is that we would like to get the maximum of information, but with the minimum dose of X-rays. Obviously we want to get information without imperiling the patient. In fact, sometimes these days' doctors choose not to take X-rays in order to avoid overexposure, but as a result they're surrendering a greater amount of information that they could learn about their patient to do a better diagnosis and ultimately a better treatment.

The advent of digital mammography, digital X-ray technologies has led to even more sensitive X-ray imaging systems that have allowed us to reduce dosages and therefore either enable us to take fewer risks with patients and X-ray exposure or to put it another way to perform X-rays a bit more liberally and therefore get more information about the patients. This arises again as a result of being able to achieve these single photon detectors very sensitive detectors for light. The other great advantage, of course, once we get our information be it visible or ultraviolet or infrared or X-ray, once we get it off of these image sensors is that we immediately have the capacity to connect it into a computer to get it onto the internet and/or to use the information and to process it to use machine recognition or image recognition to work up these images and in the case of X-rays to give the physician more information than he or she would otherwise have.

Let's talk about another spectral regime, one that's just emerged from having been in no man's land as you can tell. It seems like whenever we enter into a new spectral regime new information becomes available to us, a new and different set of colors becomes reflected and transmitted, another one is now emitting. We're able to achieve contrast, distinction based on chemical properties, compositional properties. One of these spectral regimes that until now have been very hard to access is known as the terahertz. The megahertz range is familiar because when you tune your radio in your car, you'll often see megahertz frequencies. The gigahertz is quite familiar because that's the basis for your cell phone communications. Then as we go to much, much higher frequencies than we get into the optical frequencies, the infrared, and the visible, and beyond.

In between the gigahertz and the optical is the terahertz regime. Until recently, the reason why we had little information in the terahertz regime is that we weren't able to make efficient sources of terahertz radiation. This is where quantum mechanics has come to the rescue recently. A new class of lasers and light sources and photodetectors has all been realized based on quantum phenomena that allow the creation of terahertz photons. This is a bit like a waterfall or a cascade. In fact, it reminds me of when I was in the Black Forest in Germany and I saw an ad for going to the highest waterfall in Germany. I thought well this is going to be pretty impressive and it was beautiful, but it actually wasn't a single drop of water over 163 meters; it was over seven sequential cascades

This notion of the cascade where we go down one level and another level and another level, each of those levels in the case of these cascade lasers the same height, each of these cascades produces these relatively small energy photons inside the cascade laser. The way in which this is achieved is using quantum phenomena, using quantum states whereby putting again our electrons into a box, we take advantage not just of the first level, the lowest lying electronic level, but there're in fact many levels of electronic energy states that are available inside a box and then we can couple many boxes together and achieve this sequential cascade, achieve a waterfall of electrons falling down. Every time an electron falls down one of these levels, we see the emission of a photon, of a particle of light that we can use in terahertz imaging. Terahertz imaging is now coming up in security applications because it turns out you can see through fabric and so that's transparent or transmissive, but you can see whether somebody's concealing either something metallic like a weapon or you can even get information on the chemical composition of what's behind the veil so you can learn about the presence of things like drugs based on their terahertz signatures.

Let's talk about one final example of where this could all go. The field of imaging at a standoff has been taking advantage of the fact that you can shine a beam of light over miles, kilometers, and you can image from a distance for awhile and we've been using spectral signatures to see at these distances, to see chemical compositional information at these distances. But sometimes, the kinds of molecules we're looking for are too subtle, too complex. There're spectral signatures seen from kilometers away that can't be discerned. So, there's an emerging field for biodetection at a standoff where we're looking for very, very specific and subtle differences between two organisms, such as whether something is anthrax or whether it's just posing as anthrax. Scientists have come up with new ways to launch an aerosol into the region of the positive threat, have binding occur between nanoparticles that themselves contain a distinctive fingerprint and the subject of interest, let's say the anthrax bacillus and only if the particles are sticking to the subject of interest do they change color.

They take on a different light emitting color that can be detected from these very, very long distances. As a result of that, we're able to do from a safe distance, from a safe standoff, we're able to do biosensing or biodetection using light, but we're able to see more than what you can see if you only sent photons in. Instead, by sending particles in that change their behavior—change their optical spectral signatures as a function of what they're stuck to, what they're bound to—we're able to see much more than the purely spectral fingerprints would allow us to see.

The examples that we've talked about today, there're about three coupling and interfacing the optical with the electronic. They're about using nanotechnology as a basis for transduction now from the optical into the electronic. The way they leverage nanotechnology first and foremost is through their capacity to engineer materials and their properties towards a particular application. It's our ability through nanoengineering to tailor the properties of materials to our desires to particular spectra, to being strongly absorbing, to being readily integratable with conventional silicon platforms that has led to some of the most exciting work in this field. It also illustrates the point that whereas nanotechnology may sound exotic or new, some of its most powerful and practical applications will come from using nano where we need it and building upon well-established technological platforms such as the field of micro- and nanoelectronics where these are the most powerful solutions.

Nanomedicine—DNA and Gold Nanoparticles
Lecture 7

In the first section of the course, we learned about the impact of nanoscience and nanotechnology in such areas as computing, communications, and imaging. We're now ready to discuss nanoscience in the world of biology—a world that fundamentally operates at the nanoscale—and the applications of nanotechnology to medicine. This lecture and the next one will combine discussions of basic biological processes with nanotechnological applications.

Diagnostic Testing Using Gold Nanoparticles

- Diagnostic testing using gold nanoparticles was one of the first nano-enabled diagnostic systems to come onto the market.

- In the late 1990s, a group of researchers at Northwestern University discovered how to attach DNA molecules to gold nanoparticles. They did this by identifying a sulfur atom that was very good at sticking to gold. They then attached this atom to the end of a sequence of DNA that they synthesized. With these DNA-nanoparticle complexes, these researchers showed that they could read out mutations in very long DNA sequences from patients.

- The detection of DNA mutations has tremendous relevance to the diagnosis of genetic diseases, such as cystic fibrosis. Genetic diseases are caused by small changes in an individual's DNA that are then passed down from generation to generation.

- The gold nanoparticles were able to scan DNA molecules for these changes, and if a problem with the DNA was identified, the particles changed color. To understand how something as complicated as genetic disease can be detected with a simple color change, we need to take a closer look at three components of this diagnostic approach: the gold nanoparticle, the DNA molecule attached to the particle, and the DNA genome that is scanned.

The DNA Genome

- As we know, DNA is the molecule that stores all the information our cells need to function. It does so by programming information in a biological code. If we zoom in at the molecular level (also the nano level), we find that DNA is a double-stranded molecule, in which the 2 strands are wound around each other, forming the famous double-helical structure.

- Why does this helix form, and how does it carry a code? The key feature of DNA that is relevant to both of these questions is that it contains 4 different building blocks, the DNA bases: A, G, C, and T.

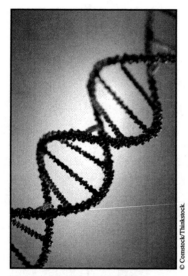

The double helix of DNA forms as a result of attractive forces between its 4 building blocks—the bases A, G, C, and T.

- All 4 of the DNA bases have different chemical structures; these are not necessarily different kinds of atoms but atoms that are arranged differently. Thus, each base has a unique structure.

- The helical structure of DNA results from specific attractive forces between bases that dictate what partners they pair with in hydrogen bonds. The base A, for example, binds to the T, and they have 2 hydrogen bonds. The Gs bind to the Cs, and they have 3 hydrogen bonds.

- The specificity here is amazing. We can take a piece of DNA that has 100 units within it, and if we introduce the complementary sequence—in which for every A, we have a T; for every G, we have a C; and vice versa—those 2 DNA molecules will line up perfectly, without any mistakes.

- Even more amazing than the way these bases are arrayed is what codes the genetic information required for life. The pattern of bases that is found in a DNA molecule gives the cell a full set of instructions so that it knows exactly what to do to keep itself alive and healthy.

The DNA Molecule
- In the 1940s, scientists were aware that DNA was most likely the molecule of life, and they knew that it included different amounts of the 4 units, but they didn't know what the molecule might look like.

- James Watson and Francis Crick got a start on finding the structure of the molecule using stick-and-ball models. At the same time, Rosalind Franklin and Maurice Wilkins were using X-ray diffraction to try to understand the molecule's structure.

- A major breakthrough came when Watson and Crick saw Franklin's famous Photograph 51. This was an X-ray diffraction pattern of a DNA sample. The fuzzy X in the middle of the molecule is not a direct image of DNA but the diffraction of X-rays bounced off of DNA. This pattern indicates a helical structure, and it was this information that allowed Watson and Crick to determine the structure of the DNA molecule.

- There are 6 billion bases in the DNA found in every cell. Each base takes up about 0.3 nanometers in a linear sequence. This means that for every 10 base pairs, you have about 1 nanometer of DNA; 100 base pairs give you about 10 nanometers; and so on. Stretched end to end, there are about 2 meters—more than 6 feet—of DNA in every cell! The reason we can fit all of this DNA in our cells is that it's not present in a linear form; it's condensed into tiny particles.

Gold Nanoparticles

- Patients affected with cystic fibrosis typically have mutations in a gene that dictates how well their cells can deal with salts. For example, the most common mutation causes 3 bases to be missing from a sequence that codes for a protein that is essential for cellular function. This causes mucus to accumulate in the lung, and serious bacterial infections result that interfere with breathing.

- How do gold nanoparticles sense mutations like this? As we've seen, DNA consists of 2 complementary strands in the cell. If we want to target a particular sequence of DNA to diagnose a disease that would result from mutations in that sequence, we can take a manmade strand of DNA and design it to stick to the region of the mutation; how well it sticks will tell us whether the mutation is present or not.

- In order to detect the cystic fibrosis mutations, two different types of gold nanoparticles can be made that will line up specifically with the region of mutated DNA. If the altered DNA sequence is present, the gold nanoparticles will bind to it, and when this happens, the nanoparticles will change from red to blue. It's that color change that tells us that the mutant sequence is present.

- Of course, macroscale gold—gold in its metallic state—isn't red and it doesn't change color. But when nanoscale gold is dispersed in solution, it has a very different set of properties. Its red color is related to the nanoscale size of those particles.

- The fact that nanoscale objects can have a completely different set of properties from macroscale versions is a key point that illustrates why nanomaterials have unique utility.
  - The color change that we've seen and the red color of gold nanoparticles in solution arise because of the interactions of the particles with light.

  - The fact that the oscillations of light are on about the same size scale as the nanoparticles allows a unique interaction.

- Macroscale gold doesn't interact with light; it merely reflects light. But with gold nanoparticles, we have electromagnetic waves that are dispersed on the surface of the particle, where there are highly delocalized electrons. The wavelengths of light and the waves on the surfaces of the particles interact and dictate what color the particles appear to be to the human eye.

- Gold nanoparticles that are surrounded by water and not close to other particles appear to be red. When the nanoparticles come close to one another, they appear blue. Again, it's the same material, but it has a different distance separating it.
  - The fact that the absorption of this material becomes blue means that the particles become electronically coupled. The electrons actually start talking to one another; they know that others are there, and that perturbs the surface waves on the nanoparticles.

  - That perturbation of the surface waves gives us the color change that we see when nanoparticles line up on a strand of DNA in the presence of a disease-related mutation.

The Technology in Use
- A company that was launched out of Northwestern University developed an instrument to automate the process of using gold nanoparticles to detect genetic mutations, and the technology is now being used in hospitals across North America.

- In a testing laboratory, a technician can take a sample of blood, extract the DNA from the cells, purify it, and inject it into a cartridge that can mix it up with nanoparticles. This mixture is then put onto an array, which picks out patterns of blue spots or pink spots, allowing doctors to know what mutations are present in the sample.

- This type of testing instrument, in addition to being used for cystic fibrosis testing, can also be used to determine whether patients have mutations that make them sensitive to certain drugs. Viruses and bacteria can also be detected with the instrument.

- As mentioned earlier, this is one of the first nano-enabled diagnostic systems to come onto the market. In future lectures, we'll discuss other types of diagnostic approaches that are a little bit earlier in their development but have just as much promise.

Suggested Reading

Maddox, *Rosalind Franklin.*

Nanosphere, Inc. (corporate Web site).

NOVA, "Secret of Photo 51."

Seeman, "Nanotechnology and the Double Helix."

Vo-Dinh, ed., *Nanotechnology in Biology and Medicine.*

Watson, *The Double Helix.*

Questions to Consider

1. How does DNA transmit genetic information from one cell to another? How does this capacity relate to the ability of DNA to link nanomaterials?

2. Why is reading out DNA sequences relevant to disease diagnosis? For what diseases is this type of diagnostic approach most relevant?

Nanomedicine—DNA and Gold Nanoparticles
Lecture 7—Transcript

Shana Kelley: In the first section of the course, you heard about the impact of nanoscience and nanotechnology in areas like computing, communications, and imaging. We're now ready to leave the physical world and enter the biological world to discuss nanoscience in the world of biology, and as well the applications of nanotechnology to medicine. Biology fundamentally operates at the nanoscale: the basic building blocks of life are all around 1 or 2 nanometers in size, so things like amino acids, sugars, lipids, even DNA molecules are all nanoscale objects.

Only slightly larger than these molecular building blocks are the vast world of molecular machines and the messengers that drive cellular function. Historically, the cell was thought of as having a few major organelles that did most of the work. For example, the cellular mitochondria, which are the power producers in the cell, they're about 1000 nanometers, so a little too big to be nanoscale. But, we now know that there are thousands of smaller different molecules that run around inside cells—and these molecules allow cells to live and replicate.

For example, proteins are synthesized by molecular machines called ribosomes. These ribosomes which perform a very complicated function are only 25 nanometers in size. As well, energy for the cell is produced by an enzyme called ATP synthase and this enzyme—again a very complicated machine that has a very important function—is about 10 nanometers in size. The cell membrane, which holds everything in the cell in place, is typically about 10 nanometers too. You can see that this idea of biology really being nanoscale spans many, many different aspects of biology. As well, certain self-replicating organisms can also be nanoscale although just barely. Certain viruses can be around 20 nanometers, others are about 400 nanometers, but then the very smallest bacteria are about 1000 nanometers, so not really nanoscale.

As you might imagine, nanoscientists derive lots of inspiration from biology. We look at the complex world of biology and we marvel at its ability to self-organize and we try to recreate what we see with the tools of nanotechnology.

It will be important for us to understand some of these nanoscale activities of the cell so that we can understand disease mechanisms and the action of nanodrugs and as well the logic behind nanodiagnostic approaches. In order to do this, we need to take a look at the biomolecules that are responsible for all the action within a cell and we need to understand how they're structured and how they function. Then we can explore how those biomolecules can be put together with nanomaterials to do something let's say like advance drug development or help with the invention of new diagnostic tools.

Our next two lectures will combine discussions of basic biological processes with nanotechnological applications. Then we'll move on to some discussions that are more focused and they'll be focused on applications of nanomedicine. We'll start in this lecture by looking at a new type of diagnostic testing based on gold nanoparticles that has very exciting potential. What is so exciting about this is that this is a completely new type of testing that can read out a variety of DNA mutations that give rise to genetic disease or drug reactions and this type of testing relies on a very simple measurement, the change of color of a nanomaterial.

This was one of the first nano enabled diagnostic systems to come onto the market. The discovery that this diagnostic approach is based on was made in the late 1990s at Northwestern University in Illinois. A group there in the Chemistry Department discovered how to attach small DNA molecules to gold nanoparticles. How did they do this? Well, they identified a type of atom (a sulfur atom) that was very good at sticking to gold. They then attached a sulfur atom to the end of a sequence of DNA that they synthesized. With these DNA-nanoparticle complexes, they showed that they could read out small changes, or what we call mutations, in very long DNA sequence from patients.

The detection of DNA mutations as I'm sure you know has tremendous relevance to the diagnosis of genetic diseases like cystic fibrosis. Genetic diseases are caused by very small changes in an individual's DNA as these changes then get passed down from generation to generation. The gold nanoparticles again developed at Northwestern were able to scan DNA molecules for these changes, and if a problem with the DNA was identified, the particles changed color and they turned from red to blue. How can something as complicated as genetic disease be detected with a simple color change? All this seems way too good to be true. Let's take a close look at this so we can really understand how it works.

In order to really have a complete picture of how this type of diagnostic approach works, we need to understand three different components that are coming together—a gold nanoparticle, a small DNA molecule attached to the particle, and the DNA genome that's being scanned. Let's start with the DNA genome so that we can understand the challenges involved in genetic disease diagnosis. As I'm sure you're aware DNA is the molecule that stores all of the information our cells need to function. It does so by programming information in a biological code. If we zoom in at the molecular level (and keep in mind that this is also the nano level) we find that DNA is a double stranded molecule. If you look closely at the structure in the figure, you'll see that there are two strands that are wound around each other and they form this very famous double helical structure that I'm sure you've seen before

.Now why does this helix form? You know of all structures to be present why do we get this helical structure? How does it carry a code? Well, I'm sure the answers are familiar to you from introductory biology. The key feature of DNA that is relevant to both of these questions is that it contains four different building blocks that we call the DNA bases. They each have one letter abbreviations either A, or G, or C, or T and don't worry too much about these names, but the one letter abbreviation either stands for adenine, guanine, cytosine, or thymine. All four of the DNA bases have different chemical structures. You'll see that A is colored red, T is yellow, G is blue, and C is green and if you look closely at these structures you'll see that they have not necessarily different kinds of atoms, but atoms that are arranged differently and so each base has a unique structure and we'll talk about why that's important in a few minutes.

The helical structure of DNA results from specific attractive forces between bases that dictate what partners they pair with. Why is there this pairing? Why are these strands attracted to one another? It turns out that hydrogen bonding is what's key in holding the structure of DNA together. Hydrogen bonds are bonds that actually hold molecules together kind of loosely, but

125

with a high degree of specificity. These types of bonds, not surprisingly, are called hydrogen bonds and they involve hydrogen so you have to have as one part of the partner a hydrogen atom, and then as the other partner we usually find things like oxygen or nitrogen. It turns out that all of life, all of the molecules that are wrapped up in our cells are held together by the attractive forces of hydrogen bonds. As I said this is a loose type of bonding, but it's very specific and it's enough to have us live and breathe and do all of the things that we do. As you look more closely at the structure, if you now can pick out a hydrogen bond, you'll see that the A moieties bind to the Ts and they have two hydrogen bonds. The Gs bind to the Cs and they have three hydrogen bonds so there are these different levels of bonding and of different base pairs.

So these attractive forces between different bases cause the strands to pair up. This is why DNA helices form. The specificity here is amazing. You can take a piece of DNA that has 100 units within it, and if you introduce the complementary sequence where for every A you have a T, every G you have a C, and vice versa, those two DNA molecules will line up perfectly and there won't be any mistakes. It works every time. Even more amazing is the way these bases are arrayed is what codes the genetic information required for life. The pattern of bases that are found in a DNA molecule gives a cell a full set of instructions so it knows exactly what to do to keep itself alive and healthy.

Now I've shown you the structure of DNA and pointed out its key, nanoscale features, but how do we know that this is exactly how it looks and how was the structure of DNA originally characterized? To answer this question, we have to go back to the 1940's. At that time, members of the scientific community were aware that DNA was most likely the molecule of life that carried genetic information. They also knew that DNA included different amounts of the four units—A, T, G and C—but nobody had the slightest idea of what the molecule might look like. There were proposals, there were models drawn on a piece of paper, but it was all really guesswork. You have to keep in mind that when this question was being answered, this was long before we had the ability to image molecules at the nanoscale.

Two men, James Watson and Francis Crick ended up being the ones that eventually did solve the structure and they got a start on getting that structure using stick-and-ball models. They were working on this problem in the 1940s at the University of Cambridge and you'll see in the picture that you're viewing a depiction of their model, the two of them working on it. It may seem funny to try to solve something as complicated as DNA structure by building something out of wire and trying to get it work and come together, but if you're thinking about something chemical it's actually quite a valuable way to build up a structure because you know what the bond angles and bond lengths can be and you can eventually put together something that makes sense.

At the same time, other scientists were using experimental methods where they were trying to directly characterize the structure of DNA. Rosalind Franklin and Maurice Wilkins, who were also in England, but they were at Kings College in London, used X-ray diffraction to understand the physical structure of the DNA molecule. When you shine X-rays on a crystal of DNA, the invisible rays bounce off the sample. The rays then create complex patterns on photographic film, but it would take hours and hours to capture a single image. Then by looking at the patterns, it was possible to get important clues about the structures that make up the crystals.

Watson and Crick were building their models, but they were having difficulty getting the strands to match up properly. Every time they would stand in front of their model and they would try to bring the two strands together they just couldn't make it such that it was stable. They knew it would just fall right apart. It was as though they were trying to solve a puzzle, but they weren't using the right pieces. They just couldn't get the whole thing to work.

A major breakthrough came when they saw Rosalind Franklin's famous "photograph 51." This was an X-ray diffraction pattern of a DNA sample, and you'll notice that it has a fuzzy X in the middle of the molecule, and this is not actually a direct image of DNA, but the diffraction of X-rays bounced off of the DNA show a pattern. This pattern indicates that there's a helical structure there and so that told them that the structure of DNA was a helix, and that it had a certain periodicity that told them about the spacing between the bases. It was this information that allowed Watson and Crick to finally get the structure right. They published their structure of DNA in the journal Nature in 1953, and this paper was published alongside of a paper from Rosalind Franklin another paper from Maurice Wilkins describing the experimental data that they had collected.

Watson, Crick, and Wilkins received the Nobel Prize in 1962 for their discovery. Unfortunately Rosalind Franklin died in 1958 of ovarian cancer and thus did not live long enough to be recognized for her very important contribution to solving the structure of DNA. Now that we know something about the nanoscale structure of DNA, let's think about the much longer pieces of DNA that are present in a cell.

There are 6 billion bases in the DNA found in every cell. Each base takes up about 0.3 nanometers in a linear sequence. That means for every 10 base pairs you have about a nanometer of DNA, 100 base pairs give you about 10 nanometers, and so on. So if you think about it and you add up the numbers, that means that there are 2 meters (or over 6 feet) of DNA in every cell if you were going to stretch it end to end. The DNA in just one of my cells, and there are trillions of cells in my body, if it was stretched out linearly and vertically, it would be taller than I am! That's just one cell's worth of DNA. If you took all of the DNA in all of your cells and laid it out end to end, it would actually stretch to the moon and back about 130,000 times. It's amazing to think about it and I really don't suggest trying to see if I am right; you'll have to just take my word for it as for one thing it would be very hard to get the DNA back in your cells after you took it out and it would also be very expensive to fly back and forth to the moon every time to check that, so hopefully again you take my word for it. But, it's really amazing to consider how much DNA it takes for us to function.

The reason that we can fit all of this DNA in our cells is that it is condensed into tiny particles and it's not present in a linear form. In the figure that you are looking at, you can see how the DNA of an X chromosome—which has 155 million base pairs, but is only about 100 nanometers in size, it really needs to come unraveled for the linear form to be the least bit visible. Now that we have an understanding of the structure of DNA, let's talk about the role of DNA in genetic disease. Then we'll be able to look at how nanomaterials can be used for DNA-based diagnosis of genetic disease.

Patients affected with a disease called cystic fibrosis typically have mutations in a gene that dictates how well their cells can deal with salts. For example, the most common mutation causes 3 bases to be missing from a sequence that codes for a protein that is essential for cellular function. This causes mucus to accumulate in the lung and serious bacterial infections result that then interfere with breathing. This is a very serious disease. Now let's come back to the gold nanoparticles that can sense these mutations. How do they do it? As you now know, DNA consists of two complementary strands in the cell. If we want to target a particular sequence of DNA to diagnose a disease that would result from mutations in that sequence, we can take a man-made strand of DNA and design it to stick to the region of the mutation and how well it sticks will tell us whether the mutation is there or not.

In order to detect the cystic fibrosis mutations, two different types of gold nanoparticles can be made that will line up specifically with the region of mutated DNA. This is depicted schematically in the graphic that you're looking at so hopefully you can see what's going where. If the altered DNA sequence is present, the gold nanoparticles will bind to it and they'll come together. When this happens, the nanoparticles will change from red to blue. It's that color change that tells us that the mutant sequence is present. That may sound a little strange, one material a gold nanoparticles changing color because it's binding to DNA so I want you to really believe me that this is what happens and so I'm going to do a demonstration of this so that you can see for yourself how it works.

What I have here is a solution of gold nanoparticles and as you see they're just suspended in solution, nothing really hanging around in the solution. These are all very soluble and stable and I've put some of that gold nanoparticles solution into two different test tubes. What we'll do is we'll add DNA to one, but not the other and we'll see what happens in terms of the color change in the tube where DNA was added and then we'll compare it with the one that was just left alone.

Here's my solution of DNA, so just a clear solution, again DNA is completely soluble, doesn't really have any color of its own so this just looks like water. I'm going to take a few drops add it to one of our gold nanoparticles solutions and then you see what happens. You can see that right away the solution is changing color and again we started out with red, I added something that's clear and now you can see that this guy is turning kind of bluish-purple. That is the color change that's affected by gold nanoparticles brought together by a complementary sequence of DNA. That's exactly the type of effect that's used to pick up on the presence of genetic mutations.

If we step back for a minute, this is kind of curious right. We are talking about gold nanoparticles. We all know what color gold is in its solid color. It's gold, right. Now why did I start with one solution that was red and then I was able to change it into a blue solution and this all of a sudden starts to seem kind of confusing. If you happen to have two rings that are made of gold and you bring them together absolutely nothing happens right. Gold in its metallic state really doesn't ever change color. Here we're not talking about macroscale gold; we're talking about nanoscale gold. When nanoscale gold is dispersed in solution it has a very different set of properties and so that red color is related to the nanoscale size of these particles.

This is a great example of how a nanoparticles or a nanoscale object can have a completely different set of properties than the macroscale version that maybe we're used to looking at. This is a key point that illustrates why nanomaterials can have unique utility. This color change that we're talking about—and the fact that the gold nanoparticles in solution start off red to begin with—arises because of the interactions of the particles with light. If you think about light and the waves that make up light, those waves are on a length scale of nanometers. We talk about the spectrum of light and the unit that we describe that in is always nanometers. The fact that you have light with these oscillations that are nanometers, you have a particle that has a set of dimensions that are about on the same size scale. There's an interaction there that is unique.

Again macroscale gold that doesn't have anything nanoscale going on doesn't really interact with light. It just reflects light. Here with these tiny gold nanoparticles, we have electromagnetic waves that are dispersed on the surface of the particle and there are highly delocalized electrons there, and so the wavelengths of light and these waves on the surfaces of the particles interact and they dictate what color the particles appear to be to the human eye.

Gold nanoparticles that are surrounded by water, and not close to other particles, appear to be red. When the nanoparticles come close to one another, they appear blue. So again it's the same material, but it just has a different distance separating it. The fact that the absorption of this material becomes blue reflects the fact that they become electronically coupled. What does that mean? Well it means that the electrons actually start talking to one another; they know that they're there, and then that perturbs the surfaces waves on the nanoparticles and it's this perturbation of those surface waves that gives us the color change that we see when nanoparticles line up on a strand of DNA in the presence of a disease-related mutation.

Now you understand how gold nanoparticles can be used to detect the DNA mutations that cause disease. You're probably wondering is this something that can be done now, or are we talking about something that is years away from being available? It turns out that nanoparticles are actually being used today for exactly this application that we've just gone over in hospitals all over North America. A company called Nanosphere that was launched out of Northwestern University where all of this research began has taken the gold nanoparticle technology and developed an instrument that can automate its use. So, me squirting my solutions here on a bench we wouldn't necessarily want somebody to be using gold nanoparticles that way to do something as important as diagnosing a disease, but the same concept has been packaged up into an instrument.

In a testing laboratory, a technician can take a sample of blood, they extract the DNA from the cells—they break the cells up and they take the DNA out and they purify it, and then they inject it into a cartridge, just a small testing unit that can mix it up with the nanoparticles. Then this mixture is put onto an array, and what the array is doing is picking out a pattern of blue spots or pink spots that allows us to know what mutations are present in the sample. This is important because there are many different DNA mutations that cause cystic fibrosis and so it's important to be able to look at many sequences at once—hence the need for lots of different spots for the same test. We wouldn't want to miss let's say a very rare mutation and miss the diagnosis for that reason so being able to look at lots of things at once is very helpful in that regard.

This type of testing instrument, in addition to being used for cystic fibrosis testing, can also be used to see if patients have mutations that make them sensitive to certain drugs. Genetic factors have much to do with why individuals react differently to the same drug, and there is a Nanosphere test now available that allows physicians to assess this genetic predisposition before writing a prescription, so before they give a patient a drug that they're going to have a bad reaction to, a very powerful capability. Things like viruses and as well bacteria can also be detected with the Nanosphere instrument. Different viruses and bacteria have different genetics, and so the same principle can be applied to diagnosis of viral infections. It's very clear that this technology has tremendous utility, and as I mentioned at the beginning, this is one of the first nano-enabled diagnostic systems to come onto the market—a very exciting piece of progress.

This advance is the first of many and in a few lectures we'll discuss other types of diagnostic approaches that are a little bit earlier in their development, but have just as much promise. We'll come back to this idea of looking at nucleic acid molecules using nanomaterials to do very sensitive and specific detection and we'll look at a variety of different approaches that can achieve this, again, all using nanomaterials. So in this lecture, we've covered some key concepts that will help you to understand nanomedical advances and how they work. You've now seen an example of a nanomaterial, a gold nanoparticle, this has come up in other lectures, but now you've seen how these materials can scan DNA for mutations.

We also discussed a special property of nanoscale objects, and that's the interaction with nanometer light waves and this gives nanomaterials like gold very different colors than their macroscale counterparts. You now know that this special light-changing capacity can be used to diagnose genetic disease resulting from DNA mutations. In the next lecture, we'll talk about nanomaterials that are given special functions by the attachment of a different type of molecule that's also nanoscale—a protein, so we'll look at the structures of proteins, go over their functions, relate how the functions of proteins can be used to manipulate nanomaterials or to make them more powerful. See you then!

Nano and Proteins—Enzymes to Cholesterol
Lecture 8

J ust like DNA, which we covered in the last lecture, proteins are a major class of biomolecules that can connect biology directly with the world of nanotechnology. In this lecture, we'll look at some of the basic features of proteins and see how these features have been used to manipulate nanomaterials or how they can be made useful for applications in nanoscience and nanomedicine.

The Structure of Proteins

- Proteins are a type of cellular molecule that—unlike DNA—have a wide range of functional roles and structural motifs. They drive all the chemical reactions that occur within cells, they provide structural support to cells and tissues, and they control what molecules are allowed in and out of cells. Proteins are also the key players in the immune system; they recognize foreign cells, such as bacteria and viruses, and target them for destruction.

- Proteins are composed of amino acids, which are no more than 1 nanometer in size. The ordering of the amino acids within a protein can have a strong effect on structure. That ordering is determined by the information in DNA.

- The first glimpse of protein structures at the nanoscale came around the time that DNA's structure was first characterized. It was much harder to interpret the protein data, however, because unlike the simple double-helical structure of DNA, proteins have structures that are highly variable.
  - Consider, for example, the protein hemoglobin. This protein carries the oxygen from our lungs to other sites in the body.

  - Notice that there are curly, helical sections in the protein structure, but it's not a straight, continuous helix like DNA. There are also sections that are not helical, that are interspersed, and these can be quite disordered. This is one of the things that made structural characterization of proteins extremely difficult.

- o Another challenge was that there are 22 different amino acids that can be present within a protein, and having so many building blocks made it much more challenging to fit everything together.

- Why are the structures of proteins so variable? The answer is probably connected to the fact that they perform so many different functions within the cell. Some proteins have evolved to very specifically recognize other proteins or even DNA or other molecules; thus, their structures are designed to find and bind partners.

  - o The helical sections that we find in proteins are rigid, so they're good at grabbing chemical functionalities on other molecules. This is where different amino acids come in. The ones that are good at making hydrogen bonds can reach out and make contact with other molecules.

  - o The linker regions that we saw in hemoglobin are quite flexible, and they're good at allowing a protein to change its shape to give off a signal. In this way, proteins can tell a cell whether it's cold or hungry so that the cell can respond.

  - o Other structural motifs that are found in proteins can provide binding pockets where chemical reactions can occur.

Proteins as Catalysts

- One of the most ubiquitous functions of proteins is the catalysis of chemical reactions. Proteins are good at making unreactive molecules do something special. They do this by binding molecules in special pockets where they can bend the molecule to put it under stress and break a bond, or they can use one of their own functionalities to cut or replace a chemical bond.

- As an example, let's consider the peroxidase enzymes, which break down peroxides, such as hydrogen peroxide.
  - On its own, hydrogen peroxide is pretty stable, but when it binds the peroxidase, it's cut in half and made very reactive. This is an important function that helps the immune system fight disease.

  - In the presence of an infectious agent—for example, a bacterial cell—the enzyme converts hydrogen peroxide into a reactive molecule that will stop the bacterium in its tracks by damaging its cell wall.

- Interestingly, the enzyme peroxidase seems to be able break down and biodegrade carbon nanotubes, which is an important discovery for drug delivery using nanotubes. This degradation process takes place from the outside layer of the nanotube and works toward the inner layers.

Antibodies
- Antibodies represent another important class of proteins. Antibodies are able to specifically recognize foreign agents in our bodies and tag those foreign agents so that they're eliminated. Most antibodies have a Y shape, with a stem and two recognition domains that are very specific sensors.

- How do these proteins recognize threats to the immune system? Our bodies have large libraries, or sets of antibodies, and every member of this set is slightly different. Once one of these antibodies finds something threatening, it gives off a signal that says it should be amplified, and many copies of it are made to ensure that an infection is cleared.

- As you know, our immune systems can sometimes turn against us. For those people who have certain food allergies, it's the immune system and antibodies that mistakenly treat a certain component of a food as a threat.

- We have also learned, however, to make our immune systems work better. We know how to vaccinate against many diseases by injecting substances that mimic infectious agents to trigger antibodies.

- We also know how to produce highly specific antibodies in large quantities so that we can exploit their binding properties for medical applications. There are several antibody-based drugs that are able to find specific proteins on the surfaces of cancer cells and selectively eliminate them just as if they were bacterial cells.

- Antibodies are a powerful tool in nanomedicine. For example, antibody–gold nanoparticle conjugates are already used as indicators in many commercially available pregnancy tests. The red lines that appear when urine is introduced onto the testing stick are formed with gold nanoparticles.
  o In these tests, an antibody that specifically binds the hormone hCG is modified with a gold nanoparticle.

  o If hCG is present, it binds to the antibody, and a large complex is formed. This complex flows along the testing stick until it reaches the test site.

  o At the site, a filter stops the large complex from flowing through and concentrates it into a line.

  o Close by, any leftover gold nanoparticles that are still present are trapped by a finer filter and used as a control (a single red line) to show that the sample was actually transported through the device.

  o In this way, the intense color and the nanoscale size of the particles are leveraged to make this type of diagnostic testing easier and more sensitive.

Passive Protein Functions

- Not all proteins have what we would consider active functions. Some of these passive functions are present to provide structure to a cell or a tissue.

- For example, collagen is a main component of connective tissue, and it represents 30% of the total protein in our bodies. It always exists as a triple-helical structure, about 1.5 nanometers wide and 300 nanometers long. These triple helices of collagen are wound into tough bundles that can be hundreds of nanometers thick, and they provide a guide that tells cells where to grow.

- Scurvy is one of a number of diseases that are related to problems with collagen. The vitamin C deficiency that causes scurvy produces defective collagen, which affects connective tissues. The gums in the mouth are particularly susceptible to this, and tooth loss was a major ramification of scurvy. The process of wound healing is also expedited by collagen, and slow healing was a major symptom of scurvy.

- Collagen is an intensely studied protein because of its role in our physical appearance. The changes that appear in our skin as we age come about because of collagen breakdown. Many cosmetic procedures have been developed that attempt to reintroduce collagen to

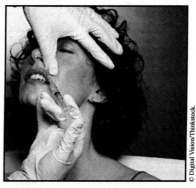

As we age, the collagen in our faces and elsewhere breaks down, causing our skin to lose structure; cosmetic procedures attempt to reintroduce collagen to repair these effects.

repair the effects of aging. Collagen is also an important component in types of artificial skin that are under development for treatment of burn victims.

- Collagen has been used as a model for the development of nanomaterials that can support cell growth. As mentioned earlier, collagen is oriented in fibers, and its directionality and the spacing of the fibers tell cells how to position themselves. This natural phenomenon has been mimicked with nanomaterials.
  - Researchers at MIT have produced nanoscale gratings that mimic the structure of collagen, and they have found that these gratings are effective at orienting cells.

  - It's important for cells to have directionality in order to be able to build up tissues and organs in an organized manner; thus, these types of materials have tremendous promise for artificial tissue engineering.

Proteins as Cellular Gatekeepers
- Delicate balances of different molecules must be maintained in cells, and there are proteins that sit on the surfaces of cells whose function it is to decide what should be allowed into and out of the cell.

- These proteins, called receptors, are inactive if they do not have anything bound, but once they bind something, they trigger an amazing chain of events, causing the cell to make pockets in its outer membrane that allow the receptor to bring materials into the cell.

- This type of process plays an important role in how cholesterol is processed.
  - One type of cholesterol is packaged in a nanoscale particle formed by a protein called low-density lipoprotein, or LDL. These particles can bump into a receptor on the surface of the cell, and the cell takes in the LDL.

  - If LDL isn't brought into our cells, then it remains in the bloodstream, and that's where it can cause harm. If the cholesterol is taken into the cell, then it can be metabolized.

  - Individuals who have a defect in one of the proteins that sends the cholesterol particles are susceptible to having high serum cholesterol concentrations and subsequent coronary and vascular issues.

• Gold nanoparticles use the same pathway as LDL to enter cells. The particles bind receptor proteins on the outsides of cells and are taken in through pockets in the cell membrane. Interestingly, researchers have recently found that the shape and size of nanoparticles can affect the efficiency of uptake into the cell. This type of study is quite helpful as new nanomaterials are designed for applications that take place both inside and outside the cell.

Suggested Reading

Cooper, et al., *Principles of Protein Structure, Comparative Protein Modelling, and Visualization.*

de la Rica and Matsui, "Applications of Peptide and Protein-Based Materials in Bionanotechnology."

Stryer, *Biochemistry.*

Vo-Dinh, "Protein Nanotechnology."

Questions to Consider

1. What are the functions of proteins in cells? Why would it be important to interface them with nanomaterials?

2. How do we know what proteins look like at the nanoscale? Why does it matter?

Nano and Proteins—Enzymes to Cholesterol
Lecture 8—Transcript

Shana Kelley: Everyone knows that protein is an important part of our diet, but do you know why? Well our bodies are actually 20% protein and it's this material that allows us to think and run and do all of the other things that we do. Protein is a very important part of our diet so that we can make the molecules that we need internally and keep ourselves running.

Just like DNA which we covered the last time, proteins are a major class of biomolecules that can connect biology very directly with the world of nanotechnology. What we'll do in this lecture is to look at some of the basic features of proteins, and see how these features have been used to manipulate nanomaterials, or make them useful for applications in nanoscience and nanomedicine. Proteins are a type of cellular molecule that—unlike DNA—have a wide range of functional roles and structural motifs.

When we talked about DNA, we talked about its very regular structure and the fact that it really only does one thing. It stores genetic information. Proteins, on the other hand, have many, many different functions so they drive all of the chemical reactions that occur within cells, they provide structural support to cells and tissues, they're also the gatekeepers of cells, controlling what molecules are allowed in and out. Proteins are also the key players in our immune system; they're able to recognize foreign cells like bacteria and viruses and target them for destruction.

Before we talk about how proteins and nanomaterials can interact, let's consider the nanoscale structure of proteins themselves. These molecules are composed of small building blocks that we refer to as amino acids and when we call them small what do we mean. They're no more than one nanometer in size. The picture that you're looking at shows the structure of tryptophan. This is an example of an amino acid you're probably familiar with because of its reputation for making us sleepy after we've Thanksgiving turkey. That's not its major function, but that's one of the things that it can do when it's floating around in cells.

It turns out that there are 22 versions of tryptophan that serve as building blocks in proteins. They're all slightly different—some are more greasy or water-friendly or they may have a molecular charge. The part of the amino acid that you're looking at that's gray is what varies from one amino acid to another—the rest of the molecule stays constant. The ordering of the amino acids within a protein can have a strong effect on structure. How is the sequence or the ordering of the amino acids within a protein determined? Well, this is what the information within DNA is used for. It's turned into a protein code that gives cells the molecules they can use for all of their various functions.

The first glimpse of protein structures at the nanoscale came around the time that DNA structure was first characterized. It was much harder to interpret the protein data, though, because unlike the simple double helical structure of DNA that is very uniform, it turns out that proteins have structures that are highly variable. Let's take a look at a protein named hemoglobin. This protein carries the oxygen from our lungs to other sites in the body, or if you happen to be a fish and you're tuning in, it carries the oxygen from the gills to the rest of the fish. This protein is roughly six nanometers across.

You'll notice that there are curly, helical sections in the protein structure, but it's not a straight, continuous helix like DNA. There are also sections that are not helical that are interspersed and these can be quite disordered and this is one of the things that makes structural characterization of proteins extremely difficult. Another challenge was that there were 22 different amino acids that could be present within the protein and having so many building blocks made it much more challenging to fit everything together.

But a breakthrough was finally made in this area in the 1950s, which, as you'll remember, was the decade after DNA structure was characterized. Two researchers working at Cambridge University, Max Perutz and John Kendrew spent an entire decade trying to deconvolute protein structure and they were finally successful in 1957. They received the Nobel Prize in Chemistry in 1962, and you'll remember probably this is the same year that the Nobel Prize in Physiology and Medicine was awarded for the structure of DNA.

Why are the structures of proteins so variable? We think this is connected to the fact that they perform so many different functions within the cell. Some proteins have evolved to very specifically recognize other proteins—or even DNA or other molecules—and so their structures are designed to find and bind partners. The helical sections that you find in proteins are very rigid, and so they're good at grabbing chemical functionalities on other molecules. This is where different amino acids come in. The ones that are good at making hydrogen bonds can reach out and make contact with other molecules.

The linker regions that you saw in hemoglobin are quite flexible, and they're good at allowing a protein to change its shape to give off a signal. Proteins are able to change shape and they can tell a cell whether the cell is cold or it's hot or it's hungry and it can give off these signals so that the cell can do something about it. Other structural motifs that are found in proteins can provide binding pockets where chemical reactions can occur. So now that you know what a protein looks like and you have a feeling for the highly variable structures of proteins, let's discuss what proteins do and connect their functions with different aspects of nanotechnology.

One of the most ubiquitous functions of proteins is the catalysis of chemical reactions. Catalysis is a term that is used to describe what needs to happen for a reaction that is not spontaneous to proceed. Proteins are really good at taking unreactive molecules and making them do something special. They do this by binding molecules in special pockets where they can bend a molecule to put it under stress and break a bond, or they can use one of their own functionalities to cut or replace a chemical bond. They're very clever about getting work done.

Let's take for, example, the peroxidase enzymes. As the name suggests, peroxidases can break down peroxides, like hydrogen peroxide. On its own, hydrogen peroxide is pretty stable. But when it binds the peroxidase, it's cut in two and it's made very reactive. This is an important function that helps the immune system fight disease. In the presence of an infectious agent—for example a bacterial cell—the enzyme converts hydrogen peroxide into a reactive molecule that will stop the bacterium in its tracks by damaging its cell wall. So this type of enzyme and the chemical catalysis that it facilitates has an important function that keeps us healthy. There are actually a variety of diseases linked to high and low peroxidase levels. Too much peroxidase seems to be linked with coronary artery disease. The peroxidase may help to speed the formation of plaques that are very harmful. But too little peroxidase is linked with immune suppression, also problematic.

A very interesting potential new role for peroxidases has been identified that is relevant to the use of nanomaterials. The enzyme peroxidase seems to be able break down and biodegrade carbon nanotubes and we'll talk more about carbon nanotubes when we discuss drug delivery and you'll appreciate why this discovery was so important as we talk about how powerful carbon nanotubes can be in an in vivo system. The discovery that carbon nanotubes could be broken down with peroxidase was made by Alex Star, a professor of Chemistry at the University of Pittsburgh. Alex worked with carbon nanotubes for several years and he first developed very powerful sensing systems using these materials.

In the course of these studies, he began to wonder what would happen to nanotubes once they were inside the human body. He was then the first person to observe that a peroxidase called myeloperoxidase could degrade a nanotube. He first showed that this was possible in a test tube, and eventually showed that it could also occur in a living animal. This finding really captivated the nanoscience community because it indicated that nanomaterials could be biodegradable.

Again, we'll come back to this, but we'll discuss how nanotubes can be used for drug delivery and you'll realize that if they were not biodegradable, this type of application just wouldn't be possible. It would be very problematic because if nanotubes were left behind once a drug was dispensed they would eventually accumulate and they could cause inflammation. There had been studies of mice, where mice that inhaled carbon nanotubes developed severe lung inflammation and went on to suffer from lung fibrosis. So this was a serious concern and this is why finding a way for nanotubes to be biodegradable was a major breakthrough.

The way that peroxidase degrades nanotubes is a really amazing process. Nanotubes sometimes exist as what we call multi-walled structures, meaning that there is a nanotube inside of a nanotube that is inside of a nanotube. This is very much like the Matryoshka dolls that maybe somebody has bought you as a present from Russia that are nested dolls. When peroxidase degrades these materials, it does so one layer at a time and Alex Star and his team were able to observe this in real time. They were also able to observe that once the nanotubes were present as a single layer, so all of the outside layers were degraded and then there was just a single nanotube left, the enzyme chewed from the middle of the carbon nanotube to break them into smaller pieces.

When I read about this mechanism in detail, it reminded me a lot of the way that my kids eat sandwiches that they don't like so I have a 2 year old, 4 year old, both boys, and if I give them a sandwich that they don't like what's in the middle, they start to eat the sandwich from the outside and they eat the bread. They eventually break one sandwich into 20 sandwiches and all that's left is whatever was the filling for this sandwich with a little layer of bread and that's exactly what happens to these carbon nanotubes that they get chewed up from the outside and then just the core is left. This discovery really highlights an important discovery in nanoscience—the enzymatic degradation of carbon nanotubes—and it also gives us a good example of a chemical reaction that a protein catalyzes.

Another important class of proteins are antibodies. These proteins do all of the heavy lifting for our immune systems. Antibodies are able to specifically recognize foreign agents in our bodies and tag those foreign agents so that they're eliminated. Most antibodies have the Y shape that's shown in this figure. They have a stem and two recognition domains that are very specific sensors. Now how do these proteins recognize threats to our immune system and how do they work to eliminate them? This seems like a hard problem to solve—recognizing an unknown agent that your body has never seen before, how on Earth do we do that? It turns out that what we do to cope with this challenge is to make large libraries, or sets of antibodies, and every member of this set is slightly different. Once one of these antibodies finds something threatening, it gives off a signal that says that is should be amplified and then many copies of it are made to ensure that an infection is cleared. The binding between an antibody and its target is very strong and many molecular interactions are made that hold the complex together.

As I'm sure you're aware, sometimes our immune systems can turn against us. For those of us with certain food allergies, it's the immune system and antibodies that mistakenly treat a certain component of a food as a threat. But we've also learned to make our immune systems work better. We know how to vaccinate against many diseases by injecting substances that mimic infectious agents. Using these types of strategies, we've been able to eradicate many terrible diseases. We also know how to produce highly specific antibodies in large quantities so that we can exploit their binding properties for medical applications. There are several antibody-based drugs out there that are able to find specific proteins on the surfaces of cancer cells and they're able to selectively eliminate them just as if they were a bacterial cell. These types of drugs are very effective at controlling cancer.

We'll find that antibodies are also a very powerful tool in nanomedicine. We'll look at several examples of antibody-functionalized nanomaterials, for example metal nanoparticles or quantum dots with an antibody tethered to the surface and this is a way to take a nanomaterial and make it very specific for a certain type of cell or a certain type of molecular target. Let's look at one example of this type of antibody-mediated targeting that relates to the gold nanoparticles from our last lecture.

It turns out that antibody gold nanoparticle conjugates are already used as indicators in many of the commercially available pregnancy tests. These are tests that can provide a result simply by introduction of urine onto a dipstick. The urine is drawn up into an analysis chamber and it reacts with two strips of material enclosed within the dipstick. One is a control, so as long as urine was introduced onto the dipstick a line is formed. The other indicates whether or not a hormone associated with pregnancy, hCG, is present. The outputs for this type of test are just red lines so you just read it by eye. Again many of these commercial tests, these red lines are formed with gold nanoparticles.

The way this works is that an antibody that specifically binds the pregnancy hormone, hCG, is modified with a gold nanoparticle. There are also larger spheres in the mixture. If hCG is present, it binds to the antibody and a large complex is formed. This complex then flows along the dipstick until it reaches the test site. At this site, a filter will stop the large complex from flowing through it and it concentrates it into a line. Then close by, any leftover gold nanoparticles that are still there are trapped by a finer filter and they're used as a control to show that sample was actually transported through the device so that you'll always have a positive signal even if the pregnancy test is negative.

So here, the intense color and the nanoscale size of gold nanoparticles are being leveraged to make this type of diagnostic testing easier and more sensitive. If it was not for the nanoscale size of the particle, the filter-based approach would not work, so small molecules that we usually use as colored dyes are difficult to stop with filters, so this just wouldn't work if all we had to work with was a dye. Now you're a little bit more familiar with antibodies, and can see how they can help a nanomaterial recognize a target molecule and sense it. We'll look at many other examples of materials functionalized with antibodies as we go along through the next few lectures.

Not all proteins have functions that we would consider active. Others are passive and they're present to provide a structure to a cell or a tissue. For example, collagen, which is a protein named after the Greek word for glue is a main component of connective tissue, and it represents 30% of the total protein in our bodies. It has a very interesting structure so rather than being variable, it's quite constant and it always exists as a triple helical structure, about 1.5 nanometers wide and 300 nanometers long. These triple helices of collagen are wound into tough bundles; they can be hundreds of nanometers thick and they provide a guide that can tell cells where to grow.

There are a number of diseases related to problems with collagen. I'm sure that you've heard of scurvy and know that this results from a deficiency of vitamin C. Scurvy was at one time a serious issue for those on long military expeditions at sea, but it is fairly rare now that its origin is well-recognized. It turns out that the vitamin C deficiency that causes scurvy produces defective collagen and the connective tissues are affected. The gums in our mouth are particularly susceptible to this, and tooth loss was a major ramification of scurvy. As well, healing of wounds is a process that's expedited by collagen, and slow healing was a major symptom of scurvy that made people affected with this disorder susceptible to infection.

Collagen is an intensely studied protein also because of its role in our physical appearance. The changes that appear in our skin as we age, those come about because of collagen breakdown, so as we age the collagen in our face and other places kind of breaks down and we lose the structure of our skin. Many cosmetic procedures have been developed that attempt to re-introduce collagen to repair the effects of aging. Collagen is also an important component in types of artificial skin that are under development and an important ingredient in treatments given to burn victims.

The relationship between collagen and nanoscience is that this protein has been used as a model for the development of nanomaterials that can support cell growth. As we just discussed, collagen is oriented in fibers, and its directionality and the spacing of the fibers tell cells how to position themselves. This natural phenomenon has been mimicked with nanomaterials. Researchers at the Massachusetts Institute of Technology have produced nanoscale gratings that mimic the structure of collagen, and they found that these gratings are effective at orienting cells. For example, here you can see a cell that is growing along a nanograting. Without the collagen mimic, the cell simply spreads. It doesn't have any directionality at all. It turns out that it's very important for cells to have directionality in order to be able to build up tissues and organs in an organized manner and so these types of materials have tremendous promise for artificial tissue engineering. We'll return to this topic in a few lectures.

For now, we're talking about the different functions of proteins at the nanoscale, and we've talked about three different functions so far. We've talked about proteins that can catalyze chemical reactions, proteins that are good at recognizing other molecules and proteins that provide structural support to tissues and cells. Now let's look at one other important function of proteins that relates to a role that they can play in nanoscience and the role that they play as cellular gatekeepers.

Cells are very picky about what they take in. They do this to protect themselves. It's a rigid requirement that very delicate balances of different molecules be maintained in cells, and there are proteins that sit on the surfaces of cells and their function is to decide what should be allowed into the cell or what should come out of the cell. These proteins, and we call them receptors, are inactive if they do not have anything bound. They just kind of sit there and wait for something to happen, but once they do bind something, they trigger an amazing chain of events that causes the cell to make pockets in its outer membrane. These pockets, if you imagine the cell membrane and it's nice and smooth and then this protein binds something that it wants to take in and then the membrane will just loop in and it'll make a pocket and the edges will reclose and then whatever the receptor wanted to drag into the cell comes in.

This type of process plays an important role in how cholesterol gets processed. One type of cholesterol is packaged in a nanoscale particle formed by a protein called low-density lipoprotein or LDL. These particles can bump into a receptor on the surface of the cell, and the cell takes the LDL in. Now LDL is what we think of as "bad" cholesterol, right, that's the one that you don't want to see showing up when you go to your physician for a checkup. But, there's a reason for this, so if we don't get that LDL into cells it's running around in our blood, and that's when it can do bad things. If this process goes smoothly and the cholesterol is taken into the cell than it can be metabolized and processed very efficiently. Individuals that have a defect in one of the proteins that sends the cholesterol particles, the LDL, if you have a defect in that you will be very susceptible to having high serum cholesterol concentrations and you'll be more susceptible to the coronary and vascular issues that come along with that.

LDL is roughly 15 to 25 nm in size, and so the cell is used to seeing nanoparticles of this size. Interestingly enough, it turns out that gold nanoparticles can use this same pathway to enter cells. They bind receptor proteins on the outsides of cells, and then they're taken in through these pockets that can be formed in the membrane that I just described. How efficient the uptake is depends quite a bit on the structure and the size of a particle.

A colleague of mine at the University of Toronto, Warren Chan, studies this issue in detail. Warren actually started his career using nanomaterials as medical imaging agents, and we'll actually talk about some of his work in the next couple of lectures. Recently he's turned away from using nanomaterials as imaging agents and turned over to looking at the details of how nanomaterials interact with cells. His lab has incredible capabilities when it comes to studying very specific and detailed cellular phenomena, but he also has significant experience in the development of interesting new nanomaterials.

Recently, Warren's group did a study where they looked at the uptake of gold nanoparticles and nanorods into cells. What they found was very interesting. While the spherical particles that they studied, and these were particles with many different sizes; they all entered the cells, but when they changed out particles for rods, they did not see any uptake into cells. It seems as though a cell can be fooled into thinking that a gold nanoparticle is a particle of something else, like cholesterol, but it knows that the aspect ratio on a rod is not right and that that material does not belong in a cell. The Chan group also observed that the closer the size of a nanoparticle was to something biologically relevant, like LDL, the more efficient he uptake was.

Now how did they do this study? How did they tell whether or not the gold particles were getting into the cells? The Chan group uses quite a bit of a technique that I think you've already heard about called scanning electron microscopy. They incubate the material with the cells that they want to study, usually human cells that you can culture in the lab, and then they take them over to the electron microscope and they actually image the cell; they look at different pockets of the cell, they look for the gold nanoparticles stuck in the membrane or maybe in the cytoplasm of the cell, that's just kind of the stuff in between the organelles or maybe even inside the nucleus or other organelles like mitochondria and they count up how many particles are there and look at the localization profile to draw some conclusions about whether or not the particles could get into the cell.

It's a very precise measurement that they use to study this phenomenon, but as you can see it gives us a tremendous amount of information. This type of study is quite helpful as new nanomaterials are designed for applications that take place both on the inside and the outside of the cell, we can use this information. We now know that if we want a nanomaterial to enter a cell, let's say perhaps to deliver a drug, then it should be spherical, and as close to the size of a natural nanoparticle as possible. On the other hand, if we want a nanomaterial to stay on the outside of a cell, perhaps to "tag" the cell as a cancer cell for detection, it should be rod-shaped.

We will return to how receptors can be used with nanomaterials in the next few lectures. In this lecture, we've reviewed the main functions of proteins, and we've linked each of these functions to the world of nanoscience. Now that we have all of this information about proteins, and all the information that we went through in the last lecture on DNA, we're ready to talk more fully about specific applications in nanomedicine. In the next lecture, we're going to discuss a cutting-edge approach to detecting cancerous tumors in the human body, and we'll talk about how sensors made of quantum dots can serve as beacons that will illuminate sites of cancer. See you then.

Nanoparticles Detect Cancer in Living Organisms
Lecture 9

S ome of the most exciting work in nanoscience first appeared, and is still taking place, in medicine. Now that we've taken a look at different types of biomolecules and how they can work together with nanomaterials, we're ready to look at a variety of applications where nanomaterials can be used in medicine. We'll start by looking at how nanotechnology is having an impact on the early detection of cancer, one of the most deadly diseases we contend with in the 21st century.

The Origins of Cancer

- There are 100 trillion cells in the human body, and the body makes 100 billion new cells every day. Every time a single cell divides, all 3 billion bases in the human genome need to be copied; that's 3 trillion bases that need to be copied per day.

- Recall from an earlier lecture that every strand of DNA is copied by a protein. The proteins that are assigned this function are fairly accurate, but they sometimes make mistakes, which result in mutations. In addition, if a person is exposed to radiation or a damaging chemical that can react with DNA, these mistakes or mutations may be even more frequent.

- Sometimes, such mistakes affect cells in ways that are harmless, but sometimes, a gene is modified in a way that affects how a cell divides and maintains itself, and once a mutation is made in DNA, it can be difficult to repair.
  - For example, free radical damage to DNA, which can be caused by radiation or chemicals, can cause the G residues in DNA to take on an extra oxygen atom.

  - When this happens, the protein that copies DNA mistakes this new form of G for a T, and when it synthesizes the strand across from it, the protein puts in an A instead of a G. This

G-to-A mutation is then perpetuated in all of the daughter cells, and it can affect the ability of the cell to self-regulate.

- If a DNA molecule that codes for a protein becomes mutated, then the new form of the protein that is produced may have some strange properties.
  o For example, the proteins called kinases attach phosphorus and oxygen to other proteins as a signal to tell the cell where it is in its life cycle.

  o If one of these kinases has a sequence that becomes mutated, it can become overactive. When that happens, the cell thinks it's time to divide earlier than it should, and it starts to divide at an accelerated rate.

- Mutated proteins can also cause cells to become dangerous by tricking them into ignoring signals that they're in trouble.
  o Normal cells know when they need to be turned over and replaced, but cells that have mutations in certain genes tend to ignore signals to turn over and become aggressive.

  o These cells divide too quickly, overtake the population in the tissue, ignore the signs that they're in trouble, and eventually, can form what's called a neoplasm, which is the start of a tumor.

  o As we know, sometimes, tumors are harmless, but sometimes, the cells that form a tumor can become increasingly aggressive and invasive. Aggressive cells can even become detached from the primary tumor and ride through the circulatory system to another organ, such as the liver or brain.

Screening for Cancer
- Cancer is a disease that's treatable if it's caught early, but the methods we use to screen for cancer are not very good at catching the disease in the early stages.

- MRI is a good method for looking at a tumor after it has formed. Here, a patient is slid into a giant magnet, and all of the hydrogen atoms in the body are used to collect an image that can reveal a tumor. An amazing amount of detail can be collected with an MRI, but it is too expensive to use as a yearly screening method.

- How might nanotechnology be leveraged to find a solution? Biomodified nanomaterials may be used to find cancer cells, either while the cells are still in the body (*in vivo*) or as samples that have been taken out of the body.

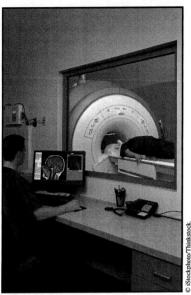

An MRI enables doctors to collect an amazing amount of detail; for example, every region of the brain can be imaged to find abnormalities or tumors.

© iStockphoto/Thinkstock.

Finding Tumors in Living Organisms

- The idea behind using nanomaterials to find tumors is to send tiny nanosensors into the bloodstream that are able to differentiate a cancer cell from a healthy cell. If the sensor finds a cancer cell, it could give off a signal that could be detected accurately.

- We've already seen examples of nanomaterials modified with specific biomolecules that make them able to recognize other molecules with very high levels of specificity. What types of molecules do we need to be able to recognize to know whether a cell is cancerous or not?
   o We can't target the mutated DNA because DNA is packaged up on the inside of the cell. A sensor that circulates inside the body can really only work with markers that are located on the

outside of the cell, such as the receptors we talked about in the last lecture.

o   Certain types of receptors are often present at very high levels on the outside of cancer cells because these receptors are involved in signaling and in some of the self-regulation processes that go into overdrive in cancer cells. These receptors, then, are good markers that nanoparticles can be targeted to.

•   One of the most sensitive ways to get a signal out of a sensor is to have it emit light, and as we've seen, quantum dots are effective materials for light emission. Another nice feature of these materials is that the color of their emission can be tuned across a broad range.

o   Because tissues also emit light, we need to think about whether the light emitted from the quantum dot will be visible so that it can be detected in the same environment as tissue. An absorbance spectrum of a typical tissue shows that light from the quantum dot can indeed make its way out to be detected.

o   In fact, nanomaterials are among the few materials that can absorb and emit light far in the red part of the spectrum, which is where it's necessary to be to get around the absorption and emission of natural tissue.

•   To ensure that a quantum dot can find a receptor that is specific to a cancer cell, we rely on antibodies. These proteins can be engineered to stick to other proteins and can be covalently bound to the quantum dots.

o   As these quantum dots are swimming around in the bloodstream, they look for a cancer cell with many receptors on the surface. If they bump into a healthy cell, ideally, they won't see its receptor, which is at a much lower level on the surface of the cell, and they will just bounce off and go on their way.

- If they hit a cancer cell, there's a high probability that they will collide with a receptor and stick because the antibody has been engineered to stick to the receptor.

The Challenges of Quantum Dots

- This process works on both cells and tissue, but does it work in a living organism? Again, the ideal situation would be to inject into the bloodstream a solution of quantum dots that are specific for a certain type of cancer cell and let the dots circulate and find their target.

- If they didn't find a target, they would be excreted, and no signal would be emitted. If they came in contact with a tumor, they would stick and accumulate and could be detected by their light.

- One challenge here is that the human body is very good at filtration. Our kidneys filter our entire volume of blood every day 25 times! But the first demonstration of quantum dot–based visualization in a living organism was performed several years ago by researchers at Emory University.
  - These researchers generated three colors of quantum dots— green, yellow, and red—with each color specific for a different kind of tumor.

  - They then implanted tumors in lab rats and injected the three different solutions of quantum dots, all mixed together. Finally, they imaged the light coming out of the animals and were able to see the three types of tumors lit up.

- There were a few unexpected discoveries along the way to this advance that are quite interesting on their own. One is that there's a "magic" quantum dot size—4 nanometers in diameter—that allows this type of approach to conform to FDA regulations concerning the length of time in which materials must be cleared from the body.

- Another interesting discovery relates to the mechanism by which the quantum dots accumulated in the tumor.

○ While we know that the matching of the antibody on the quantum dot surface to the cancer cell receptor helps targeting to be efficient and specific, it turns out that the structure of the blood vessels that feed oxygen to tumors also played a role.

○ The blood vessels around a tumor are quite leaky because they experience pressure from the tumor. The small holes and breakages that result make it easier for a nanoparticle to get out of the blood vessel and into the tumor.

• The quantum dot approach has enormous promise for targeting tumors with nanoparticles and reading their signals from outside.
  ○ However, because quantum dots are very stable and because they are sometimes made with toxic materials, such as lead and cadmium, we need to look at the long-term effects of a quantum dot injection to ensure that we understand the risks.

  ○ These toxic materials are currently used because of their emissive properties, but researchers are now looking for alternatives, such as nanomaterials made from carbon.

  ○ Another challenge lies in the "scaling-up" of quantum dot–based materials for use in medical imaging. For this application, the synthesis of quantum dots must be highly reproducible and consistent.

Suggested Reading

Heath, Davis, and Hood, "Nanomedicine Targets Cancer."

Riehemann, et al., "Nanomedicine: Challenges and Perspective."

Weinberg, *The Biology of Cancer*.

Zrazhevskip, Sena, and Gao, "Designing Multifunctional Quantum Dots for Bioimaging, Detection, and Drug Delivery."

Questions to Consider

1. What signs do cancer cells exhibit that differentiate them from healthy cells? Why is it a challenge to read out these differences?

2. Why is the development of *in vivo* sensors (those that detect analytes within living organisms) so much more challenging than *in vitro* sensors (those that detect analytes in samples taken from a living organism)?

Nanoparticles Detect Cancer in Living Organisms
Lecture 9—Transcript

Shana Kelley: Some of the most exciting work in all of nanoscience first appeared, and is still taking place, in medicine. Now that we've taken a look at different types of biomolecules and how they can work together with nanomaterials, we're ready to look at a variety of applications where nanomaterials can be used in medicine. We'll start by looking at how nanotechnology is having an impact on the early detection of cancer, one of the most deadly diseases we contend with in the 21st century.

Let's start by talking through why cancer happens in the first place. To understand the origins of this disease, we first need to think about the cells that make up the human body. As you know cells are the basic physiological unit that make up tissues and organs. They're micron sized, and they hold all of the proteins and DNA molecules that are needed to support life. Humans have an incredibly complex set of cells. We have over 300 different types of cells that perform different functions. Overall, if you count up all the cells in the human body there are 100 trillion; I think that's a really staggering number. I never really stopped to think about how many cells I'm made up of, but that's an awful lot.

We're constantly making new cells. We need to regenerate our tissues and replace old cells with new ones. Every day, about 0.1% of our cells divide to replace old or dead cells. That's 100 billion cells every day in every one of us! If you've not gotten much done in a day, just remember how busy your cells have been and call it a great day.

Now when these 100 billion cells are made every day, there's a chance that a mistake could be made. Every time a single cell divides, all three billion bases in the human genome need to be copied—so that's three trillion bases that need to be copied per day. You'll remember from two lectures ago that every strand of DNA is copied by a protein and it reads a single strand to generate a complement. The proteins that are assigned this function in the cell are really pretty good at not making a mistake; they've evolved over time to become more and more accurate, but nobody's perfect and given that many assignments to copy, that much DNA, every once in a while, they do make mistakes.

In addition, if a person is exposed to something like radiation or a damaging chemical that can react with their DNA, these mistake or mutations may be even more frequent. Sometimes, these mistakes affect cells in ways that are harmless. If you were to roll out all of the DNA in our cells and look at what parts the DNA code for proteins and which parts are just there, most of our DNA is just a spacer, so if a mistake or mutation happens in one of these regions, it doesn't affect the cell and we just go on with our cells doing what they did without the mutation. But sometimes, a gene is modified that affects the way a cell divides and maintains itself. Once a mutation in made in DNA, it can be difficult to repair. For example, free radical damage to DNA, which can be caused by radiation or chemicals, can cause the G residues in DNA to take on an extra oxygen atom. When this happens, the protein that copies DNA mistakes this new form of G (we call it oxo-G) for a T and when it synthesizes the strand across from it, it puts in an A instead of a G. This G to A mutation is then perpetuated in all of the daughter cells, and it can affect the ability of a cell to self-regulate.

How does this happen? We touched briefly in the last lecture on the idea that protein sequences are encoded by DNA sequences. You now know that proteins have many important chemical, structural, and regulatory functions in the cell. If a DNA molecule that codes for a protein becomes mutated, then the new form of the protein that is produced may have some strange properties. For example, there are proteins called kinases and these proteins run around the cell and they attach phosphorus and oxygen to other proteins. Why do they do this? It's a signal, and the purpose of the signal is to tell the cell where it is in its life cycle. If one of these kinases has a sequence that becomes mutated, it can become overactive and then it runs around in the cell too fast and it does too much modifying and then the cell thinks it's time to divide earlier than it should, and it starts to divide at an accelerated rate.

Mutated proteins can also cause cells to become dangerous by tricking them into ignoring signals that they're in trouble. Normal cells know when they need to be turned over and replaced, and there is a process called programmed cell death that healthy cells use when it's time for them to go. Cells that have mutations in certain genes tend to ignore these signals to turn over, and they become aggressive. They divide too quickly, they overtake the population in the tissue, they ignore the signs that they're in trouble, and eventually they can form what's called a neoplasm. This neoplasm is really the start of a tumor. It's the thing that can become a tumor. Sometimes tumors are harmless—we call them benign in this case—and the cells within them are a little too aggressive in that they divide too much, but they're not aggressive enough to cause damage and that benign tumor just stays contained and doesn't do any harm.

Sometimes, the cells that form a tumor can become increasingly aggressive and invasive. It's kind of like a cascade or a snowball effect: Once a cell starts mutating, more mutations may build up. What do I mean by a cell becoming aggressive? Very aggressive cells that are part of a tumor can take advantage of the fact that tumors are very well-connected to the bloodstream. They're wired right in; they need oxygen, and so there's usually blood vessels that connect them. These very aggressive cells are good at becoming detached from the primary tumor and then they hitch a ride in the circulatory system to another organ. Then they colonize in these remote sites. This could be the liver, or the brain, or the bones, and these are places where these tumor cells can do real harm.

This is why cancers in tissues like the breast or the prostate—tissues that don't really have that much function as we age—can be deadly. You are looking at an image of metastatic breast cancer cells that have made their way to the liver and formed a tumor there. It is the metastatic tumors, not the primary ones that formed in the breast, but the secondary ones that formed in the liver, these are the one that are problematic that eventually affect the health of people with cancer.

Cancer is a disease that's treatable if it's caught early. For example, a small breast tumor can be surgically removed and a patient made disease free if it's caught early. Same thing goes for prostate cancer. But, the methods that we use to screen for cancer are not very good at catching it at the early stages.

There are methods that are good at looking at a tumor after it's formed, like MRI. Here we slide a patient into a giant magnet and all of the hydrogen atoms in the human body are used to collect an image that can reveal a tumor. The blue map that you're looking at shows the incredible amount of detail we can collect this way. We can see every single region of the brain and we can see where there might be abnormalities or a tumor. But, MRI is really expensive so it's about $1000 a scan just for a localized region, that's just for a brain scan, it would be much more expensive if we were to MRI the whole body. It just turns out that the healthcare system cannot support this level of cost and MRI is just too expensive to be used at a yearly checkup to screen everyone for cancer. Maybe more importantly, MRI doesn't help us find cancer cells in the blood. The cells basically have to be still. They can't be swimming around as the blood is circulating in your body and this then would not tell us about cancer cells that were spreading in the body because those one are usually in the bloodstream. So we need other solutions.

Think about this, using what you know so far: How might nanotechnology be leveraged here to find a solution? You already know that it's possible to make nanoscale structures and modify them with biomolecules. It turns out that if we're clever about using bio-modified nanomaterials, we can use them to find cancer cells, either while the cells are still in the body or if they're in samples that we take out of the body. In the next two lectures, we'll look at different approaches that can be used inside or outside of a human being. For many types of cancers—the ones where solid tumors are formed—detecting cancer inside the body makes sense because we have to send a sensor around and figure out what tissue the tumor is in. For others, like leukemia or for cancers that are becoming metastatic and traveling through the bloodstream, taking a sample from a patient and analyzing it outside probably makes more sense.

In this lecture, we'll talk about nanomaterials that are good at finding tumors "in vivo," meaning that they can find them in a living organism. The idea here is that if we could send tiny nanosensors into the bloodstream and make them "smart," we could then find the smallest of tumors, hopefully before it becomes metastatic. Now by "finding" a tumor, what I mean is that these sensors would be able to differentiate a cancer cell from a healthy cell and that sensor would then give off some type of signal that could be detected accurately. Let's take a look at how we do this with nanomaterials.

You've already seen examples of nanomaterials modified with specific biomolecules that make them able to recognize other molecules with very high levels of specificity. So what types of molecules do we need to be able to recognize to know if a cell is a cancer cell or not? We can't target the mutated DNA that I just mentioned because as you know DNA is packaged up on the inside of the cell. If we're going to send a sensor that's going to circulate around the body, it really only has markers that are located on the outside of the cell to work with. There are protein molecules that we talked about in the last lecture that are called receptors, and these proteins sit on the outside of the cell and they look at the environment and they let things in and they take things out.

Certain types of receptors are often present at very high levels on the outside of cancer cells because these receptors are involved in signaling and involved in some of the self-regulation processes that I just mentioned that kind of go crazy in cancer cells. These receptors then are good markers that we can target nanoparticles to. In the images that you're viewing, you are looking at a normal cell and a breast cancer cell. The cancer cell has about five times as many receptors on its surface relative to the healthy cell. So, the receptors are an excellent target to go after so that a tumor can be imaged.

Now, what type of material would be useful for finding a tumor in a living organism like a human? One of the most sensitive ways to get a signal out of a sensor is to have it emit light. If you think back through all the nanomaterials you've seen so far, think through all the things that we've looked at and think about the subset of those that emit light, you probably remember that quantum dots are some of the best materials for light emission. Another nice feature of these materials is that the color of their emission can be tuned across a broad range. Now, it turns out that tissues also emit light, so we need to think a bit about whether the light emitted from the quantum dot will be visible if it needs to be detected with tissue in the way. We can actually look at the absorbance spectrum of a typical tissue and this is shown on the graph that you're looking at in black. Now if we overlay the spectrum of an orange quantum dot, you can see that the emission from the human tissue is pretty weak in that region, so light will indeed be able to make its way out to be detected.

You may be wondering why human tissue absorbs and emits light and if you think about the components of tissues and cells, many of them are things that are colored, obviously our blood is highly colored. It absorbs lots of light because of all the hemoglobin that's in our red blood cells. This is a major issue when it comes to in vivo imaging. How do we get around the natural absorption of tissues? This is one of the key advantages of nanomaterials. There are not that many materials out there that can absorb and emit light as far in the red part of the spectrum, which is where we need to be to get around the absorption and emission of natural tissue. The fact that nanomaterials do have these properties is one of the things that's very special about them.

How are we going to help a quantum dot find a receptor that is specific to a cancer cell? We'll rely on proteins called antibodies. We talked about these too in the last lecture and these proteins can be engineered to stick to other proteins, and so we can attach these proteins to the quantum dots. How do we make these? We can prepare the quantum dots; we can give them an outer layer that is easily functionalized, meaning that it's easy to come in with the antibody that we want to attach and we link it and then it's covalently bound and that complex will stay together basically irreversibly.

If you think about these quantum dots swimming around in the bloodstream, they're looking out for a cancer cell with lots of receptors on the surface. If they bump into a healthy cell, hopefully they don't see that receptor that's at a much lower level on the surface of the health cell and they just bounce off and keep on going their way. If they hit a cancer cell, there's a high probability that they collide with a receptor and then they stick because that antibody has been engineered to stick to the receptor.

You are looking at an image of a cancer cell that has been bound by green quantum dots. The quantum dots are actually stuck to the outside of the cell where the receptors sit on the surface. The blue part of the image is just showing us where the nucleus of the cell is—this is the middle of the cell so you can see that the quantum dots are stuck on the outside and there's none on the inside of the cell.

This works on cells, but it also works on tissue. The image that you are viewing now shows a tissue that was collected during a breast cancer biopsy.

It's glowing red in this case because the quantum dots that were used are red. So this really does work—we can get quantum dots to show us where cancer cells are.

The key question of course is does it work in a living organism? I've shown you pictures of cells and tissues where quantum dots have stuck to the cancerous cells. Now, how do we think about whether this would work on a live subject? Ideally, we would take a solution of quantum dots that are specific for a certain type of cancer cell, inject it into the bloodstream and let the quantum dots circulate and find their target. If they don't find a target, hopefully they're excreted and we don't get a signal. As they're traveling through the bloodstream, they would flow through different areas of the body and if they came into contact with a tumor, they would stick and accumulate. Then they could be detected if we looked for the light coming out. Basically you would need to put the person in a dark room, have a light source there that's a irradiating the quantum dots and then we take a picture and see if anything is glowing.

If you think about the quantum dots circulating and doing their thing as they're looking for a tumor, this may sound like a pretty grand challenge because we know that the human body is very good at filtration, right. Our kidneys filter our entire volume of blood every day 25 times! That's their main function. Will these quantum dots that don't really belong in our bloodstream be able to stay in circulation long enough to find their targets?

The answer to this question, and the first demonstration of quantum dot-based visualization in a living organism, was obtained several years ago by a group working at Emory University in Atlanta. The group of Shuming Nie was able to show that they could see tumors lit up by quantum dots in a lab rat. The Nie group generated three different colors of quantum dots. They made green ones, yellow ones, red ones and they made each color specific for a different kind of tumor. Believe it or not, you can take a rat or a lab mouse and implant different tumors in that animal, so you introduce the tumors, you let them take hold and grow, and then if you're going to do this type of imaging analysis, you introduce your imaging agent and watch how well it localizes.

They did this. They took their three different solutions of quantum dots all mixed together. They injected it into the tail vein of the rat, and then they let the animal go do its thing for a few hours, its last few hours. Then they imaged the light coming out of the back of the animal, and low and behold they were able to see the three types of tumors lit up. They knew which tumor was where and they knew that the green quantum dots went to the right tumor, the yellow ones went to the right tumor, and the red ones went to the right tumor.

You may remember me mentioning a guy named Warren Chan in my last lecture. He's a colleague of mine from the University of Toronto who is a nanomaterials specialist. We spoke about his work on tracking nanoparticle uptake in cells, and I also mentioned then that he had started in the field of nanomaterials-based medical imaging. It turns out that this is actually the system that he worked on as a Ph.D. student. He published a landmark paper about quantum dot sensors in 1998 in the journal Science, and this paper has been cited thousands of times by researchers around the world. It is a very impressive contribution that has made a real impact on nanoscience.

There were a few unexpected discoveries along the way to this advance that are quite interesting on their own. One is that there's a magic quantum dot size that allows this type of approach to be feasible. A few minutes ago we talked about the fact that with this type of approach, one concern is that the kidneys would remove the quantum dots so quickly that they wouldn't be able to find their target, but this didn't appear to be the case and we saw efficient targeting of the quantum dots to the tumor. However, we don't want to take this too far. It would not be desirable at all to have the dots in circulation indefinitely. The U.S. Food and Drug Administration insists that any material that gets injected into the body whether it's a drug that's going to treat disease or if it's some type of diagnostic agent like this one, they insist that that material is cleared completely from a human being in a reasonable amount of time. It's not completely specified, but it has to be reasonable. It has to be finite so that long-term side effects are avoided.

For these quantum dots, it was observed that particles with an 8 nanometer diameter were not cleared fast enough—they're still present after 24 hours and if the animal is taken apart after the experiment and their different organs are analyzed, you can see that there are very high levels of accumulation in the liver of the animal. Quantum dots that are 50% smaller with a 4 nanometer diameter are cleared within about two hours and they don't accumulate in any organs and they do hit the tumor specifically. So the difference of 4 nanometers here makes all the difference when it comes to whether these materials are useable for in vivo imaging.

Another interesting discovery that was made about the targeting of the quantum dots relates to the mechanism by which they accumulated within the tumor. While we know that the matching of the antibody on the quantum dot surface to the cancer cell receptor helps targeting to be efficient and specific, it turns out that the structure of the blood vessels that feed oxygen to tumors also played a role. The blood vessels around a tumor turn out to be quite leaky. That's because the tumor puts pressure on the blood vessels. It's pressing against them and this may cause them to have holes and become quite perturbed. So if there are little holes and breakages this makes it easier for a nanoparticle to get out of a blood vessel and into the tumor. We now realize that even though we a specific antibody immobilized on a quantum dot and we realize that that's important for recognizing a tumor cell and ignoring the healthy cells, the structure of the blood vessels that feed tumors may also really help the sensor reach its target.

So where is this approach heading? It has enormous promise, we've looked together at the data that demonstrates that it is indeed possible to target tumors with nanoparticles and read that signal from outside. This is truly noninvasive imaging where we don't even have to really put a needle into a patient, take a blood sample, anything. We just send the sensor inside.

It's very promising that there are further advances that will need to be made for quantum dot-based tumor imaging to be used in the clinic routinely. We need to look at the long-term effects of a quantum dot injection to make sure that we understand the risks. Quantum dots are very stable: You can make them, let them sit around in the lab for months or a year, and they're the same material after that amount of time as they were to begin with. If you take a look at the components of quantum dots, they can be made from materials that can be quite toxic—metals like lead and cadmium—so we do need to look very closely at the in vivo stabilities of these materials.

It may seem a bit odd that these materials were engineered and they've been brought this far with such rudely toxic components. Why did we go with these materials in the first place? Why were they brought forward as the most promising materials for this application? Well it really relates back to the emissive properties. We talked about the fact that biological tissues have a lot of absorption, they have emission in a certain range within the visible spectrum, and quantum dots get around that because of their special electronics and the wavelengths at which they can emit light. That's a really hard set of properties to match. But, people are certainly looking for alternatives. There are some very interesting results now starting to come out with things like nanoscale diamond. As you know diamond is a very stable material. It's made of carbon. We have lots of carbon in our bodies so this is a material that should in principle be very nontoxic. There may also be ways to coat quantum dots with different materials to make them more biocompatible and more stable; things like gelatin, a very nontoxic substance could basically rescue the properties of quantum dots if they're found to be problematic.

Another challenge lies in the "scale-up" of quantum dot based imaging materials. As I mentioned, the synthesis of the quantum dots is quite straightforward, the materials are stable, but if we think about now scaling this up to have enough to actually use for medical imaging, the synthesis needs to be highly reproducible and consistent. Most of the work that has been done in this area so far has relied on small batches of materials, so it remains to be seen if the materials can be made in sufficient quantities.

Many think of the successful scale up and clinical validation of quantum dot-based tumor imaging as a holy grail in the field of nanomedicine. It holds a great deal of promise for the detection of tumors that are too small to cause symptoms, but these tumors should be treated aggressively anyway to ensure that cancer does not spread. Now that we've taken a look at the challenge of tumor sensing inside the body using nanomaterials, we'll look at some other systems, still ones that use nanomaterials and ones that are aimed at doing early cancer detection, but these systems will function outside of the body. Here we'll be taking samples out of human patients and then using nanomaterials to analyze them ex vivo. In the next lecture, we'll see how this type approach differs from what we just discussed and we'll look at the advantages and disadvantages and really pull together all of this information to understand what the options are and what the promise is of nanomaterials-based cancer diagnosis. See you then.

Detecting Only a Few Molecules of a Disease
Lecture 10

—————————————————————————————————————

Testing for cancer inside the body using circulating nanosensors, as we discussed in the last lecture, is a promising approach that may eventually allow us to screen for cancer in a way that's completely noninvasive. But this approach is challenged by both regulatory hurdles and the fact that not all cancers respond equally well to *in vivo* testing. In this lecture, we'll look at *in vitro* testing, which offers a reduced regulatory burden and the ability to analyze cells or cancer markers in the blood.

Early Cancer Detection
- Many of the tests currently used for cancer screening look for blood-borne markers and are performed *in vitro*, that is, outside the body. For example, the PSA test that is used for prostate cancer screening is performed using blood samples drawn from patients. This *in vitro* test and most others are not accurate or sensitive enough for early cancer diagnosis.

- The key feature that a testing strategy must have to be effective for early cancer detection is a very high level of sensitivity.
  - In a sample taken from a patient, the molecules that can be used as markers of cancer will be present at levels that are correlated with the burden of the disease or the size of the tumor.

  - If a tumor is small and still localized, it will not release many molecular markers into the bloodstream. With a blood cancer, such as one that affects the white blood cells, the cancer cells will be a tiny population compared to the red blood cells.

  - This means that if we're going to use a sample of blood for cancer screening, whatever method we use must be able to track very low levels of a targeted molecule in the presence of a background of excess cells and molecules that may interfere with the detection strategy.

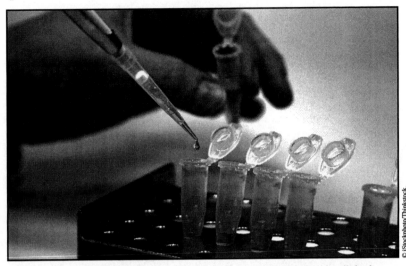

In vitro diagnostic tools using nanomaterials may appear sooner in clinical practice than *in vivo* approaches because of the reduced regulatory burden associated with this type of testing.

- Nanomaterials show great promise for achieving this type of sensitivity. The fact that nanoparticles are almost the same size as proteins or nucleic acid molecules means that there is the potential for each particle to need only 1 molecule to make it give off a signal.

Nanosensors

- A research group at the University of Toronto has developed a powerful chip-based system that uses nanomaterials to very sensitively detect DNA sequences that are the markers of cancer.

- The chip is made using the same processes used in consumer electronics applications. The underlying substrate of the chip is silicon, and it has a gold pattern on it, generated using photolithography. On the surface of the chip are tiny holes that allow the introduction of nanomaterials.
  - The chips are placed in a bath of metal salt, and a potential is applied, which causes metal to electroplate onto the chip. As

the metal plates onto the chip, it forms nanostructures that are actually quite easy to manipulate.

- o For example, using three different conditions for electroplating yields three different levels of nanostructuring.

- These chips can be used to detect biomolecules by, first, designing and synthesizing a DNA sequence that is complementary to the target for detection. That sequence is then attached to the sensor surface.
  - o When the target sequence is present in a sample, it binds to the sensor through hydrogen bonding and base pairing. This binding event causes an electrical current to be given off, and that's what is measured.

  - o A variety of sensors can be put on 1 chip to collect a profile of signals that can tell us about the type of cancer cell present in a sample.

- The presence of nanostructures on the sensors has a dramatic effect on the sensitivity of this approach.
  - o With a smooth sensor, at least 1 million DNA molecules are needed in a sample in order for the sensor to give off a response. If the sensor has nanostructures measuring 20 nanometers, only 100 molecules in solution are needed to trigger detection.

  - o The closer a nanostructure is in size to the molecules targeted for detection, the better the sensors work.

Testing the Chip-Based System
- Chronic myeloid leukemia (CML) affects the granulocytes (one kind of white blood cells) that are important for fighting infection. It's one of the most treatable cancers, but it's important that it is diagnosed and classified very specifically so that the right drug is used to treat it.

- This disease arises because a specific break occurs on chromosomes 9 and 22, and they then recombine to form a fusion. This creates a new DNA sequence that is not present in healthy cells. As a result of the presence of this sequence, a mutant protein is produced that causes the cells to be overactive and divide too quickly. This is what increases the number of white blood cells to a level that the body can't sustain.

- A drug is available that specifically targets this protein and shuts the mutant cells down. Because the mutant protein is present only in the leukemia cells, the drug has no effect on other cells and has few side effects.

- The method for diagnosing this type of cancer is expensive and slow and can be performed only in specialized laboratories by experienced laboratory technicians. For this reason, the microchip-based method was tested as a possible substitute. Instead of amplifying the CML gene, this method tries to turn up the volume of the signal that it produces.

- To test the chip-based approach for leukemia detection, a chip was designed that would display a DNA sequence specific to the CML gene fusion on a nanostructured sensor. The sequence was attached to the sensor by putting a sulfur atom at its end, enabling it to stick to the metal of the sensor. Once the chip was ready for a measurement, it was calibrated, and a sample was introduced containing an unknown number of cancer cells.

- The chip was designed to produce electrical signals that tell whether or not the target sequence is present. The chip also produces data that allow a determination of the levels of CML cells in the sample.

- The Toronto group has developed a prototype instrument to validate this sensing approach. Eventually, the chip will be embedded in a cartridge into which a physician can inject a sample. That cartridge will then be slid into the instrument, and the analysis will be performed in about 5 to 10 minutes. The testing unit uses only a simple set of circuits to apply potentials to the leads on the chip and collect signals from the sensor.

Gold Nanoparticles in Cancer Diagnosis

- As we discussed, gold nanoparticles are good sensors to report on genetic disease and the presence of hormones that can confirm pregnancy. These materials can also detect proteins, making them powerful for cancer detection. The red color that a gold nanoparticle produces can be concentrated on a chip, and the fact that these red-absorbing nanoparticles are nanoscale makes them much easier to handle.

- A recent study using gold nanoparticles for protein detection looked at detecting PSA, the protein that is a marker for prostate cancer.
  - o The commercially available PSA test is good at detecting large changes in levels of PSA, but it's not as good at looking for small variations or very low levels of the protein.

  - o Men who are treated for prostate cancer with a prostatectomy have trace levels of PSA in their blood postoperatively that are not measurable using the existing test. But how fast the PSA comes back after the operation can tell a physician quite a bit about what treatment regime to use.

  - o Again, the methods that are currently used for PSA screening simply can't look at these low levels. A study published in 2009 showed that the very sensitive gold nanoparticle approach could predict recurrence quickly and accurately.

- In this study, PSA detection data were collected for a large cohort of patients. The data sets showed a dramatic difference in PSA reappearance in different patients. For some, PSA levels stayed low after the operation, but for others, the levels started to creep up about a year after the prostatectomy.

- With prostate cancer, there are many treatment options that can be helpful for patients who aren't cured by surgery. And with access to the nanoparticle screening approach, oncologists have the information that further treatment is needed many months before they would know using conventional diagnostic assays.

In Vivo and *In Vitro* Approaches

- *In vivo* approaches to cancer diagnosis may help us do whole-body screens for early tumors, while *in vitro* approaches provide information on cancer cells and markers in the blood.

- With the *in vivo* approach, we may be able to send nanosensors into a patient, let them circulate and accumulate in tumors, and then get a snapshot of the patient's profile. This approach has the promise of detecting tumors at very early stages.

- As we continue to develop *in vivo* methods, we will also use the *in vitro* approach. One of the unique advantages of working with a sample is that we can look for many markers at once, as opposed to just 1 marker with the *in vivo* approach.

Suggested Reading

Choi, Kwak, and Park, "Nanotechnology for Early Cancer Detection."

Giljohann and Mirkin, "Drivers of Biodiagnostic Development."

Questions to Consider

1. Contrast the conventional approach to *in vitro* cancer detection (making billions of copies of suspect DNA material) with the increased sensitivity to small amounts of potential cancer offered by nanotechnology. Explain for yourself how the newer approaches both resemble and differ from the fictional tricorder in *Star Trek*.

2. Based on what you know so far about current achievements in nano-based testing, speculate about what advances might be necessary to create a panel profile of *every* molecule in a cell.

Detecting Only a Few Molecules of a Disease
Lecture 10—Transcript

Shana Kelley: Testing for cancer inside the body using circulating nanosensors, as we discussed last time, is a very promising approach that may eventually allow us to screen for cancer in a way that's completely non-invasive. But there are limitations. First, as you're aware, any time a substance is being developed for use in a human, there are significant regulatory hurdles that must be dealt with—the FDA protects all of us by having a very rigorous process in place to ensure that new medical procedures or treatments are tested thoroughly on human patients before they become accepted practice.

Second, not all cancers respond equally well to testing within the body. In particular, we talked about the fact that in vivo imaging approaches can only really catch solid tumors. Leukemia, for example, is a blood cancer, and it does not have as many malignant cells that stand still. Same thing goes for tumors that are metastasizing where there are cancer cells traveling through the bloodstream. The cells that are leaving the primary tumor are moving around and before they colonize as a metastatic tumor, they wouldn't show up by imaging.

Let's zoom in on some different approaches that may be usable outside of the body, and that are especially relevant in the short-term. These are the approaches that may be relevant when we want to analyze cells or cancer markers in the blood. It's also quite possible that we will see nanomaterials appearing sooner as cancer diagnostic tools when they're used "in vitro"—or outside the human body given the lower regulatory burden of getting these things into clinical practice.

Many of the tests currently used for cancer screening look for blood-borne markers and are performed with this type of in vitro or test tube approach. For example, the PSA test that is used for prostate cancer screening is performed using blood samples drawn from patients. The PSA test measures a protein that is released from the prostate if a tumor is creating pressure within the organ. This in vitro test and most others actually, are not accurate or sensitive enough to catch cancer early, so there's a real need for improved testing systems.

The key feature that a testing strategy has to have to be effective for early cancer detection is a very high level of sensitivity. Now what do I mean by high sensitivity. If we think about what's going on in this sample that's going to be taken from a patient, the molecules that can be used as markers of cancer and other diseases are going to be present at levels that are correlated with the burden of the disease or the size of the tumor. If a tumor is very small and still localized, it will not release many molecular markers into the bloodstream. Or if we're thinking about diagnosing a blood cancer, like one that affects the white cells found in blood, the cancer cells will be a tiny population compared to the red blood cells. That means that if we're going to take a sample of blood and use it for cancer screening, whatever method we use must be able to track very low levels of a targeted molecule in the presence of a background of an excess of cells and molecules that can't interfere with the detection strategy.

Nanomaterials show great promise for achieving this type of sensitivity. As we've touched on before, the fact that nanoparticles are almost the same size as proteins or nucleic acid molecules means that there is the potential for each particle to only need one molecule to make it give off a signal. This is actually an area that my own research group works in at the University of Toronto, so I'll take the opportunity today to tell you about some of our work and this is work that is focused on developing new types of nanosensors and in particular nanosensors that will assist with early cancer diagnosis. At the end, I'll also touch on another approach developed in another lab that's also extremely promising.

We got started in the area of developing new cancer diagnostics about ten years ago. I first started my own laboratories at Boston College, and very soon after I got my lab going, I was offered a grant from the National Cancer Institute. This is part of the National Institute of Health in the United States and I was asked to start up a project that would develop a new cancer diagnostic system. The NCI liked some of the preliminary results we had and they thought the approaches we were pursuing—all of which relied on nanomaterials—had significant promise. Now, ten years later, we have a very powerful chip based system up and running that uses nanomaterials to very sensitively detect DNA sequences that are the markers of cancer. Let me tell you a bit about how this works.

The chip we developed is a device that is made using the same processes that are used in consumer electronics applications. We print chips at the wafer level, meaning that we can make thousands at a time and this is really important if we eventually want to mass produce the devices we're developing for clinical use. I have one of these chips with me and we can take a closer look at it. As you can see, this chip is tiny. It looks like it couldn't do much of anything, but as I'll tell you it's very powerful. This chip allows us to monitor a whole panel of markers at once and it does it with a very high level of sensitivity that lets us go directly into a clinical sample and see what's there.

The underlying substrate of this chip is silicon, and then if you're able to zoom on this and see what's here, you'd see a gold pattern. This gold pattern is generated using a process called photolithography. You heard about photolithography when Ted was telling you about information technology. Photolithography, as you know, is the main tool that's used to pattern metals and other materials on chips. It uses light to define the areas where patterning should take place. We don't need this particular capability to make our chips, but there are now types of photolithography that can be used to make nanostructures so this is a huge tool in nanotechnology and the resolution of photolithography gets better every day.

Now back to the layout of our chip so rather than making you squint at that tiny chip we can look at a drawing so you can see the features more clearly. The yellow squares that you can see, those are made out of gold, and that's where we're going to contact the chip to read out the signal. The pointy things that you see are leads that separate the sensors from the contacts so we don't get any short circuiting. We put our sensors at the ends of the leads. Now, the printing of this chip on a silicon wafer is not what gives us our nanoscale features—instead, it's what we do once we bring the chip in the lab, so the chips get fabricated at a semiconductor fabrication facility and then they come back to us and we post process them.

If you look at the surface of our chip you wouldn't be able to see this by eye, but it turns out that there are tiny holes in the surface of the chip and they were put there purposely to provide a place for us to introduce nanomaterials. We take our chips, we put them in a bath of metal salt, we apply a potential, and that causes metal to electroplate onto the chip. This is what gives us our nanostructuring. As the metal plates onto the chip, it forms tiny nanostructures that are actually quite easy to manipulate. For example, if we use three different conditions for electroplating, we can get three different levels of nanostructuring.

You're looking at images that are collected using scanning electron microscopy and these are three different sensors that we made and they were all made side by side on our chip. The one on the left has no nanostructuring; it's basically smooth, while the one in the middle has pretty large nanostructures that are about 200 nanometers. The sensor on the right has very fine nanostructures that are about 20 nanometers. Why do these different levels of nanostructuring appear? We actually used the same materials to make them, same conditions and solution, except for one condition and that has to do with how fast we do the electroplating process. If we make it go very fast, the metal plates onto the chip very chaotically, and the voids formed in the sensor don't get filled in. If we go slowly, we don't get any nanostructures because all of the voids are filled so you get this nice smooth sensor. This is a nice easy way to control nanostructuring.

Now how can we use these to detect biomolecules and what role do the nanostructures that we've created play? We can design and synthesize a DNA sequence that is complementary to whatever we want to detect. We know about the genetics of cancer cells. We know about the genetics of pathogenic organisms where this approach might also be valuable and so we can identify that sequence, program it into our DNA synthesizer, and then attach it to our sensor surface. When the sequence that we're looking for is present in a sample, it binds to the sensor through the type of hydrogen bonding and base pairing that we talked about a few lectures ago. This binding event causes an electrical current to be given off and that's what we're able to measure. We can put a variety of sensors on one chip and collect a profile of signals that can tell us about the type of cancer cell present in a sample.

It turns out that the presence of nanostructures on our sensors has a dramatic effect on the sensitivity of the approach. If we use a smooth sensor and we have a solution that contains a known number of DNA molecules, we have been able to determine that we need at least a million molecules in a sample in order to get that sensor to give off a response. So a million molecules; that's quite a large number, that's not typically what you have to work with in a clinical sample so we obviously need to push past there. If we take our sensor with 200 nanometer nanostructures, our sensitivity gets better, but we still need hundreds of thousands of molecules present to get an accurate reading. When we move over to the sensor that has 20 nanometer nanostructures all the sudden we only need 100 molecules in solution to trigger detection. This is a huge improvement over state-of-the-art that allows us to contemplate using these sensors to analyze clinical samples for cancer biomarkers so when we study these different levels of nanostructuring and we were able to pull out this trend and show that the nanostructuring gave us much better sensitivity, we were very excited about making that discovery.

Why does this work so well? And why does nanostructuring matter? One thing that we discovered in the course of our work is that the closer a nanostructure is in size to the molecules that are being looked at for detection, the better the sensors work. If we think about what's going on at the nanoscale, the molecules that are immobilized on a sensor that are being used as molecular bait; they're trying to reach out to find their complementary sequences in the sample. If they're on a surface that is flat on their size scale, they aren't really accessible. It's kind of a sea of bait molecules and they can't really see over their neighbors. If instead they're displayed on a small nanostructure—one that has a radius of curvature that they can feel—they're much better at finding the molecule they're trying to detect.

The nanostructuring, and again this size matching, creates room around the DNA strand trying to see the molecule that it's looking for. It's a bit like being in a movie theater. If you're in an old theater that has the seats arrayed on a flat floor and you're vertically challenged the way that I am, as soon as somebody sits down in front of you your vision is obscured and you can't see what's going on. But, if you go to one of these nice new theaters that has the tiering, it doesn't matter how short or tall you are or how short or tall the person in front of you is; you have an unobstructed view and you're able to see what's going on in the entire room. If the seats n that theater were only tiered by an inch that wouldn't help, right, the spacing of the seats need to be approximately on the human size scale to make a difference. Same thing with our DNA strands. The nanostructuring needs to be on the order of the molecular size scale to give them some room to see what's in the solution.

Let me tell you about a specific study we did using this chip. There is a certain form of leukemia, chronic myeloid leukemia, that affects white blood cells. Specifically, it affects the granulocytes that are important for fighting infection. It's one of the most treatable cancers, with very effective drugs available to arrest it. However, it's very important that it's diagnosed and classified very specifically so that the right drug is used to treat it. There are many different form of leukemia and it's really just this certain form that will respond to the drugs that I'm mentioning.

The origin of this disease is very interesting. It arises because a specific break occurs on chromosomes 9 and 22, and then they recombine to form a fusion. This creates a new DNA sequence that is not present in healthy cells. As a result of this sequence being present, a mutant protein is produced that causes the cell to be overactive and divide too quickly. This is what increases the level of white blood cells to a level that the body can't sustain. We don't know why this chromosome break occurs, but there have been suggestions that it could result from exposure to radiation. There must be other causes though because there are people affected with this type of leukemia that we know haven't been exposed to radiation so that's still a bit of a mystery.

The good news is that a drug is available that very specifically targets this protein and shuts the mutant cells down. Since the mutant protein is only present in the leukemia cells, the drug has no affect on other cells and has few side effects. There are very few drugs on the market that are this specific.

Let's talk a bit about how this type of cancer is diagnosed presently. If someone has a high white cell count, a sample of their blood is drawn and then it's taken to a lab. Once it's at the lab, a research technician will take the sample, they'll isolate all of the DNA from the blood, and then they'll start analyzing it. Even from a large sample of blood, that 10 mL that usually goes into a Vacutainer, there's not enough DNA to analyze using most methods that are available in clinical laboratories, so a process called PCR—the polymerase chain reaction—is used to amplify the CML gene. PCR makes many copies of the DNA molecule. Just like a Xerox machine it just runs lots and lots of copies off of a single original. It can produce billions of copies from a single original molecule. Once you have this much DNA in a sample, it's much easier to use pretty simple methods, for example monitoring the emission of light coming from a DNA-binding dye, to analyze the sample. In the figure that you're looking at the vials are showing you the strong fluorescence signal that's obtained once the CML sequence is amplified.

This works, but it's expensive, it's slow, and it can only be done in specialized laboratories with very experienced laboratory technicians running the tests and so that's why we decided to test whether or not our microchip-based system could be used as a substitute. Here, instead of amplifying the thing that we're trying to detect by running off copies of it, we're trying to turn up the volume of the signal that it produces—seems to us that it's more straightforward to do detection that way.

To test our chip-based approach for leukemia detection, we designed a chip that would display a DNA sequence specific to the CML gene fusion on a nanostructured sensor. Recent advances in the synthesis of artificial DNA make it possible for us to have a machine in the lab that is able to make any DNA sequence we need. Once the DNA sequence is made and ready, we attach it to the sensor by putting a sulfur atom at its end—we touched on the fact before that sulfurs are very good at sticking to the metals that make up our sensors. That allows us to take a specific sequence and anchor it to our chip. Once the chip is ready for a measurement, we calibrate it, and then we introduce a sample containing an unknown number of cancer cells.

Data is produced from the chip that allows us to determine how high the levels of CML cells in the sample are. What you're looking at is raw data generated from our instrument that reads the chip and it shows how much current is generated in the presence of varying numbers of cancer cells. We were able to do this kind of measurement both with samples taken from patients where the white blood cells were isolated, and also in whole blood samples. The fact that we could get these kinds of readings in whole blood presents the possibility that maybe someday rather than having to take a

10 mL blood draw from a patient, we could just do a pinprick and take a tiny drop of blood and analyze it, something that could be done right in the doctor's office.

We're very excited about the potential of this technology. What will it take to put it on the market and make it available to the clinical community? Well, we have a prototype instrument that we're using to validate the sensing approach and I've brought a prototype of this instrument with me to let you take a look. The way that this will eventually work is that our chip will be embedded in a cartridge that a physician can inject a sample into. If you're able to see this up close, you would see the contacts of the chip sticking out here so the chip is embedded in the cartridge and these foil packs, those are what hold our reagents and so those are the things that we need to be able to run this assay. What will happen is that the sample gets introduced into this cartridge. The cartridge then gets slid into the instrument, locks in, and then all one has to do to start the analysis is to press one button on the instrument and then within 5–10 minutes, an answer will appear to indicate whether or not there are cancer cells in the sample.

Why are we able to make such a small testing unit? Why is this possible? All of the signals that come off of our chip are collected electronically so we don't need any optics in this instrument. We don't need any type of fancy detectors or excitation sources, we just need a pretty simple set of circuits that can apply potentials to our leads and then collect the signals from the sensor. Inside of this box is just a collection of very simple electronic parts. We think that this is an instrument that can be produced very inexpensively and put at t price point where every physician could have one in their office.

Very often, when I tell people about this technology, they tell me that it sounds like a Star Trek tricorder and it's too good to be true. But this type of approach, where information on species or molecules in blood can be reported very quickly, is slowly but surely making its way into clinical medicine. Take for example the way that diabetics can now manage their illness with handheld monitors that report on blood glucose levels. These are very simple instruments that are quite inexpensive. The premise here is the same; we use the same guts in our instrument that you find in the handheld glucose monitor. But our analytes are much scarcer in the samples that we analyze, hence the need for nanomaterials. But there is every reason to believe that disease diagnosis will be made much faster, cheaper, and straightforward in the next decade, and nanomaterials will play a big role in this paradigm shift.

Let's look at another advance is cancer diagnosis and management made possible by nanoscale sensors. We've discussed gold nanoparticles as good sensors to report on genetic disease and also the presence of hormones that can confirm pregnancy. These materials, it turns out, are also very powerful for cancer detection. They can detect proteins in the same way that we discussed for the case of determining whether a woman is pregnant. The red color that a gold nanoparticle produces can be concentrated on a chip, and the fact that theses red absorbing nanoparticles are nanoscale makes them much easier to handle.

A recent study using gold nanoparticles to do protein detection looked at detecting PSA—the protein I mentioned at the beginning of the lecture that is a marker for prostate cancer—and they used the gold nanoparticles approach rather than conventional methods that are currently used. The commercially available PSA test is good at detecting large changes in levels of this protein, but it's not as good at looking at small variations. It's also not good at looking at very low levels of the protein.

Men that are treated for prostate cancer with a prostatectomy have trace levels of PSA in their blood post-operatively and so the levels of PSA go way down and are actually not measurable using the existing test. Why does this matter? Well it turns out that how fast the PSA comes back after the operation can tell a physician quite a bit about what treatment regime to use—and this decision should be made just when the PSA is starting to creep back up, not once it's already kind of on a steep trajectory. Again, the methods that are currently used for PSA screening simply can't look at these low levels that are present. A study published in 2009, showed that the very sensitive gold nanoparticle approach was a great solution and it could predict recurrence very quickly and accurately.

In this study, again done using gold nanoparticles, PSA detection data was collected for a series of patients, a pretty large cohort of patients. The data sets that were collected showed a dramatic difference in PSA reappearance in different patients. For some patients, the PSA stayed nice and low after the operation was complete—this must have given this subset of patients' really great peace of mind. For other patients, however, about a year after they had their prostate removed, their PSA levels started to creep up again. There are many treatment options that can be helpful for patients that surgery doesn't cure. Here, with access to this technology, the oncologist treating these patients had the information that the cancer was not gone many months before they would've known using the conventional diagnostic assays. It's clear that adoption of this approach should improve treatment outcomes for prostate cancer patients significantly.

So we've looked at two approaches to in vitro cancer diagnosis that have significant promise. While in vivo approaches may help us do whole body screens for early tumors, in vitro approaches are probably also here to stay as they provide information on cancer cells and markers in the blood. Before we leave this topic, let's take a step back and think about these two different approaches and how they may be complementary and potentially used at the same time to more effectively manage cancer. We have the in vivo approach where we send the nanosensors into the patient, let them circulate, let them take advantage of the leaky vasculature of tumors, let them accumulate into tumors, and then we get a snapshot of the patient's profile that tells us where there may be an accumulation of cancer cells so this is a very powerful approach. Again, it has the promise of detecting tumors when they're at a very early stage and it should be a very simple measurement. We just need to look for light shining through the tissue and skin.

That is an approach that we'll continue to advance as we mentioned when we talked about that material that the safety of the imaging agents needs to be assessed, the regulatory burden on that type of approach is higher so we then turn to our in vitro methods to look at how nanomaterials can be leveraged to look at samples that are taken out of patients. We looked at two different systems, one that is a chip based system that allows cancer related nucleic acids to be analyzed, and another, a gold nanoparticles system that is very good at looking at low levels of protein. Here, one of the unique advantages of doing things on a sample, doing things on a chip or with particles, is that we can look for many markers at once. If we do things in vivo we're usually looking for one marker. If we do things in vitro we can look for panels. Again, these approaches are very, very complementary and eventually they'll probably both be available and used together for more specific diagnoses and more earlier diagnoses.

In the next lecture, we're going to switch gears and we'll start talking about nanomaterials as drugs. That's right: nanotechnology not only has the possibility of detecting medical problems, but it may also be just as useful in treating medical problems. So we'll get a way of thinking about how you find trace analytes and samples or in the human body and we'll really start focusing on the solution and new treatments for cancer that are based on next generation nanomaterials. Next time, we'll really hone in on how treatments can be developed to selectively eliminate harmful cells. See you then.

Nanomaterials That Seek and Destroy Disease
Lecture 11

S cience fiction fans may remember the movie *Fantastic Voyage*, in which a miniaturized submarine, complete with crew, zooms around a man's body to repair a blood clot in his brain. In this lecture, we'll see how gold nanoparticles are being used to achieve something similar—to target and eliminate diseased cells in living tissue. We already know that these particles can be modified to recognize specific molecules and diagnose disease; here, we'll see how they use heat-producing vibrations to kill cells.

Properties of Gold Nanoparticles

- Like quantum dots, gold nanoparticles are good at moving around the circulatory system, but how good they are depends on their size, which can range from about 1 nanometer to more than 100 nanometers. Studies have shown that smaller seems to be better in using nanoparticles to selectively eliminate diseased cells.

- What allows gold nanoparticles to kill diseased cells is their ability to absorb light and convert it into heat.
  - Recall that when quantum dots are photoexcited, the energy is released in the form of emitted light. It turns out that the electronic structure of quantum dots makes them good at holding the energy in an excited state that can be emitted as photons.

  - For gold nanoparticles, when light goes in, the energy comes back out as heat. This effect can be used to kill cells that gold nanoparticles selectively enter.

- Most biomolecules lose their shape when they're heated up, which interferes with their ability to function.
  - Several years ago, it was discovered that a 1.4-nanometer gold particle was exactly the right size to sit in the major groove of DNA, the larger of the 2 spaces between the 2 strands of DNA.

o   If light causes a nanoparticle nestled in this space to give off heat, that heat will cause the 2 strands of DNA to dissociate, interfering with the cell's ability to function properly.

o   Roughly the same thing can happen with protein molecules. Certain proteins will even nonspecifically attach themselves to gold nanoparticles, and these proteins can also be denatured when heat is produced. Thus, exciting gold nanoparticles with light can basically turn a good detection sensor into a sensor that can both seek and destroy a cell.

Gold Nanoparticles in Action

•   Many types of cancer cells overexpress a protein called the epidermal growth factor. A team at the Georgia Institute of Technology attached an antibody to this protein to gold nanoparticles to study the particles' ability to achieve targeted ablation of cancer cells.

•   The researchers first verified that the nanoparticles were very specific for cancer cells. To do this, they tested the activity of the nanoparticles with two types of epithelial cells, one healthy and one cancerous. Epithelial cells are those that line the surfaces of tissues, such as skin, and cavities, such as the mouth or the stomach. Healthy cells don't have much of the receptor that the particles were designed to bind to, while cancer cells have high levels of this receptor.

•   The results of this research showed a distinct difference in gold nanoparticle binding to the two types of cells. When the researchers irradiated the particle-containing cells with light, they saw much higher levels of cell death for the cancer cells.

•   This same approach can be used to selectively kill bacterial cells. In a study done at the University of Arkansas, researchers generated gold nanoparticles that carried an antibody specific to the bacterium *Staphylococcus aureus*.

- o When these particles came into contact with the bacteria, they didn't penetrate the cell but sat on the cell membrane.

- o When the particles were excited with a laser, they disrupted the cell and caused the bacterium to break open and die.

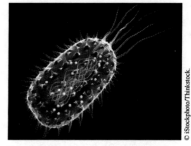

Bacterial cells can be targeted for destruction by gold nanoparticles bound to specific antibodies.

The Challenge Presented by Living Tissue

- The challenge with using the gold nanoparticle approach to cancer or bacterial cell elimination in a living system relates to the issue of absorption of light by tissue that we discussed in a previous lecture.
  - o Gold nanoparticles typically absorb light in the 500- to 600-nanometer range, and the larger the particle, the more that absorption shifts to a higher wavelength (the red part of the spectrum).

  - o But in this part of the spectrum, there is a great deal of absorption by tissue. If the surrounding tissue is absorbing the light, that means that very little light will make it to the gold nanoparticles, even using a powerful light source, such as a laser.

  - o Although gold nanoparticles give us an important proof of concept for using nanomaterials to target and damage specific cell types, this absorption of light by surrounding tissue appears to limit the use of gold in living systems.

- One way to solve the absorption problem is to make a modified type of gold-based nanoparticle, as was done by researchers at Rice University. Instead of using nanoparticles composed of gold, these researchers coated a core material, such as silica, with a thin layer of gold. This shifted the absorption of the particle far into the infrared, which is a much better region of the spectrum for getting light to pass through tissue.

- As the coating gets thicker on these gold-based nanoparticles (nanoshells), the absorption peak shifts from the more red part of the spectrum to the more blue part of the spectrum, making these materials very tunable.

The Power of Nanoshells
- In a study done at the University of Texas Southwestern, a mouse model of prostate cancer was generated by implanting tumors that grow from human prostate cells. Once the tumors had grown to about 40 cubic millimeters, the mice were injected with gold nanoshells. After about 18 hours, the researchers irradiated the tumors with 800-nanometer light for about 3 minutes. They then measured the tumors over the course of 3 weeks.

- In the control group of mice that didn't receive treatment, the tumors tripled in size over this period. In the treated group, however, the tumors shrank so small that they couldn't be measured by the end of the 3-week period.

- Despite the success of this study, the researchers highlighted some limitations. For example, when they measured the penetration of infrared light into the tissue, they found that once they went further than 1 centimeter, they had trouble getting light into the tissue. Many types of tumors, such as lung or breast tumors, would need greater penetration depths than this in order to be accessible.

- One solution to this problem might be to deliver light directly to different places in the body, for example, by bringing a fiber optic bundle into the lung. But instead of using visible or infrared light, we might also think about using a different type of radiation that doesn't have these absorption problems.

Gold Nanoparticles as Antennae

- One of the most common methods of cancer treatment relies on radiation therapy. Here, much smaller wavelengths of light are used to directly damage cancer cells.
  - This therapy is called ionizing radiation because when it hits molecules, they are forced to give up electrons, becoming charged ionic molecules. This, in turn, triggers DNA to release electrons and causes it to self-destruct.

  - This type of external beam radiation therapy is very effective at shrinking tumors and is much easier to get through human tissue. But it's often difficult to cleanly target the tumor because there are always healthy cells in the vicinity.

- The fact that we can make gold nanoparticles specific for cancer cells gives them the potential to be used as antennae for ionizing radiation, to help radiation therapy be more selective for tumor cells versus healthy cells.

- The dose enhancement effect comes into play when radiation interacts with the junction between two materials that have different atomic numbers.
  - At the interface between gold (atomic number 79) and the atoms of human cells (atomic numbers ranging from 1–8), very high doses of radiation will be generated.

  - We've seen that gold nanoparticles can be directed at cancer cells, bind them, and enter them selectively, and here, we could potentially use the good penetration properties of ionizing radiation to more effectively get at tumors that are buried under skin and tissue but leave healthy cells untouched.

- Scientists at the University of Connecticut Health Center, collaborating with a company called Nanoprobes, were among the first to explore how ionizing radiation could be used in combination with gold nanoparticles. In a study of mice implanted with breast cancer tumors, treatment with a combination of gold nanoparticles and radiation eliminated the tumors and resulted in a survival rate of 86% 1 year after treatment.

Gold Nanoparticles as an Internal Source of Radiation

- Using gold nanoparticles as an internal source of radiation eliminates the need to have radiation passing through healthy tissue at all; thus it's even cleaner than the amplifier approach of using the particles in combination with radiation.

- The use of radioactive particles to shrink tumors is referred to as brachytherapy. This approach is particularly effective for the treatment of prostate cancer. It is much less invasive than surgery and much less prone to complications. It can also be used to make surgery more straightforward by shrinking the tumor before a surgeon tries to excise it.
  - o Here, small seeds made of radioactive gold are implanted near a tumor. The overall effect that results, the death of cells close to the particles, is the same as what's achieved with external radiation, but it's much more localized and doesn't affect healthy cells.

  - o One problem with this approach is that the radioactive seeds can be difficult to work with and exhibit a great deal of variability in size. Seeds of varying sizes are less likely to focus on the tumor and more likely to focus elsewhere, perhaps causing inflammation, pain, and other side effects.

  - o Of course, as we know, it's pretty straightforward to precisely control the size of nanoparticles. Thus, well-defined nanoparticles made of radioactive gold could greatly improve the reproducibility and reliability of brachytherapy.

- A group at the University of Missouri tested the efficacy of radioactive gold nanoparticles for brachytherapy. They were first able to show that the gold nanoparticles had very little variation in their sizes, especially compared with conventional gold seeds, and in the levels of radioactivity they emitted. Further, the volume of prostate cancer tumors in mice treated with the radioactive gold particles was reduced by about 82%, with no side effects.

- This discovery may present a way to effectively deal with tumor metastases, particularly micrometastases, which are difficult to detect using imaging. Radioactive gold nanoparticles could actually find tumors and shrink them, irrespective of size—a much more effective way to halt the progression of metastatic cancer.

Suggested Reading

Kennedy, et al., "A New Era for Cancer Treatment."

Kumar, ed., *Nanomaterials for Cancer Therapy*.

Morton, Day, Halas, and West, "Nanoshells for Photothermal Cancer Therapy."

National Cancer Institute, "NCI Alliance for Nanotechnology in Cancer."

Questions to Consider

1. What are the advantages and disadvantages of using nanomaterials, such as gold nanoparticles, in medical testing?

2. Which of the three broad approaches to using nanomaterials against cancer do *you* regard as most promising? Why?

Nanomaterials That Seek and Destroy Disease
Lecture 11—Transcript

Shana Kelley: If you are a science fiction fan or a Raquel Welch fan, I bet you've seen the movie Fantastic Voyage. This 1966 movie has a plot that involves the invention of a miniaturization technology that allows a submarine to be scaled down so small that it can zoom around the human body and repair problems—like clogged arteries or blood clots. You may remember from the movie that the team goes into the submarine and it has a series of misadventures. It encounters turbulence in the heart and attacks it by white blood cells. In the end, they're finally able to repair a brain blood clot and escape from the body through the tear duct.

This is clearly science fiction. We can't miniaturize people and we probably never will be able to. Down at the nanoscale, a human-type body wouldn't even work because of the way we need to take things in from our environment. Yet, we'll see in this lecture how nanomaterials are being able to achieve something similar, but without the miniaturized people. You already know how gold nanoparticles can be modified to recognize specific molecules and diagnose disease. You also know about how semiconductor quantum dots can be used to seek out tumors in vivo by selectively accumulating in cancer cells.

We'll look at how nanomaterials that seek diseased cells in the body can also be used to destroy those diseased cells just like the micro-submarine in the Fantastic Voyage—except without the tiny people inside, which is good news actually. In the Fantastic Voyage, the miniaturized people were somehow able to breathe regular oxygen, even though one molecule of oxygen would've actually been too large to fit in their mouths! So things simplify quite a bit if we think about making tiny submarines to do these kinds of jobs—but ones that don't need a human crew onboard.

We'll see in this lecture three different ways that a familiar material—gold nanoparticles—can target and eliminate diseased cells. Gold nanoparticles are really good at moving around the circulatory system. Just like quantum dots, they're small enough to move through even the smallest of capillaries.

But how good they're at doing this actually depends on their size, which can range from about 1 nanometer to over 100 nanometers.

A recent study compared 20 nanometer and 100 nanometer particles that were introduced into a mouse that carried a tumor. The animals were examined after different time intervals and then portions of their tumors were analyzed. So as we look at gold nanoparticles that can selectively eliminate cells, we've to keep an eye on the sizes of the particles. Smaller seems to be better to enable the particles to travel away from a blood vessel and penetrate a tumor. This makes sense, as the particles need to be able to slip in between the cells that make up a blood vessel.

What properties do gold nanoparticles have that allows them to kill diseased cells? We've discussed to some extent how these materials interact with light, for example, when we talked about the color changes that result depending on the spacing between particles. In that case, the nanoparticle was emitting a signal that we were following.

Here, we'll be looking at a different phenomenon—the ability of gold nanoparticles to absorb light and then convert it into heat. If you think back to our discussion of quantum dots, you'll remember that when they're photoexcited, light goes into the particles, and then the energy contained within comes back out in the form of emitted light. It turns out that the electronic structure of quantum dots makes them good at holding the energy in an excited state that can be emitted as photons.

For gold nanoparticles, when light goes in, the energy actually comes back out as heat. These nanoparticles are not good at keeping the light in an excited state, and so the light is instead converted into vibrations that produce heat. As we'll see, this effect can be used to kill cells that gold nanoparticles selectively enter.

Why would a bit of heat kill a cell? Well, most biomolecules lose their shape when they're heated up, and this interferes with their ability to function. In certain cases, gold nanoparticles get really close to molecules. For example, it was discovered several years ago that a 1.4 nanometer gold particle was exactly the right size to sit in the major groove of DNA. You'll remember that the double stranded structure of DNA contains two grooves or spaces between the two strands of DNA. These grooves are actually asymmetric and the larger one, which is 2.2 nanometers wide, is referred to as the major groove, while the smaller one, which is about 1.2 nanometers wide, is the minor groove. So if a 1.4 nanometer gold nanoparticle nestles itself into this major groove space, and light causes the particle to give off heat, local heating is going to result. That heat can cause the two strands to dissociate—and when DNA strands dissociate, well, that really interferes with a cell's ability to function properly.

Roughly the same thing can happen with protein molecules. Certain proteins will even nonspecifically attach themselves to gold nanoparticles, and these proteins can also be denatured when heat is produced. Really, all cellular structures, which are held together by non-covalent interactions like hydrogen bonds and van der Waal interactions, can be perturbed by heat. So exciting gold nanoparticles with light can basically turn a good detection sensor into a sensor that can both seek and destroy a cell.

Let's take a look at an example of how this can work. A group at Georgia Tech has done some very nice work with gold nanoparticles that selectively enter and kill cancer cells. They were able to use a trick that we've already talked about in order to get the particles to recognize the cells. Basically, they attached an antibody to their gold nanoparticles. You'll remember that many types of cancer cells overexpress a protein called the epidermal growth factor, and there is an antibody to this protein that's available. So they attached that antibody to gold nanoparticles and verified that the nanoparticles were very specific for cancer cells.

To do this, they took two types of epithelial cells, one healthy and one cancerous, and they tested the activity of the gold nanoparticles. Epithelial cells are the kind of cells that line the surfaces of tissues, like skin, and cavities like the mouth or the stomach. The healthy cells don't have much of the receptor that the particles were designed to bind to, while the cancer cells, which were derived from an oral cancer tumor, have high levels of this receptor.

If you look at this image, you can see the difference in gold nanoparticle binding to the two different types of cells. On the left are the healthy epithelial cells, and on the right are the cancer cells. You can see that there are many more nanoparticles inside the cancer cells. When these researches irradiated these particle-containing cells with light, they saw much higher levels of cell death for the cancer cells. So this provided really good proof of principle because it showed that gold nanoparticles could be used to get targeted ablation of cancer cells.

It turns out that we can use the same approach to selectively kill bacterial cells. We can also get antibodies that are specific for certain types of bacteria and basically play the same game. In a study done at the University of Arkansas, a group in the Microbiology Department there generated gold nanoparticles that carried an antibody specific to the bacterium *Staphylococcus aureus*. You've probably heard of the infections caused by this bug; they're typically referred to as Staph infections, and they can be quite serious, especially if the bacteria ends up in the blood. When these particles came into contact with the bacteria, here the nanoparticles didn't actually go inside the cell, but instead they just sat on the membrane.

When the particles were excited with a laser, they disrupted the cell and caused the bacterium to break open and die. The images that you are looking at show this quite clearly. On the left, you can see a bacterium with the nanoparticles attached to its surface, and on the right you can see how the cell wall has broken open. So the use of nanoparticles to seek and destroy certain cell types is applicable not only to human cells, but also to bacterial cells and it's potentially a very powerful way to kill and target problematic cells, while leaving other nearby cells unharmed.

So far we haven't looked at whether this gold nanoparticle approach to cancer or bacterial cell elimination works in a living system. Why not? Well, here's the catch. Gold nanoparticles typically absorb light in the 500 nanometer to 600 nanometer range. The larger the particle, the more that absorption shifts to a higher wavelength, or the red part of the spectrum. But in this part of the spectrum there is lots of absorption by tissue, as we discussed in a previous lecture. So if the tissue all around is absorbing the light, that means that very little light will make it to the gold nanoparticles, even if we use a powerful light source like a laser. So, while gold nanoparticles give us really important proof of concept for using nanomaterials to target and damage specific cell types, this absorption of light by surrounding tissue really appears to limit the use of gold, at least this kind of gold, in living systems.

Let's take a look at a clever approach that circumvents this issue, and uses gold in a slightly different way that solves this problem. It turns out that one way to solve the absorption problem is by making a modified type of gold-based nanoparticle. Several years ago, researchers at Rice University figured out that if instead of using nanoparticles entirely composed of gold, they instead used a core of another material like silica and then they coated it with a very thin layer of gold and what they observed is that this shifted the absorption of a particle way into the infrared. Infrared is a much better region of the spectrum for getting light to pass through tissue; the absorption of tissue is really minimal in this part of the spectrum, so the light can actually reach the nanoparticle.

First, let's take a look at how these gold-plated nanoparticles are made. You start off with a particle composed of silica, which basically has the same composition as sand, but the particles are obviously much smaller than those that you find in sand. They then get coated with tiny particles of gold until the gold shell grows together.

What's really neat about these materials is that as the coating gets thicker, the absorption peak shifts from the more red part of the spectrum to the more blue part of the spectrum. This makes these materials very tunable: that is, the thicker gold plating, the more the absorption peak shifts to lower wavelengths. These nanomaterials really illustrate why being able to control materials at the nanoscale is so important. Just by varying the amount of gold plating, we can really tailor their optical properties and their heat absorbing properties to make them really effective in particular applications.

In order to use these as better cell targeting and killing agents, we obviously want to focus in on the materials with the thinner coatings that will absorb light more in the red and the infrared part of the spectrum. It was found that these gold nanoshells could be used in the same way as the original gold nanoparticles. But, we'll see that the shift that was achieved in the absorption spectrum allowed them to then be studied in real tissues.

A study done at the University of Texas Southwestern provided a very compelling example of an in vivo study showing how powerful these nanoshells are. In this study, a mouse model of prostate cancer was generated by implanting tumors that grow from human prostate cells. The tumors were allowed to grow until they were about 40 cubic millimeters. (This is about the size of a pencil eraser, just so you know how big it is.) The mice then had the gold nanoshells injected through their tail veins. After about 18 hours had gone by, the researchers then irradiated the tumors with 800 nanometer light for about three minutes. They monitored the mice over three weeks and measured the tumors over the course of this time period. Now in the control group of mice that they monitored that didn't get any treatment, the tumors tripled in size over this time, but the tumors in the treated group, the group that got the gold nanoshell therapy, they shrank so small that the researchers couldn't measure them by the end of the three weeks. This was a really striking result.

Despite the success of this study and the proof of principle they achieved for using gold nanoparticles in a tumor that was buried under a little bit of tissue, the authors of the study pointed out an important consideration in how this work should be moved forward. It turns out that they got to the goal that they wanted to achieve. They were able to use the nanoshells to improve the absorption properties of the particles, and they were able to do a study in living animals. But, they knew that there were still limitations. When they measured the penetration of infrared light into the tissue, they found that they could go a good distance, but once they went further than a centimeter, they had trouble getting the light into the tissue.

If you think about many types of tumors, like lung or breast tumors, these would need better penetration depths in order to be accessible. But, there are solutions that may allow us to use these materials. One would be to deliver light to different places in the body directly, for example by bringing a fiber optic bundle into the lung or another part of the body. If we continue to run into trouble with getting light through tissue, there's always a way to solve that by bringing the light closer to the particles. But, there's another way to think about this. Instead of using the type of light that we've been talking about, visible light, infrared light, we could think about using a different type of radiation that doesn't have these absorption problems.

One of the most common methods of cancer treatment relies on what we call radiation therapy or radiotherapy. Here, we're using radiation, but it's at very high energy radiation and it has much smaller wavelengths than the light we were just talking about. These wavelengths of light can be used to directly damage cancer cells. We call this kind of radiation ionizing radiation because molecules when they are hit with it, they're forced to give up electrons, and they become charged ionic molecules. This triggers DNA to release electrons and causes it to self destruct. In other words, ionizing radiation typically causes a cell to die. This type of external beam radiation therapy focuses a really powerful beam towards a tumor, and it's very effective at shrinking tumors. The type of energy that we're talking about here is much easier to get through human tissue, so tumors that are buried under the skin can be treated this way. But in this approach, it's very difficult to cleanly target the tumor because there are always healthy cells in the vicinity.

What if we could use gold nanoparticles as an antenna for ionizing radiation and we could use the fact that we can make them specific for cancer cells to help radiation therapy be more selective for tumor cells versus healthy cells. Now how can gold, or any other type of nanoparticle, act as an antenna? Well, there is an effect called the dose enhancement effect that comes into play when you have radiation interacting with the junction between two different materials that have very different atomic numbers.

What we find in the human body are elements that mostly have pretty low atomic numbers: so carbon has an atomic number of 6, oxygen is 8, hydrogen is 1, and these are the common elements in cells. Gold, in contrast, has a high atomic number (79). At the interface between the gold and the atoms of human cells, very high doses of radiation will be generated. The enhancement in radiation dose can be as much as 500%—this is a really powerful effect. We've seen before that gold nanoparticles can be directed at cancer cells, bind them and enter them selectively, and here, potentially we could use the good penetration properties of ionizing radiation to more effectively get at these tumors that are buried under skin and tissue but will leave the healthy cells untouched, hopefully.

Let's take a look at a study where this idea was tested. A group of scientists at the University of Connecticut Health Center, collaborating with a company called Nanoprobes that is based in New York, were one of the first to explore how ionizing radiation could be used together with gold nanoparticles. They generated a mouse model of breast cancer, and they generated tumors within the mice that grew to about 50 cubic millimeters, about that eraser size again. They separated these mice into four different groups—one that didn't get any treatment, one that received radiation only, one that received only the gold treatment, and one that got both gold and radiation. For the gold only and the no treatment groups, the tumors grew very quickly and they enlarged by 1000% within 5 days. The radiation only group had slower growing tumors, but within 20 days these mice had tumors that were actually identical to the control group.

Amazingly, the tumors in the group of mice that had been treated with both the gold nanoparticles and radiation were completely gone; they were too small to measure. What was particularly neat about this study is that these researchers then followed the mice in each group for an entire year so that they could evaluate whether the animals that received the gold plus radiation treatment were healthy in the long term. When they did, they observed an improvement in survival rate from 0% for the control group to 86% for the highest dose of gold nanoparticles. This is an amazing result—if we were able to see this same type of effects in humans, cancer would be a much more treatable disease.

Now let's take a look at a third way that nanomaterials can be use to selectively ablate cells. We've worked through a photothermal approach, where gold is used to generate heat, and an external radiation approach where gold is used to amplify radiation coming from an external source. So I think you'll be able to appreciate this third approach. It turns out that gold nanoparticles can also be used as an internal source of radiation—this then eliminates the need to have radiation passing through healthy tissue at all, and so it's even cleaner than the amplifier approach we just spoke about.

First let's talk through how internal radiation has traditionally been used without nanotechnology, and then we'll turn to how nanomaterials can improve the efficacy of this approach. The use of radioactive particles to shrink tumors is referred to as brachytherapy—from the Greek word for short-distance. This approach is particularly effective for the treatment of prostate cancer. It is much less invasive than surgery and much less prone to complications, and so it's quite popular as you can imagine with patients. It can also be used to make surgery more straightforward by shrinking the tumor before a surgeon tries to excise it. What is done here is that small gold seeds made of radioactive gold are implanted near a tumor. The gold is radioactive because it has an unstable nucleus that gives off gamma emission. The overall effect that results—the death of cells close to the particle—is the same as what's achieved with external radiation; but here, it's much more localized and you don't have any healthy cells in the way.

One problem that can be encountered with this approach is that the radioactive seeds can be difficult to work with and somewhat heterogeneous with lots of variability in their sizes. Radioactive seeds of varying sizes are less likely to focus on the tumor and more likely to focus elsewhere, perhaps causing inflammation, pain, and other side effects. This is where nanotechnology comes in. As you now know, it's pretty straightforward to very precisely control the size of nanoparticles. So what people realized is that by using well-defined gold nanoparticles made of radioactive gold, they could greatly improve the reproducibility and reliability of brachytherapy. Let's look at a study where this idea was tested.

At the University of Missouri, a group of clinicians and scientists got together and made radioactive gold nanoparticles to test their efficacy for brachytherapy. They were able to show that the gold nanoparticles had very little variation in their sizes and in the levels of radioactivity that they emitted. You are looking at a set of traces that illustrate how nanomaterials can be sized. A technique called dynamic light scattering is used to estimate the size of the particles and also to judge how much heterogeneity is present. The sizes of these particles were nicely clustered just around 100 nanometers, right around 85 nanometers, with little variability. At most, the particles varied in size by about a factor of 5, from the lowest size observed to the highest size observed, and when the conventional gold seeds are used, their sizes can vary by a factor of 100 so we've cut down the variability in size quite a bit by using nanoscale gold.

Once this group knew that they had a good material to test, they made sure that the gold nanoparticles did not affect the blood of the mice injected with them, just to look at the side effects that might result. They looked at the aggregation of platelets; they also checked that the hemoglobin levels didn't change, and this made it apparent that the gold nanoparticles didn't have any adverse effects on the mice. Then, using mice that had prostate cancer tumors, they tested their materials. What they observed was that the tumors in the group of mice that were treated with the radioactive gold particles had a reduction in the volume of the tumors of about 82%, and no side effects like weight loss or hair loss.

What's really exciting about this discovery is that it may present a way to effectively deal with tumor metastases. Usually, these tumor satellite sites are detected using imaging, and then depending on where they're located, external beam radiation is used to decrease their size. Small tumors, what are called micrometastases, are difficult to pick up with this type of imaging, so we usually don't even get the chance to treat them until they're larger. With the approach I just described to you, the particles could actually find the tumors and shrink them irrespective of size. This would likely be a much more effective way to halt the progression of metastatic cancer.

Now you know how nanomaterials can be used to seek and destroy cancer cells and other dangerous cell types. We talked about examples of cancer cells and also bacterial cells that can be destroyed using the same approach. For the cancer cells, we actually went through three different ways that we can use gold nanoparticles. We can get them to give off heat; we can get them to act as an antenna for radiation coming from outside of the body, or we can actually use them to deliver radioactivity directly inside the body. In each of these cases, the ability to manipulate matter at the nanoscale was absolutely essential so particles of particular sizes and with high levels of uniformity this was critical in order to make these materials effective killers of cancer cells, without harming other nearby cells. The materials that we looked at may not be as smart as the micro submarine in the Fantastic Voyage, but you can see that they certainly get the job done.

They would do it cheaply. You may be thinking about the fact that the price of gold per ounce is pretty high, and you might wonder how much gold we would actually need to treat a patient. It turns out that it would probably just add up to about 10 milligrams of gold. So, if someday the price of gold went up to $10,000 per ounce, we're still only talking about $3 per patient in terms of the cost of treatment. That's one thing to keep in mind that even when we're using expensive materials, if we're using them in their nanoscale form it's not going to be cost prohibitive.

The work that I described on nanomaterials being used as drugs to kill cancer cells or bacterial cells is just beginning and we talked about some of the challenges that still exist with getting light into tissue and really getting these materials to be effective, but it's clear that we're going to find solutions to make these materials work. There are many other applications or the same types of the approaches including the treatment of heart disease where destroying harmful plaques can be very important. Even though we don't yet have those nanoscale submarines, you can see that very powerful tools for medicine can be developed using pretty simple components.

In the next lecture, we will explore a, what you can think of as a, division of labor in the mission to seek-and-destroy diseased cells. Here we'll look at nanomaterials used as delivery agents for other drugs. We'll find that this approach is actually farther ahead than the one we just discussed: several drugs that are already approved by the FDA use nano delivery systems, and they're already on the market and in clinical use. See you then.

How Nanomaterials Improve Drug Delivery
Lecture 12

H ave you ever thought about what happens to a pill once it lands in your stomach? Think, for example, about aspirin—in addition to curing your headache, it may also give you a stomachache. The way we administer drugs is often untargeted, which can lead to side effects. In this lecture, we'll look at how nanomaterials may be used to allow more targeted drug delivery.

The Challenges of Drug Delivery

- Getting a drug to work in the human body is all about getting it to the right site at the right level. The reason this is difficult is that we almost always rely on a delocalized means of distribution.

  o In all of our drug delivery methods, the drug has to pass through a barrier, which may be the small intestine, the tissue in our ears or eyes, or the epidermis of our skin. Our bodies have several kinds of densely packed protective cells, and the drug must be able to get through these barriers and into the bloodstream.

  o In addition, many drugs don't survive the acidic conditions of the stomach. In these cases, drugs are typically injected into the bloodstream, but this is not a particularly well-liked means of administering drugs.

- Drugs that are injected into a vein go first into the heart and then to the lungs, along with the blood, to get oxygenated. Once it picks up oxygen, the drug will then travel through the body in the arteries and flow into the capillaries. This is where the drug has the opportunity to make it into a tissue. Capillaries are about 10,000 nanometers in diameter, so nanoscale drug particles can easily flow through them.

- Among the toughest challenges in drug delivery are those encountered in anticancer therapy. Tumors are difficult to penetrate, in part because the blood supply reaches only the outside of the tumor. In addition, many of the drugs used to treat cancer have significant toxicity if they reach healthy cells; thus, it's important to engineer some type of targeting into their delivery.

- In the scenario in which a drug is circulated by tagging along with blood, it will go through the lungs, liver, heart, and kidneys as it travels, and there are many harmful things that can happen to these organs when they're exposed to drugs. If we are trying to target a drug to the pancreas, for example, it would be best to send it right there and not have it pass through any other organs.

- It's also true that many drugs are difficult to formulate; for example, some drugs are difficult to make into powders, so they can't be made into pills. For intravenous drugs, sometimes the solvents that are needed to get a greasy drug molecule into solution can have more side effects than the drug itself.

Drugs in Current Clinical Use
- Only a few classes of drugs are used for cancer chemotherapy.
  - Some of these are molecules that react with DNA; this is a good approach for an anticancer drug because it can shut down rapidly dividing cells by depriving the cells of instructions for making more copies.

  - Other drugs interact with structural components of cells, interfering with cell division.

  - Yet another approach to cancer chemotherapy involves molecules that act like natural metabolites and interfere with DNA synthesis. They shut down the enzymes that are responsible for copying DNA and, again, deprive the cell of instructions needed to replicate further.

- Cisplatin is a drug used to treat ovarian cancer, lung cancer, leukemia, and quite a few other cancers. The activity of cisplatin is termed DNA alkylation, which basically means that the drug hits one of the functionalities on the DNA base and interferes with its structure. Because they affect both normal and cancerous cells, DNA alkylators would definitely benefit from more specific delivery.
  - Cisplatin was first characterized in 1845, and in the 1960s, it was found to stop cells from replicating. It was approved as an anticancer agent by the FDA in 1978.

  - Cisplatin has a range of side effects, including kidney problems, hearing loss, weight loss, and nausea; thus, minimizing the exposure of healthy cells to cisplatin would be beneficial.

- Another effective anticancer drug is doxorubicin, used to treat certain leukemias, bladder cancer, breast cancer, tissue sarcomas, and others. Doxorubicin works by slipping in between the DNA base pairs and shutting down the DNA copying, which helps to shut down cell division.
  - Doxorubicin was originally isolated from a microbe that has a bright red color. The bug that produces it probably uses the molecule to fight off other bugs. It was originally thought of as an antibiotic, but later it was discovered to have antineoplastic activity, or anticancer activity.

  - The main problem with using doxorubicin is that it causes damage to the heart and lungs. The cardiotoxicity that's seen after doxorubicin treatment is a major side effect and can actually be life-threatening once a certain dosage is reached. It's important, then, to find ways to keep doxorubicin out of the heart.

- TAXOL®, originally derived from the bark of the Pacific yew tree, is widely used for the treatment of lung, ovarian, and breast cancers. TAXOL works by binding to a cell's microtubules, parts of the cell that are important for structure. When TAXOL is bound, the cytoskeleton of the cell can't be broken down to make way for new cells. This is another way to shut down rapidly dividing cells.

o   The major problem with using TAXOL is that it is a large, greasy molecule. It's very hydrophobic, which makes it difficult to formulate.

o   Castor oil is used to make TAXOL stable in solution, but when castor oil is injected intravenously, it can cause some people to experience neurotoxicity.

A program in the 1950s to find naturally occurring drugs resulted in the development of paclitaxel, a drug derived from the Pacific yew tree and used to treat lung, ovarian, and breast cancers.

Nanoscale Drug Carriers

•   A carbon nanotube looks similar to a drug capsule, and nanotubes are hydrophobic, which means that drug molecules that are difficult to formulate will work well inside carbon nanotubes. As we've mentioned, carbon nanotubes can be biodegraded. It's also possible to cork carbon nanotubes—to snip the ends shut but have them open back up once they're in the right environment. Further, nanotubes can also be coated with drugs on the outside.

•   Liposomes represent another major class of nanoscale drug carriers. Liposomes are soft materials, mainly made out of the lipids that make up the membranes around all of our cells. Drugs are encapsulated inside the lipid bilayer. Again, these carriers offer excellent biodegradability.

•   Protein nanoparticles are also great vehicles for delivering drugs because not only are they biodegradable, but the cells recognize them as just being proteins. If we can find a way to make a particle out of protein and fill it with a drug, it would be an effective way to move a drug around the body and get it to tumors very specifically.

- Nanomaterials are also good at getting around some of the resistance mechanisms in cells, which can be a major problem. Cancer cells are very aggressive and can pump drugs out of cells; they can also introduce enzymes that will deactivate drugs. But packaging drugs in nanomaterials disguises the drugs from the cancer cells.

- Nanovalves sense pH levels, which differ in healthy cells and cancer cells. If the nanovalve senses the pH of a cancer cell, only then will it release the drug into the cell.

Studying Drug Delivery with Nanomaterials
- The most popular way to study drug delivery with nanomaterials is to use cultured cells. Such studies look at the effects of drugs with and without the nanomaterial-based carrier.

- Once we have some proof of principle with cultured cells, we can then move into an animal to see if we can reproduce the same effect, but here, we have the circulatory system to contend with and all the other intricacies of a live animal.

- Another way to study drug delivery that's unique to using nanomaterials as delivery agents is to use scanning electron microscopy. Here, we use a particle that can be seen as a carrier and then image the cells we're testing to determine exactly where the particle went. This gives us a full profile for what's happening at a very fine level.

Suggested Reading

Allen and Cullis, "Drug Delivery Systems."

Ferrari, "Frontiers in Cancer Nanomedicine."

Hillery, Lloyd, and Swarbrick, eds., *Drug Delivery and Targeting.*

Langer and Folkman, "Polymers for the Sustained Release of Proteins and Other Macromolecules."

1. Why can't every drug be packaged into a pill?

2. How can nanomaterials help with drug delivery? What's special about their properties that provides a solution in this area?

How Nanomaterials Improve Drug Delivery
Lecture 12—Transcript

Shana Kelley: Have you ever thought about what happens to a pill once it lands in your stomach? Think, for example, about aspirin—in addition to curing your headache—it may also give you a stomachache. The way that we administer drugs is very often untargeted and we introduce a drug and we let it distribute itself throughout the body. This can lead to a lot of side effects, and irritation like the aspirin-induced stomachache. What we'll talk about today is how nanoscience may provide a solution allowing more targeted drug delivery. What do I mean by that? Well we know that nanomaterials can be targeted to certain types of tissues. We've looked at examples where that has worked, for example imaging cancer tumors. If we could turn this paradigm around and learn how to use nanomaterials as drug capsules and target specific tissues we could leverage this type of specificity for better treatments.

This lecture will be the first of two focused on nanoscale drug delivery. By that I mean that we're going to be focusing on systems that allow us to take a drug, package it up, and allow it to be delivered to the site within the body where it's going to exert its action. We'll start by trying to understand the challenges of drug delivery, and then we'll look at a variety of nanomaterials that can be used to meet those challenges. We'll also discuss several of the leading anticancer drugs so that you are familiar with the agents that will be involved once we shift over to look how nanomaterials can be involved in their delivery. That will be this lecture and then in the next lecture, we'll look at specific examples of nano-packaged drugs that are either on the market or in development. By the time we get through all of this material, I think you'll understand how drug delivery is one of the areas where nanoscience is making a really significant near-term impact on medicine.

Getting a drug to work in the human body is all about getting it to the right site at the right level. Why is this hard? We almost always rely on means of distribution for a drug where the drug just goes all over the body. If we take a drug orally in a table, like aspirin, it goes into the stomach and is absorbed through the small intestine. We can also administer drugs through the eye, or the ear, or the nose; all of these places will take drug up into our system, but each of these are also delicate tissues that we don't want to perturb. You might also be aware of the fact that in the last decade, we've become better and better at delivering drugs using patches and so we've put a patch containing the drug on the skin and the drug then goes into the skin, but it does actually end up in the bloodstream. This is not really a localized type of drug delivery, but something that's fairly delocalized.

Maybe the one way that we're able to deliver a drug in a way that is very specific and localized are topical drugs. For example, if you get poison ivy, you don't take a pill, you put a cream on your skin and that works very well and there are no side effects from that type of approach. But, the skin is really one of the only places that we can do that and anything that's affecting an internal organ obviously needs to be addressed from the inside. For all of the drug delivery challenges, the main thing that is difficult is that the drug has to pass through a barrier and this barrier may be our small intestine or it may be the tissue that's in our ears or eyes or mouth and the epidermis of our skin is just one example of a layer of epithelial cells. Our bodies have several kinds of these densely-packed protective cells, and, the drug has to be really good at getting through these barriers and into the bloodstream.

In addition, many drugs just won't survive the acidic conditions of the stomach and they get stuck in some of the other places that we mentioned. So in this case we typically inject them right into the bloodstream. This is obviously not a very convenient way to administer a drug—nobody likes needles, but in some cases it is the way to go because it gets more of the drug into circulation where it can start doing its thing.

Now what happens once a drug is in the bloodstream? Well, let's say we're injecting a drug into a vein, the simplest case we can consider. That drug will first go into the heart, and then over to the lungs along with the blood to get oxygenated. Once it picks up the oxygen, it will then travel through the body in the arteries and then flow into the capillaries. The capillaries are where the drug within the blood has the opportunity to make it into a tissue. The arteries and veins are designed for physical transport of blood and really that's it. While it's the capillaries, the much smaller vessels, that handle chemical transport and so they're really there to feed oxygen and other agents to tissues. So they have good exchange properties, whereas again, the veins and arteries don't. It's the capillaries that will really allow drugs to travel into tissues.

How big are these capillaries? You probably have a picture in your mind of them being quite small and we have to think about are they so small that we can't really envision nanomaterials in them. But, it turns out that they are about 10 microns, or 10,000 nanometers, so we don't really need to worry about nanoscale drug particles getting stuck. They'll be able to flow through just like the blood cells.

Some of the toughest challenges in drug delivery are in the area of anticancer therapy. Tumors are some of the hardest places to reach in the body. They're very dense, and by that I don't necessarily mean that the cells are more closely packed, but they're much harder to penetrate in part because the blood supply only reaches certain parts of the tumor. It really only comes to the outside and then the cells inside can really be protected from the blood supply, which is how we're going to get drugs in so that's a major challenge. In addition, many of the drugs that are used to treat cancer have significant toxicity if they reach healthy cells so it's quite important to try to engineer some type of targeting into their delivery.

We've touched on a feature of the blood supply around tumors that does help nanomaterials reach them. If you remember when we were discussing tumor imaging, we went over the fact that blood vessels or capillaries can be quite leaky around the tumors. The leaks that are there actually create openings that measure about 500 nanometers. This type of opening is too small for a red blood cell to leak out, but it's large enough for a drug packaged up with nanomaterials to leak out if it's packaged properly and if the size scale of the particle is right.

That's how drugs travel around the body and into tumors. The problem that needs to be solved here is how to more specifically target drugs. In the scenario that I just discussed where we considered a drug would be circulated by tagging along with blood, the drug will go to the lungs, it'll pass through the liver, it'll go through the heart and the kidneys, and there are lots of bad things that can happen to these organs while they're being exposed to drugs. If we are trying to target a drug to the pancreas, it's really unnecessary, if

213

only we could send it right there and not have it stop any of these other places. What we'll find as we start to discuss nanomaterial-based solutions is that some nanomaterials can be very good at keeping drugs out of trouble in non-target areas.

We'll also find that nanomaterials can be helpful for drug delivery in a different way. Many drugs are difficult to formulate, and by that I mean that in order to take a compound and then administer it to a human you have to have it either as a pill or in solution or in a patch in some type of formulation so that you can give it to the patient. Many drugs are really difficult to work with. If they're too hydrophobic they won't dissolve in water. If they're not very good at making powders you can't make them into pills and so in certain cases nanomaterials have really been able to solve this part of the drug delivery problem, what you get is a formulation problem. For drugs that get turned into intravenous drugs, one that we administer as a solution in a needle, it turns out that sometimes the solvents that are needed in order to take a very greasy drug molecule and get it into that solution can be quite nasty and they have more side effects than the drugs themselves.

You can think of things that are good at solubilizing greasy molecules, these organic solvents like benzene and chloroform and you probably know the names of these and know that these are not things we would want in a human body and that's very true. There are other things like castor oil that can be effective at dispersing a drug, but we'll talk about why that's undesirable for other reasons. We'll see that nanomaterials can be quite good at getting drugs that are difficult to work with into a better state, and then they'll also help us avoid some of the common side effects.

Before we start talking about how we can use nanomaterials for anticancer drug delivery, let's look at a few examples of clinically used drugs and review some of the issues with using them as a treatment. It turns out that there are just a few classes of drugs that are used for cancer chemotherapy. Some of these are molecules that react with DNA and this is a good approach for an anticancer drug because this can shut down rapidly dividing cells because it deprives the cells of instructions for making more copies. Others drugs interact with structural components of cells and this also interferes with cell division. A third approach to cancer chemotherapy are molecules that act like natural metabolites and they interfere with DNA synthesis. They shutting down the enzymes that are responsible for copying DNA and again they deprive the cell of instructions that they need to replicate further. We'll look at a few examples of these.

One of the anticancer drugs that's been around the longest is a molecule called cisplatin and this is used to treat ovarian cancer, lung cancer, leukemia cancer, and quite a few others. The type of activity that it has is called DNA alkylation. What does that mean? It's just kind of a dumb chemistry term, but maybe I can explain it. This molecule sees a piece of DNA and it sees the guanine residues within DNA and it modifies them. It attaches the drug to them. Now you have a piece of DNA that's there to be copied right, it's carrying the genetic information, but it has this platinum molecule sticking off of it. That really messes up the copying of DNA so the alkylation just refers to the fact that we're hitting one of the functionalities on the DNA base and then interfering with its structure.

Cisplatin has been around for quite a while. It was actually first characterized in 1845 when scientists were basically just messing around and looking at reactions occurring at platinum electrodes. They saw this interesting molecule being formed. People continued to play around with this platinum based complex and then somebody decided to look at it in the 1960s to see what it did to cellular function and observed that it really stopped cells from replicating. It was then put into a series of tests and through a clinical trial and that it was approved as an anticancer agent by the FDA in 1978. Now drugs like these, the DNA alkylators, affect both normal and cancerous cells so they would definitely benefit from more specific delivery. Cisplatin has a range of side effects. It's really not a fund drug to be on. It causes kidney problems, it can cause hearing loss, it causes weight loss, and nausea. This type of drug is really dangerous to all cells and so it's something that we would just like to minimize the exposure of healthy cells to.

Another effective anticancer drug is doxorubicin. This is a drug that is used to treat certain leukemias, and bladder cancer, breast cancer, tissue sarcomas and lots of others. Doxorubicin works a bit differently. It doesn't modify DNA, but it just slips in between the DNA base pairs, and what this does is it makes it difficult for cells to copy their DNA because there's this extra

215

molecule between the bases and then part of what needs to happen during the copying is the two strands need to be pulled apart and with this molecule in there that's tough to do. The DNA copying gets shut down and then this helps to shut down cell division. This is another way to interfere with the dividing of cancer cells. .

Doxorubicin, where did we find this molecule? It was actually originally isolated from a microbe that had a bright red color. It's actually the color of a ruby and that's where the name of the drug comes from with Doxorubicin. The bug that produces it probably uses the molecule to fight off other bugs. This molecule was originally thought of as an antibiotic, but then we figured out later on that it has this antineoplastic activity, or anticancer activity, and so this class of molecules is sometimes called antineoplastic antibiotics and I don't suggest that you try to say that ten times fast, but just in case you ever hear the term, that's what it means.

It's interesting that organisms like bacteria bother to make these very complicated molecules, but you have to realize that bacteria live in a world of thousands of other kinds of bacteria. There's lots of bacterial warfare that goes on and the way that they protect themselves from their neighbors is sometimes to have a molecule on hand that is harmful to somebody else, but not harmful to them. Many of these compounds have been found to be good at killing cancer cells while having some selectivity against healthy cells.

The main problem with using doxorubicin is that it causes damage to the heart, and also to the lungs. The cardiotoxicity that's seen after doxorubicin treatment is a major side effect and it can actually be life-threatening once a certain dosage is reached. So we obviously need to find ways to keep doxorubicin out of the heart.

The second approach that I mentioned are drugs that interact with the structural components of a cell. Taxol, which is the name that it was originally given for reasons that I'll get to in a minute, the name of the drug when it's used clinically is actually paclitaxel. This is a drug that is widely used for the treatment of lung, ovarian, and breast cancer. Interestingly enough, this is where the name comes from, it was originally isolated from the bark of a Pacific yew tree, *Taxus brevifolia*, and so that's where the name came from. Now why were we looking at tree bark for drugs? That may seem like a pretty crazy thing to do, but it turns out that in the 1950's the U.S. National Institute of Cancer started up an aggressive program to look for naturally occurring drugs.

We know that, for example, Native Americans and other populations that don't have access to what we call westernized medicine or modern medicine very often rely on natural remedies. They look at things around in their environment. They've kind of tried different things. They know what cures they may have out in their backyard for different ailments and so there was a move by the U.S. government to try to collect some of this same information by studying the molecule in plants and in the environment. There was a group of botanists that were recruited from the USDA who were sent out in the field and they were told to gather as many samples as they could of different kinds of plants. They would bring them back into the lab, they would extract all the molecules from the plant, and then they would see if it had any effect on either cultured cells, so cells that can just be grown in a flask in the lab, or on mice. In the mid 1960s, an extract from the Pacific Yew tree was tested and very high levels of activity were observed.

This is a great finding, but it also presents a bit of a problem so are we going to cut down every Pacific Yew tree in the world to get this drug. No, obviously not. That's not a sustainable solution. How did people contemplate taking this drug and moving forward with clinical testing? Well, it turns out that Taxol is a very complicated molecule. It has lots of bonds and the bonds have specific orientations that nature is very good at programming. Nature is great at making complicated molecules like this one.

For synthetic chemists, and they're the people that would be able to make large batches of the molecule, making this compound was quite a bit of work and very challenging, and eventually what happened is that pharmaceutical companies were basically able to marry the biology and the chemistry, get cells to do a lot of the work, and then they were able to produce the drug in a way that didn't involve cutting down any yew trees so that was a very good solution. This drug was eventually approved by the FDA in 1992 and Bristol Myers Squibb was the first company to offer it. The sales of this drug peaked in 2000, this was before there were any other analogues with the same activity available, and in a single year 1.6 billion dollars worth of this drug was being sold. It's now off patent and it's available as a generic drug and it's used widely in anticancer therapy.

How does Taxol work? It binds to a part of the cell that is quite important for structure, a part of the cell called the microtubules. The microtubules are actually nanoscale structures that are about 25 nanometers in diameter. They provide support for the cytoskeleton of the cell. When the cell divides, the cytoskeleton actually needs to be disassembled. But when Taxol is bound, this is made much more difficult: the cytoskeleton can't be broken down to make way for new cells. So this is another way to shut down rapidly dividing cells.

The major problem with using Taxol is that it is a large greasy molecule. As I mentioned it's a very complicated structure and it's very hydrophobic. It doesn't like water and that makes it very difficult to formulate. It needs something really kind of greasy to make it stable in solution. What was arrived on as a way to get it into solution is a form of castor oil. Again, it might seem like kind of a strange thing to test, but castor oil's been around for a long time. It doesn't taste very good, but it's at least kind of a biological substance. It turns out that many people react badly to the solvent and I'm not talking here about the bad taste and wanting to spit it out, but instead that castor oil when it's used as an intravenous injection can cause certain people to experience neurotoxicity. So clearly we need better ways to deliver drugs like Taxol.

Now you have a better appreciation for why we need better solutions for drug delivery. We need to keep drugs out of sites in the body where they can be harmful, and we need to be able to introduce them into the body without carriers that produce side effects of their own. Let's use what we know about the world of nanoscience to survey the range of approaches that are being explored to solve the problems of drug delivery.

One of the first classes of materials that we can look at are carbon nanotubes. If you think about the structure of a carbon nanotube, you have this very hydrophobic s as capsules—can be corked, can also carry drug on the outside, can also shallow carbon and then an empty space in the middle, so that almost look likes a drug capsule doesn't it. The fact that carbon nanotubes are very hydrophobic means that these drug molecules that I've talked about as being very problematic to formulate will be happy inside of a carbon nanotube.

We've also talked about the fact that carbon nanohorns can be biodegraded so they can be attacked by enzymes like peroxidase and that allows them to be broken down in the body. That's a very useful property that carbon nanotubes have. It also turns out, and this is a very interesting development, that people have learned how to cork carbon nanotubes so if you think about the way the structure usually appears it's an open-ended capsule. That wouldn't be all that useful, right if you just have an open capsule floating around let's say in the bloodstream it's eventually going to spill the drug into the blood.

People have figured out how to kind of snip the end shut, but then have them open back up once they're in the right environment. That's a very nice type of switchability that allows these materials to be used with quite a bit of flexibility. Another neat thing, and we'll come back to this in the next lecture, is that you can actually coat carbon nanotubes with drug on the outside. So rather than putting it on the inside you can layer a bit of drug on the outside of a carbon nanotube and that then gives you kind of a finite dosage carried on that nanomaterial.

What we have here is also a picture of a very neat kind of carbon nanotube that's actually a carbon nanohorn. This is a type of carbon nanotube, which has solved the open capsule problem by actually growing one side of the carbon nanotube into a horn shape. You'll see in this image that there's actually cisplatin particles in this nanohorn, and they're sitting there waiting to be released once they get into a tumor.

Now let's talk a bit about liposomes. This is another major class of carriers for drugs that are in nanoscale. We just looked at carbon nanotubes. Those are kind of a hard nanomaterial. Their structure is really fixed. Liposomes are different. Liposomes are really soft materials and they're mainly made out of the lipids that make up all of our cells, that make the membrane around all of our cells. What happens here is that we formulate a drug by putting it in the middle of a liposome and then we form the lipid bilayer around the drug and so you have this capsule of drug, lots of drug molecules inside, encapsulated by something that the cell is very used to seeing so again excellent biodegradability here. We'll come back to this in the next lecture with some very specific examples, but these liposomal carriers have turned out to be very powerful for getting around some of the side effects that we see with drugs that don't have any kind of nano-packaging.

Another class of nanomaterial based drug delivery that we'll look at are protein nanoparticles. Protein nanoparticles are a great vehicle for drugs because not only are they biodegradable, but the cells recognize them as just being proteins. If you can find a way to make a particle out of protein, stuff it with drug, this is a great way to move a drug around the body and get it to tumors very specifically.

Another thing that we'll find that nanomaterials can do is get around some of the resistance mechanisms in cells. Drug resistance and drug resistance to anticancer agents is a major problem. We have people that start responding very well to a therapy and then after a few dosages their tumors become resistant. This is because cancer cells are very aggressive and they're very good at coming up with ways to get rid of a drug so they can pump it out of the cell. They can overexpress that pump in a very short amount of time. They can also introduce enzymes that will deactivate a drug, but if you package the drug up with a nanomaterial that really fools the cell into thinking that it's not there. If you can have the action of the drug be much faster you give the cells much less time to become resistant. That's another advantage that we'll revisit, packaging drugs into nanoscale delivery vehicles.

There are some other very interesting things that are just being developed for drug delivery based on nanomaterials. There are things that are referred to as nanovalves, so these are drug packages that can come up to a cell and they will sense the pH of that cell so the pH tells us whether something is acidic or basic. It turns out that healthy cells have a different pH it is and if it has the pH of a cancer cell, only then will these things release the drug into the cell so that's very specific, very powerful. Now, we've just gone through a survey of different nanomaterials and how they can be used for drug delivery, how do we study this? How do we take a drug package it up and then figure out whether we've done anything to improve it?

There's lots of ways to do this, but the most popular way is to use cultured cells. We have cells in flasks that we can grow in the lab and we can introduce the drug, always do controls to make sure we're not looking at artifact, and we can look at the effect of the drug kind of with and without the nanomaterial based carrier and see if there's an increase in activity. Another way that we can look at drug efficacy, of course, is to use animals.

Once you have some proof of principle, some experiment that you've done with cells, you can then move into an animal to see if you can reproduce that same effect, but here where you really have the circulatory system to contend with and all of the other intricacies of a live animal. Another way that we can study drug delivery that's very unique to using nanomaterials as drug delivery agents is that we can use things like scanning electron microscopy. If we have a particle that we can see we can use that as a carrier and then we can image either the cells that we're testing or even an animal and figure out exactly where the particles went, see if they got into the cell, see where they went within the cells, and really get the full profile for what's happening at a very fine level.

Now we've looked at many of the key concepts that are important to appreciate so that we understand the challenges and solutions that exist in the area of drug delivery. We've considered how conventional drugs are distributed in the body and what the issues are with the conventional approaches. We've also worked our way through the major classes of drugs that are used to treat cancer. We've looked at the major classes of materials that can be used to solve the delivery problem.

With all this information covered, we have all the pieces—both the available drugs and the available delivery mechanisms—so that now we're ready to turn, in the next lecture, to how this all comes together. In the next lecture, we'll look at examples of nanoscale drug delivery systems that are already playing an important role in cancer treatment, and we'll also look at examples of some newer systems that are in very early stages of development that are quite promising. See you then.

Delivering Drugs with "Smart" Nanocapsules
Lecture 13

In the last lecture, we looked at some of the powerful drugs that are available to fight cancer and discussed the challenges of delivering drugs within the human body. We also examined a variety of carriers, including nanotubes, liposomes, and others, that are potentially programmable to bring drugs to specific tissues. In this lecture, we'll look at some recent studies in which these nanomaterials have been shown to be effective in improving drug activity.

The FDA Approval Process

- Many of the studies we'll look at in this lecture are preclinical trials. These studies are typically done in academic labs to test whether modifications to an existing drug or a completely new drug show significant activity.

- Once the preclinical data are collected on cultured cells and mice, the next step in the FDA approval process is to organize a Phase 0 clinical trial. This study is conducted on a small number of patients and is designed to enable researchers to quickly understand what a drug does to the body and what the body does to the drug.

- Next, a Phase 1 trial is conducted. This trial uses a large group of healthy volunteers to assess the safety of a drug. The thinking here is that if a healthy person can't tolerate a drug, it's unlikely that someone who is sick will, particularly a cancer patient.

- If everything goes well with the healthy volunteers, the Phase 2 trial then looks at how well the drug works in a cohort of cancer patients. Here, information on how the drug should be dosed is also collected.

- If effectiveness is observed in Phase 2, then a large a Phase 3 trial is set up. Here, testing is conducted with a large group of patients;

half of the group is given the drug and the other half is given a placebo. Because the improvements in survival can be small in drug trials, especially cancer drug trials, it's important to look at placebo effects.

- If the results of a Phase 3 trial are positive, then the drug will typically be approved by the FDA. This entire process can take about 8 years, and the preclinical work with mice needed before a trial can be started can take about 6 years. For every 1000 drugs that begin preclinical testing, only 1 goes to clinical testing.

DOXIL®

- The drug DOXIL, coupled with a nanoscale carrier, has made it through the FDA approval process and into clinical use. DOXIL is based on doxorubicin, which as mentioned earlier, causes cardiotoxicity and can impair heart function.

- In the 1990s, researchers at the University of San Francisco and a small company called Sequus Pharmaceuticals developed a new form of doxorubicin packaged inside a liposome. The drug molecules inside this nanoscale package are held in place by a lipid bilayer and a layer of polyethylene glycol.
  o The lipid bilayer keeps water on the inside of the particle. The polyethylene glycol helps the particle stay in circulation by keeping the immune system from attacking it.

  o This liposomal packaging system helps a dose of the drug stay in the body longer. This means that the drug has more time to find the tumor and that repeated doses aren't necessary, which seems to have lowered cardiotoxicity.

- Cardiotoxicity also seems to be suppressed as a result of the nanoscale structure of DOXIL. Because they are larger than regular molecules, the DOXIL particles are kept out of the crevices of the heart where they can do damage.

- DOXIL also takes advantage of the passive tumor-targeting effects that we've discussed. It was approved by the FDA in 1995 and has been shown to be particularly effective in treating Kaposi sarcoma, a skin tumor often seen in AIDS patients.

TAXOL
- As we discussed in the last lecture, the drug TAXOL is made into a liquid formula by dissolving it in a form of castor oil, Cremophor®. The drug itself, which binds to microtubules and disrupts the replication of cancer cells, has a fairly good side effect profile, but Cremophor may cause neurotoxicity. To make matters worse, Cremophor can also dissolve the plasticizers in the tubing that is used to administer the drug intravenously.

- A company called Abraxis has developed a form of paclitaxel that allows it to be administered without any toxic solvents; this form is packaged into nanoparticles of the protein albumin.
  - This protein is water soluble, occurs naturally in humans, and has a tendency to form nanoparticles that are about 100 nanometers in size.

  - Even more important, albumin can bind to receptors in blood vessels and give them a signal that allows the drug-protein complex to travel out of the blood vessel.

- The activity of the drug is very impressive. In a trial focused on metastatic breast cancer patients, the tumor response rate was twice as good for the nano-formulated drug. Dramatically reduced side effects have also been shown. This form of paclitaxel was approved by the FDA in 2005.

Dual-Layer Nanoparticles
- A study done at MIT and reported in 2005 showcases the advantages of nanomaterials. This study involved nanoparticles with 2 layers—a core of doxorubicin and an outer layer with a molecule that interferes with angiogenesis, a process by which new blood vessels are made.

- The efficacy of these dual-layer nanoparticles was tested in a mouse model of melanoma. When the mice were treated with either doxorubicin or the anti-angiogenesis agent on its own, they survived for only 20 or 30 days. With the combined nanoparticle, they lived three times as long.

- Without the control to make these nanoscale layers, this type of approach wouldn't be possible. This is why nanotechnology is so powerful: because it allows us to manipulate things at a fine level that can make a significant difference for drug delivery.

Next-Generation Nanodelivery Systems
- Researchers at Duke University are currently developing a peptide-based nanoparticle that has produced dramatic results as an anticancer treatment. They started off by engineering a peptide that would self-assemble around the drug doxorubicin.
  - A domain on these peptides has a section that has a good ability to grab the drugs. On the other side of the peptide is a group of hydrophilic amino acids.

  - In a solution of these peptides and a drug with water, the drug and the sticky part of the peptide go inside, and the hydrophilic part of the peptide goes on the outside. The result is a water-soluble particle with the drug encapsulated inside it.

  - These peptides will spontaneously form 100-nanometer particles, a good size for a drug delivery system.

  - A single dose of these nanoparticles increased the 60-day survival of mice with tumors by 90%.

  - These researchers also discovered that the conjugates are good at preventing cells from becoming drug-resistant, likely because the drug is very fast-acting.

- A group at Northwestern University has come up with the idea of producing nanobins that can sense pH and selectively release a drug in response to a pH change. To create these bins, the researchers developed a polymer that could be cross-linked to hold the particle together, which allows them to load the particle with doxorubicin.

- o Because they are pH-responsive, the bins shrink when the pH is lowered. In other words, as pH goes down, the bin collapses on itself and eventually squeezes all of the drug out. As we've said, cancer cells have a lower pH than healthy cells.

- o These nanostructures worked extremely well in tests in a mouse model of breast cancer.

- A group in Japan has done some interesting work with carbon nanohorns to deliver cisplatin. These nanohorns bind to the surface of the cell and seem to be able to poke through the cell membrane and deliver the drug directly into the cell. The researchers in Japan showed that the potency of the drug improved by about sixfold in a mouse model, and there was no weight loss in the mice, which is a common problem with cisplatin.

- At Stanford, a group is working with using carbon nanotube transporters. As mentioned earlier, a small amount of drug can be contained inside a nanotube or adhered to the outside and released when it reaches its target. In a test of the latter approach in a mouse model of lymphoma, tumor growth was completely arrested and there was decreased damage caused by the drug in non-tumor sites.

- Finally, a group at MIT has developed a targeted polymer nanoparticle. In addition to an anticancer drug, this system incorporates a recognition domain that allows the particle to specifically pick out prostate cancer cells, which have a special protein on the surface. In a test with mice, prostate tumors virtually disappeared.

The Future of Nanoscale Drug Delivery

- Of all the examples we've see in this lecture, the one with the most specificity—the one that had a recognition element that was able to specifically bind to prostate cancer cells—was the one that achieved the most dramatic results. It's likely that obtaining heightened specificity to lessen effects on healthy cells will be an increasing focus of this field.

- It's also important to note that nanoscale drug delivery has applicability in a variety of disease states—not just cancer—and there is interesting work going on in a number of different areas, such as cardiovascular medicine and treatment of diabetes.

- In general, it's clear that the pace of progress in nanoscale drug delivery is rapid, and it will likely continue to produce exciting advances in the short term.

Suggested Reading

Peer, et al., "Nanocarriers as an Emerging Platform for Cancer Therapy."

Petros and DeSimone, "Strategies in the Design of Nanoparticles for Therapeutic Applications."

Weintraub, "A Nano Drug's Giant Promise."

Questions to Consider

1. What's the difference between using a macroscale capsule for a drug and using a nanocapsule? Why would the activity of the same drug in these two forms differ?

2. How do nano-based drug delivery approaches limit side effects?

Delivering Drugs with "Smart" Nanocapsules
Lecture 13—Transcript

Shana Kelley: The effective treatment of diseases like cancer relies on our ability to come up with drugs that are potent and safe. In the last lecture, we discussed the challenges of delivering drugs within the human body. We also looked at some of the most powerful drugs that we have at our disposal to fight cancer, and we also examined the limitations and their use that comes from side effects and formulation challenges.

Nanoscience, as you know, brings a unique set of tools to problems like this one and that's particularly true for the drug delivery challenge. It gives us a variety of structures at the nanoscale that could potentially be used to bring drugs to tumors in a way that is much more directly targeted. We've already talked about a variety of carriers, including nanotubes, liposomes, protein nanoparticles, and nanovalves and a common feature of all of these is that they can carry drugs and they're potentially programmable to get to certain tissues to give us more specificity in the way that drugs are delivered. We're now ready to look at some specific examples where these nanomaterials have been shown to be very effective at improving drug activity.

First let's touch on how we evaluate the efficacy of a drug and how we evaluate improvements that could be realized when nanomaterials are used as carriers. In the studies that we'll review, mice turn out to be a very important system in which to gauge drug efficacy. We have methods at our disposal that actually allow tumors to be transplanted into mice, and so they can serve as a good model and mimic what happens in human patients. We can use mice to understand how much of a drug is in circulation as a function of time and this is important so that we understand how much drug is there and how long it stick around.

In other lectures, we've talked about the fact that our kidneys and livers are good at removing chemical agents from our bodies, and so again it's quite important to look at the kinetics of drug clearance and we understand how long it's present in a living organism. In analyzing the efficacy of new drugs, we'll also look at tumor volumes so monitoring the size of a tumor in the presence and absence of a drug is a very direct measurement that tells us how well a drug is reaching the desired site and how well it's working. You may wonder, how do we measure tumor volume? It's usually a simple measurement basically done with a ruler, so it's a crude type of evaluation, but it tells us exactly what's going on. We'll also look at response rates and survival rates. These values look at the overall effect of the drug and not only how the tumor responded to the drug, but how the animal as a whole responded.

Many of the studies that we'll take a look at represent what we refer to as pre-clinical trials. These are studies that are typically done in academic labs to test whether modifications to an existing drug or a completely new drug has significant activity. Here we'll be looking at the influence of the inclusion of nanocarriers. We'll also be looking at drugs that went all the way through a series of clinical trials, from the preclinical stage all the way through the clinical trials that were needed in order to gain FDA approval so that the drugs could be used in human patients.

Just so that you have an appreciation of what this process with the FDA involves, I want to quickly take you through the steps. Once the pre-clinical data is collected on cultured cells and mice, the next step is for a Phase 0 clinical trial to be organized. This study is collected or conducted on a small number of patients, and is designed to very quickly understand what a drug does to the body and what the body does to a drug. Here safety and the degree of efficacy for a drug are not really being assessed and it's more about trying to match up studies that may have been done in a mouse with a study being done in a patient.

After Phase 0, a Phase 1 trial is conducted and this Phase 1 trial uses a large group of healthy volunteers and the healthy subjects are used so that the so that the safety of a drug can be assessed. If a healthy person can't tolerate a drug, it's pretty unlikely that a cancer patient will, so this is an important thing to assess early on. If everything goes well with the healthy volunteers, the Phase 2 trial then looks at how well the drug works in a cohort of cancer patients. Here, information on how the drug should be dose is also collected. If up until this point effectiveness is observed, then a large a Phase 3 trial is set up. Now here a large group of patients is collected, sometimes into the thousands of patients and these trials are randomized so that one half of the group is given a drug and the other half of the group is given a placebo. The improvements in survival can actually be small in drug trials, especially cancer drug trials, so it's quite important to look at these kinds of placebo effects and really document them. If the results of a Phase 3 trial are positive then a drug will typically be approved by the FDA.

This entire process can take about eight years, and the preclinical work with mice needed before you ever start a trial and all the discovery that needs to take place can take about six years, so this is a very long process that is involved with the development of a new drug. For every 1000 drugs that begin preclinical testing and are tested in research labs, only one goes to clinical testing. Now you should be able to appreciate why the list of drugs that we have to fight cancer is so small, and why pharmaceutical companies really struggle to make progress—time and the odds of success really work against drug development.

With all of this in mind, let's now take look at an example of a drug that was coupled with a nanoscale carrier and this new form of the drug was able to make it through this entire FDA process into clinical use. The name of this drug is Doxil, and as you might guess, it's based on the drug doxorubicin that we discussed in the last lecture. The vials of the drug that you're seeing in this image show you that bright ruby red color that I mentioned in the last lecture. Some people actually refer to this drug as "red death" though because it's not well tolerated. We talked about the fact that this drug causes cardiotoxicity and can impair the function of the heart. The images that you are looking at show a comparison between healthy heart cells and those that have been exposed to doxorubicin and you can see that those cells are really perturbed and this is a consequence of the drug passing through the heart once it has been injected into the body.

In the 1990s, researchers at the University of San Francisco and then a small company called Sequus, also based in the Bay Area, developed a new form of doxorubicin packaged inside a nanoscale carrier. The carrier that they used was a liposome. On the inside of this particular liposome, floating around in a drop of water, was a collection of doxorubicin molecules. Every particle has many, many drug molecules within it.

What's holding them in place is a lipid bilayer and then a layer of polyethylene glycol. What are these layers doing? Why do we need them? It turns out the lipid bilayer is very good at keeping water on the inside of a particle. The lipids are greasy in the middle, but then they have charged groups that the water really likes. The lipids are molecules that are abundant in cells, so they're biocompatible. On the surface of the liposome, the polyethylene glycol helps the particle stay in circulation. It helps the circulation of the particle by keeping the immune system from attacking it and by making it think that the particle actually belongs in the human body.

This liposomal packaging system helps a dose of drug stay in the body longer. If we look at the kinetics of how fast unmodified doxorubicin stays in the blood, we see that the levels drop off precipitously—within hours the drug is basically gone. If we look at Doxil—the drug package in liposomes, it stays around much longer. This means the drug has more time to find the tumor, and it also means that repeated doses don't need to be administered. One of the first things that was noticed during the Doxil clinical trial was that levels of cardiotoxicity were lowered, and the immediate conclusion was that since we didn't have to re-administer the drug there was less build up of the drug in the heart and so we were suppressing cardiotoxicity that way.

Another very interesting thing that was discovered is that the cardiotoxicity was also suppressed because of the nanoscale structure of Doxil. By being bigger than a regular molecule, the Doxil particles were kept out of the crevices of the heart where they could do damage. This was another thing that helped the drug be more effective.

Doxil also takes advantage of the passive tumor targeting effects that we've discussed. One of the first conditions it was approved for was to treat Kaposi's sarcoma. This is a skin tumor that is very often seen in AIDS patients. I once saw Frank Szoka, one of the inventors of Doxil, he's a professor at UCSF, I saw him talk about the clinical trials that were done with Kaposi's sarcoma patients and the images that he showed were really dramatic.

One of the patients that they studied basically had tumors covering many parts of his body. In this study, they labeled the drug with a dye that allowed them to see where it went. In the images that were shown, you could see almost perfect overlap between where the tumors were and where the drug went. It was really amazing to see that targeting really taking place and again this is just a targeting that happens because of the leakiness of the blood vessel around tumors, even tumors on the skin. Doxil was approved for use by the FDA in 1995. It was shown to be particularly effective in Kaposi sarcoma patients who didn't respond to other treatments. It's now been approved for the treatment of several other cancer types.

Now let's move on to another nano drug delivery success story. In the last lecture, we talked about Taxol—or paclitaxel—and the problems with its solubility and formulation. When this drug is used clinically it's administered as a solution. It's made into a liquid formula by dissolving it in a liquid called Cremophor, which is a form of castor oil. While Taxol, which as you know binds to microtubules and disrupts the replication of cancer cells, has a pretty good side effect profile. In addition to make matters worse, because it is good at dissolving things, this solvent can dissolve the plasticizers in the tubing that is used to administer the drug intravenously. Cremophor as a solvent not only has bad side effects, it's even dissolving parts of the delivery system that we need to get the drug into the body at all.

A company called Abraxis, located in Los Angeles, developed a form of paclitaxel that allows it to be administered without any toxic solvents and they packaged it into nanoparticles of a protein called albumin. This protein is water soluble and it occurs naturally in humans and it also has a tendency to form nanoparticles that are about 100 nanometers in size. Even more important is that this protein can bind to receptors in blood vessels and it can give them a signal that allows the drug protein complex to travel out of the blood vessel. The drug is packaged inside the particle and goes along for the ride.

By packaging this drug within a protein nanoparticle, the ultimate biodegradable vehicle, we get around the need to use toxic solvents. The activity of the drug is very impressive. In a trial focused on metastatic breast cancer patients, the tumor response rate was twice as good for the nano-formulated drug. To make things even better, only 30 minutes were needed for a complete IV dose of the drug instead of three hours. This benefit, it may seem somewhat minor, but it really offers improved quality of life for patients being treated for metastatic breast cancer to shorten their time that they need to be in a hospital to get a drug dose definitely makes this easier to bear. This type of treatment is in addition to being faster, it's more effective, and it's safer.

This form of paclitaxel was approved by the FDA in 2005. The clinical trials that were done—in addition to showing better patient responses—also showed dramatically lowered levels of side effects. The clinical community has really embraced the use of this drug, and over 300 million dollars worth of the drug is sold every year. The company that developed it—Abraxis, was sold to a New Jersey-based pharmaceutical company, Celgene for about 3 billion dollars in 2010. Now that we have looked at two major advances in the development of more effective drugs that were made possible by nanoscale delivery vehicles, let's turn to some next generation systems that also have significant potential.

There are lots of things that we can do with nanomaterials that are simply not possible without nanoscale structural control. Let me walk you through a very clever study that was done at MIT and reported in 2005 that really showcases the advantages of nanomaterials. The particles that this MIT group made actually had two layers, so the core of the article was made of doxorubicin and as you know, this drug will keep cancer cells from replicating. The outer layer of the nanoparticle had another molecule encapsulate with it—one that interferes with a process call angiogenesis.

Angiogenesis is the process by which new blood vessels get made. Tumors need lots of angiogenesis to happen because they need a good blood supply to be provided to them so that they can survive. It's been hypothesized for some time that a way to shut down the growth of a tumor would be to starve the tumor of its blood supply. So these nanoparticles that should be able to do that would deliver a double whammy. They would hit the DNA inside the tumors cells and then they would also hit the blood vessels outside of the tumor.

Are these nanoparticles, these dual layer nanoparticles effective? Very much so. Their efficacy was tested in a mouse model of melanoma. When these mice were treated with either doxorubicin or the anti-angiogenesis agent on its own, the mice only survived for 20 or 30 days. With the combined nanoparticle, they lived three times as long. If we could reproduce that in human subjects, that would obviously be huge, to extend the lifetimes of cancer patients by three times would be really amazing. Now again, without the control to make these nanoscale layers, this type of approach wouldn't be possible. Again, I just want to emphasize that this is why nanotechnology is so powerful, because it really allows us to manipulate things at a fine level that can make a big difference for drug delivery.

We'll spend the last part of this lecture looking at a variety of system that are all in the pretty early stage of development, but they all show tremendous promise. One nanoparticle based drug delivery system that I learned about very recently is something that's under development at Duke University in North Carolina. I was just down there a few weeks ago visiting some collaborators and got to meet a group of people in the bioengineering department there that were doing some very interesting work. What they have been developing is a peptide based nanoparticle that has produced some really dramatic results when used as an anti-cancer treatment, again at an early stage in models that the early results are quite interesting.

What they did is they started off by engineering a peptide that would self-assemble around the drug doxorubicin. The sequences that they developed they thought long and hard about how to design these sequences to do this and what they ended up with, once I describe it you'll realize that they were able to mimic some of the features of a liposome with a peptide sequence. On these peptides, there's a domain that has a section that is really able to grab the drugs, so this part of the peptide is kind of greasy and the drug is kind of greasy so they come together and they stick. On the other side of the peptide is a group of amino acids that are very hydrophilic, so they love water so they really want to be in water, the other part of the peptide wants to be near the drug, and so what that means is that if you take a solution of these peptide and a drug and water, the drug and the sticky part of the peptide goes inside and the hydrophilic part goes on the outside and you get a nice water soluble particle with the drug encapsulated inside it.

These peptides will spontaneously form 100 nanometer particles, so that's a good size for a drug delivery system. What's really astonishing is that these nanoparticles when they were tested in mice, after a single dose, increased the 60-day survival of these mice by 90%, so these were mice with tumors. They had an untreated population and watched their survival rates and then they looked at the population treated with the peptide nanoparticles and there was an improvement of 90%. That's just absolutely amazing relative to some of the other things that we've looked at. What's special about these particles? Well the peptide sequences were very carefully engineered. The peptides that they used are pretty small, so the nanoparticles are a little bit smaller than what we've been looking at, and they seem to be pretty speedy at distributing the drug.

It was also discovered that these conjugates are good at allowing cells to not become drug resistant. This is likely because the drug is very fast acting. It seems as though this system has been able to provide a very effective drug delivery vehicle, but with some really special properties that gives it a very special level of activity and it will be quite interesting to see what happens as this nano-packaged drugs goes through clinical trials.

Now let's take a look at a pH-sensing nanocarrier. We quickly touched on how these work in the last lecture. The person who led this study, his name is SonBinh Nguyen, was a classmate of mine at Caltech—he's a really smart and very creative guy. He's now a professor at Northwestern, and his group came up with the idea of producing "nanobins" that could sense pH and selectively release a drug in response to a pH change. If you look at the SEM image of these materials, they really do look like shallow bins. You can see how they could carry the drug around using that depressed space. To get these bins, they were able to develop a polymer that could be cross-linked and the cross-linking is to hold the polymer together, to hold the particle together, and it allows them to load it with the drug doxorubicin. The polymer bins because they're pH responsive, they shrink when the pH is lowered so as that pH goes down, the bin just collapses on itself and eventually that squeezes all the drug out. This is almost like a nanosponge.

Why were they focusing on pH as a way to release the drug? It turns out that cancer cells have a lower pH than healthy cells. The metabolism of cancer cells is really perturbed. They don't function as normal cells do and that drives the intracellular pH down. The idea here is that they would be able to get preferential drug release in the cancer cells. When they tested these interesting nanostructures in a mouse model of breast cancer, it worked extremely well. They imaged the tumors while they were still in the animal and they could see them shrinking significantly. Importantly, just injecting the animals with the bins on their own had no effect.

We haven't really talked about this, but it is always extremely important to test an empty carrier when it's being evaluated as a delivery agent. There are many structures or molecules out there that look pretty innocuous and you think yeah that's a good carrier, it probably won't do anything, but you never know. Structures again that seem like they should be pretty stable can have strange effects when they are taken up into cells, so it's always important to look at the empty carrier to make sure there's no effect there.

In the last lecture we looked at carbon nanohorns that could hold cisplatin. We just took a brief look at this as we were surveying different types of nanomaterial carriers. These nanohorns do something really interesting— they bind to the surface of the cell, and they seem to be able to poke through the cell membrane and deliver the drug right into the cell. The group that did this work, which is based in Japan, was able to show that the potency of the drug improved by about six-fold in a mouse model, and there was no weight loss observed with these mice, and that's a common problem with cisplatin. This group also checked very carefully to make sure that the carbon nanohorns didn't cause any toxicity on their own, again an important check for this type of material, which could cause inflammation or other problems if it accumulated to high levels.

Let's also look at the use of a carbon nanotube transporter. Drugs can be put on the inside of carbon nanotubes, we've talked about that a little bit, and we've also mentioned the fact that it can be adhered to the outside. This is a really cool idea because it allows just a small amount of drug to be carried on the nanotube, and then released when it reaches its target. This work on culling carbon nanotubes was done at Stanford in the lab of Hongjie Dai. Hongjie is one of the pioneers in carbon nanotube chemistry. He's done all kinds of things with carbon nanotubes.

His group tested this doxorubicin/nanotube approach in a mouse model of lymphoma, and the results looked really good. This conjugate, just like DOXIL which we talked about at the beginning of the lecture, seemed to decrease damage in non-tumor sites. Interestingly, when they looked at doxorubicin on its own, they saw significant damage in the intestine of the mice that they were testing, but this damage basically disappeared once they attached or absorbed the drug on to carbon nanotubes. Most importantly, tumor growth was completely arrested, survival rates went way up, and the side effects were minimal.

Now let's look at one last example: a targeted polymer nanoparticle. This drug delivery system was invented at MIT by the group of Bob Langer, and you'll hear lots about Bob Langer's work when we discuss nanoscale tissue engineering, but his group also works in drug delivery. They came up with the first targeted, drug containing particle. This particle has a polymer core that's very good at binding an anticancer drug. In this case they used a drug called docetaxel, and this is a relative of paclitaxel. What is unique about this system is what they attached to the outside of the particle. Here they incorporated a recognition domain that allows the particle it to specifically pick out prostate cancer cells. These types of cells have a special protein on their surface, and so this is what the Langer group directed the recognition element towards. To test the drug, they implanted prostate tumors into mice. What was really remarkable here is that the tumors in the treated mice basically disappeared; they shrank and shrank and shrank and then disappeared. This is a really dramatic result and we think it results from the specific targeting of this system and directing the drug right to prostate tumors.

Now we've looked at a variety of nano-enabled delivery systems. We've looked at protein nanoparticles and liposomes that are used clinically to deliver drugs with greater potency and fewer side effects. We've looked at next generation approaches that combine some very interesting activities and also specificity domains and it's really probably this last angle—where heightened specificity is obtained to lessen effects on healthy cells—that will be an increasing focus of this field.

Of all the examples we looked at, the one with the most specificity, the one that had a recognition element that was able to specifically bind to a prostate cancer cell, this was the one that achieved the most dramatic results with complete ablation of a tumor observed. I think we'll be seeing more and more work in this area. It's also important to realize that nanoscale drug delivery has applicability in a variety of disease states, not just cancer, and there is very interesting work going on in a number of different areas, so cardiovascular medicine, diabetes, there are nanoscale drug delivery systems under development for these diseases that have some similarities to what's going on in cancer drug delivery, but with some subtle differences that have to do with the exact type of disease that's trying to be treated. In general, it's clear that the pace of progress in nanoscale drug delivery is rapid, and it will likely continue to be producing very exciting advances in the short-term.

In the next lecture, we'll look at nanoscale surgical tools. These can be used to perform surgical procedures one cell at a time. We'll survey a variety of literally cutting edge systems that can be used to make surgical excisions cleaner and faster to heal. We'll also look at very small surgical tools that can excise diseased cells with incredible precision—a very exciting capability. See you then.

Nanoscale Surgical Tools
Lecture 14

Surgery is currently the most effective and widely used procedure in treating human cancers and other diseases, but to be curative, surgery must be incredibly precise. Incomplete removal of a tumor can decrease survival rates significantly. In this lecture, we'll look at nanoscale surgical tools, such as tweezers and scalpels, that will improve the precision of surgery, as well as nanomaterials that enable more accurate diagnosis and aid in healing.

Assessment of Tumor Margins

- In order to completely excise cancer, a surgeon must be able to identify tumor tissue and distinguish it from healthy tissue. Where these two types of cells come together are called the "margins" of a tumor. It's important to take as little of the healthy tissue as possible, because there could be important nerves or blood vessels in the tissue; thus, surgeons are very conservative in taking extra tissue.

- Typically, when an operation is complete, a surgeon will take a small sample of tissue that he or she considers to be outside the margins of the tumor for post-surgery testing. In breast cancer, up to 50% of partial mastectomy cases require a second procedure because tumor is found in such samples, and in early-stage lung cancer, residual tumor deposits after surgery are associated with up to a 35% reduction in survival.

- The limiting factor in detecting microscopic tumors or defining the borders of a tumor at the time of surgery is the sensitivity of the human eye, which can resolve only objects that are about 250 microns in size. Further, tumor cells are not usually visually distinct from healthy cells, making them even more challenging to selectively remove.

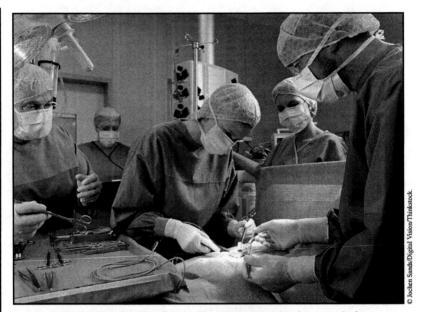

Nanotechnology has significant potential to improve what happens before, during, and after surgery; nanoscale tools and materials can aid diagnosis, enhance surgical precision, and speed recovery.

- In 2002, a group of researchers at Massachusetts General Hospital and Harvard Medical School showed that iron nanoparticles could be used to improve surgical removal of brain tumors in lab animals.
  - Here, iron oxide nanoparticles helped with visualization of brain tumors before surgery using MRI and included a chemical dye that would emit light on excitation to light up the tumors during surgery.

  - Once the surgery was done, the researchers performed postmortem testing and determined that all of the cancer cells were gone.

  - In order for these nanoparticles to work, they had to cross the blood-brain barrier, a shield of capillaries around the brain. Molecules measuring about 1 nanometer, such as sugar, alcohol, and nicotine, can penetrate this barrier, but typically, larger molecules cannot. Surprisingly, the iron nanoparticles—measuring 50 nanometers—were able to pass through.

Visualization of Lymph Nodes

- The lymphatic system is a network of vessels that carries lymph, a fluid that contains much of the waste generated by cells and is used to transport foreign cells to the lymph nodes, where they can be destroyed. The lymphatic system provides another route for cancer cells to move around the body.

- With some cancers, before they spread to other parts of the body, their first stop is a lymph node or gland close to the tumor. The lymph node closest to the tumor is referred to as the sentinel lymph node (SLN). The idea behind surgery on SLNs is to see if the cancer has spread.

- The way that SLNs are typically imaged for surgery involves the injection of a radioactive tracer near the tumor. A Geiger counter can then be used by the surgeon to track the tracer as it moves into the SLN. Using radioactivity for this procedure is not ideal because, of course, radioactive substances can be harmful. But nanomaterials may be able to provide an alternative solution.

- In 2006, researchers noticed that when infrared-emitting semiconductor quantum dots were injected into a tumor, they localized directly to the SLN. The quantum dots clearly found the same path that metastatic cancer cells take through the lymphatic system to reach the SLN. The time required for the lymph nodes to light up was only 15 seconds, which would allow a surgeon to visualize the right lymph node and take samples for biopsy in real time.
  - The pig model system used for these trials is the Sinclair™ Miniature Swine, a type of pig that has been engineered to spontaneously develop melanoma. Melanoma is a relevant type of cancer for SLN mapping because about 70% of melanomas in humans metastasize by passing through the lymph nodes.

o The pig form of melanoma is similar to the human form, making this system relevant for testing the quantum dot imaging approach.

o Another feature of these pigs that is indirectly useful is that they have highly pigmented skin and dark hair, which makes detecting light given off by the quantum dots difficult; thus, getting proof of principle in this system makes it that much more likely that it would work in humans.

• The use of nanomaterials to find lymph nodes is likely several years away from application in humans, but the potential for impact on surgical outcomes is significant. Lymph node resection is one of the most difficult things for surgeons to learn when they use existing techniques for visualization. Being able to use nanoparticles to illuminate lymph nodes should make the learning curve much less steep.

Robotic Surgery
• The most common types of robotic surgeries actually have a human being controlling the robotics, but using the robot as an interface to the patient helps eliminate tremors and allows for finer manipulations. One thing robots lack, however, is a sense of touch, and for most types of surgery, this is quite important.

• A device that may be able to give robots a sense of touch is a kind of nanoparticle sandwich, with 2 layers of gold nanoparticles on the outside, a layer of cadmium sulfide on the inside, and a layer of squishy plastic separating the 2 kinds of particles.
  o When stress is placed on the gold nanoparticles on the outside, they couple with the cadmium sulfide, causing light to be emitted. In a sense, the particles can feel the presence of others.

  o Someday, this type of device may allow a robot to be able to "feel" the tissue that it's operating on and sense fine features within the tissue.

Nanoscale Surgical Tools and Medical Nanomaterials

- A 1999 study reported in the journal *Science* described a clever approach for manipulating nanomaterials at the macroscale for medical uses.
  - In this study, a 1000-nanometer glass rod was attached to 2 carbon nanotubes, with the attachment sites made of metal so that they could serve as electrodes.
  - When there was no potential applied to the electrodes, the carbon nanotubes remained apart. But when 8 volts were applied, the tips of the 2 nanotubes were drawn together.
  - This device acts just like a pair of tweezers and could be able to pick up a single cell.

- Another way that increased precision could be achieved during surgery is through the use of nanolasers. Very fast and focused laser pulses are able to target single cells or even substructures within cells. This type of approach has been used to cut single nerves in worms that are just 1 millimeter in length.

- Brain researchers have also discovered a new nanomaterial that could be effective at stopping bleeding during neurosurgical procedures and other types of surgery. This material is a peptide that self-assembles into a nanofiber. It may someday be an important tool for treating acute trauma or could even replace the Band-Aid®.

- Nanomaterials can also be used to speed wound healing and limit infection. Silver nanoparticles, which kill bacteria, are particularly promising for this application.
  - In a study comparing silver nanoparticles with antibiotics for treating burns, the burns healed 4 days earlier when treated with silver nanoparticles, and scarring was reduced.
  - Having silver present as a nanoparticle seems to enhance the effect of the metal. The nanoparticles may fool the immune

system into not overdoing the immune response, which cuts down on inflammation.

- In addition to promoting healing, nanoparticles can also be used to solder a cut shut, eliminating the need for stitches. In a study at Rice University, researchers applied gold nanoparticles to cuts in rats, then exposed the nanoparticles to 800-nanometer near-infrared light and heat-soldered the wounds shut. There may be the potential to use a similar approach to repair nerves or blood vessels.

- Clearly, there is significant potential for nanotechnology to improve what happens before, during, and after surgery. Many types of tools are becoming available to make surgery more precise, and recovery from surgery may be sped up using better agents for wound healing and treatment. Although we've focused on cancers, similar kinds of techniques have begun to make progress for cardiovascular diseases, as well.

Suggested Reading

Asiyanbola and Soboyejo, "For the Surgeon: An Introduction to Nanotechnology."

Ben-Yakar and Bourgeois, "Ultrafast Laser Nanosurgery in Microfluidics for Genome-Wide Screenings."

Jain, *The Handbook of Nanomedicine.*

Singhal, Nie, and Wang, "Nanotechnology Applications in Surgical Oncology."

Questions to Consider

1. What are the greatest challenges surgeons face? Which presents more problems postoperatively, the surgical procedure or the healing process? How can nanomaterials and nanotechnology help in both of these areas?

Lecture 14: Nanoscale Surgical Tools

2. How can nanomaterials aid the precision of the human eye and human hand?

Nanoscale Surgical Tools
Lecture 14—Transcript

Shana Kelley: Surgery is currently the most effective and widely used procedure in treating human cancers, and it's also essential in the treatment of other diseases like kidney failure and heart disease. A recent study indicated that for particular types of cancer, surgery can cure 45% of cancer patients when it's used for treatment, whereas radiation or drugs only provide a 5% cure rate. But to be curative, surgery has to be done incredibly precisely. Incomplete removal of a tumor can decrease survival rates significantly.

In order to completely excise cancer, a surgeon needs to be able to identify tumor tissue and distinguish it from healthy tissue. Where these two different types of cells come together are called the "margins" of a tumor. It's very important to take as little of the healthy tissue as possible, because there could be important nerves or blood vessels in the tissue. So getting the "margins" of a tumor defined precisely is very important, and it's also really hard. Surgeons need to get all the tumor, yet nothing but the tumor.

Surgeons use different types of guides like radioactive tracers or visual or tactile inspection of tissue to make a call on whether tissue is diseased. Studies have been done looking at how often surgeons are correct in thinking that they have removed all of the cancer cells in a patient, and almost 40% of the time cancer cells are actually left behind. It's obviously difficult to get this right with the tools that we have available.

The lymphatic system complicates things further. Lymph nodes are present throughout our bodies to trap foreign particles. Cancer cells spreading from a tumor site will often first travel to lymph nodes, and so surgeons usually take samples of the lymph nodes close to a tumor and then the lymph node samples that are acquired can tell you whether the cancer has started to spread. But figuring out where these nodes are can be very tricky.

When Richard Feynman first started talking about nanotechnology in 1959, one of the things that fascinated him was the possibility of producing nanoscale surgical tools. The material we'll talk about today shows that this is becoming a reality. In fact, there is a whole toolbox now of nanoscale surgical tools that will improve surgery, in more ways than Feynman originally suggested. Not only can surgeons perform the operation using nanoscale tweezers and scalpels, they will eventually also be able to use nanomaterials for more accurate diagnosis and assessment, for example, by identifying tumor margins and lymph nodes with greater precision. When the procedure is over, other nanomaterials can be used therapeutically to speed up the healing of a wound.

Let's start by talking about how nanomaterials can make the assessment of tumor margins more precise, and allow surgeons to see the boundaries of tumors more clearly. As I mentioned, there are nerves and blood vessels near tumors that have to be avoided at all costs, making surgeons very conservative when taking extra tissue. Typically when an operation is complete, a surgeon will take a small sample of tissue that they consider to be outside the "margins" of the tumor, and this tissue is tested post-surgery. In breast cancer, as many as 50% of partial mastectomy cases require a second procedure owing to the fact that there's tumor found outside where surgeons thought the margins were. Surgeons are obviously very conservative when they remove breast tissue in order to lessen adverse impacts on a woman's health or self-image, and this is a tough thing to balance with making sure that all the tumor cells are gone.

In early-stage lung cancer, residual tumor deposits after surgery are associated with up to a 35% reduction in survival. Here, it's critical to take as little lung tissue as possible because the tumors are typically located near airways. Likewise with brain tumors, the stakes are extremely high as every extra cell that is taken can interfere with the survival of a patient.

The limiting factor in detecting microscopic tumors or defining the borders of a tumor at the time of surgery is really the sensitivity of the human eye. The eye can only resolve objects that are about the size of a dust mite, so that's about 250 microns in size, so most microscopic tumors or cell clusters can't be spotted with a background of normal tissue around. Really only in special cases are tumor cells visually distinct from healthy cells so this makes it even more challenging to selectively take them out. Now, if residual tumor cells could be detected in real time—in the operating room—surgical resection of the tumor could be more accurate and then survival rates would increase dramatically.

The imaging of tumor cells during surgery using nanoparticles has already been shown to be a very powerful approach to improving surgical removal of brain tumors in lab animals. In 2002, a group of researchers in Boston at the Massachusetts General Hospital and Harvard Medical School showed that iron nanoparticles could be used very effectively for this application. They made a really cool type of iron oxide nanoparticle that would help with the visualization of a brain tumor before surgery using MRI, and that would also help light up a tumor with luminescence during surgery. MRI is a very powerful tool for the visualization of tumors, but it's incredibly expensive to use. The instruments are really expensive and so it can't be used in every operating room.

On the other hand, luminescence is pretty easy to track and requires only a cheap excitation source, sometimes just a handheld lamp will do. The researchers that made these bifunctional nanoparticles managed to make something that was good at giving off both types of signals, so the MRI signal and the luminescence signal. The iron oxide core that they used had magnetic properties that were really great for getting a strong MRI signal, and then they joined this core with a chemical dye that would emit light when it was excited.

They injected this compound material into mice that had brain tumors, and then they allowed the nanoparticles to circulate for 24 hours. They collected MRI images and these images showed the researchers exactly where the tumors were. With these images in hand, knowing where the tumors were, they opened up the skulls of the animals and used the luminescence signal to make a second call on precisely where the tumor tissue was. The image that you're looking at shows the tumor lighting up because of the presence of the nanoparticles.

Once the surgery was done, they looked at the entire brain of the animals with methods that can only be used postmortem and they were able to determine that all of the cancer cells were gone. How did they do this, how did they look at the brain once the animal had been taken apart? Well, basically, they sectioned the brain tissue and then they incubated the tissue slices with stains that give a visual clue about whether a cell is diseased or healthy. This type of analysis works for post mortem analysis, but it's obviously not something we can do to a living subject who would need the tissue back. Clearly, giving the human eye some more help in the form of glowing nanoparticles is an extremely powerful approach to improving the surgical removal of brain tumors.

This was a really amazing study that back in 2003 was one of the first to prove the utility of nanomaterials for surgery. The fact that this test case involved brain tumors makes it that much more incredible. This may not have occurred to you yet, but in order for these nanoparticles to do what they did they had to cross something called the blood-brain barrier.

As the name implies, this barrier is a shield around the brain that is very difficult to get through. There is a network of capillaries that surround the brain; if you placed all these capillaries end-to-end they would span about 400 miles. On top of that, the capillaries are very densely packed and they have lots and lots of cells in them to ensure that only certain things make it to the brain. Small molecules that are about a nanometer, things like sugar, alcohol, nicotine, also certain antidepressant drugs are good at getting through this barrier, but typically large molecules can't get through. The fact that iron nanoparticles that were 50 nanometers were actually able to make it across is really surprising and obviously very fortuitous. Exactly how this works though, we really don't know yet. Many people around the world are trying to understand which combinations of properties allow these particles to trick the capillaries into letting them through, but it looks like we're going to have to wait a little while in order to have that answer.

Another type of surgical precision that can be enhanced by nanomaterials is the visualization of sentinel lymph nodes. As you may be aware, the lymphatic system is a network of vessels that instead of carrying blood, carries lymph. Lymph is a fluid that contains much of the waste generated by cells and it's also used to transport foreign cells to the lymph nodes where they can be destroyed. The lymphatic system provides another route for cancer cells to move around the body, and some cancers spread in a predicable fashion from where the cancer started, and their first stop is a lymph node or a gland close to the tumor and it goes there before the cancer spreads to other parts of the body.

The lymph node closest to the tumor is referred to as the sentinel lymph node, or SLN. The idea behind surgery on SLNs is to see if the cancer has spread. If the sentinel lymph node does not contain cancer, then there is a high likelihood that the cancer has not spread to any other part of the body. The way that SLNs are typically imaged involves the injection of a radioactive tracer near the tumor. A Geiger counter can then be used by the surgeon to track the tracer as it moves into the SLN. Now, using radioactivity for this is not ideal, lots of radioactive substances are somewhat harmful. This is where nanomaterials may be able to provide an alternative solution.

In 2006, researchers working with semiconductor quantum dots noticed that when infrared-emitting semiconductor quantum dots were injected into a tumor, they localized right to the sentinel lymph nodes. The quantum dots clearly found the same path that metastatic cancer cells take through the lymphatic system to reach the SLN. It took only 15 seconds for the lymph nodes to light up and so this would allow a surgeon to visualize the right lymph node and take samples for biopsy in real time.

The pig model system that they used for these trials is what's called the Sinclair mini-swine. This is a type of pig that has been engineered to spontaneously develop melanoma. Melanoma is a very relevant type of cancer for sentinel lymph node mapping because about 70% of melanomas in humans metastasize by passing through the lymph nodes. The pig form of melanoma is quite similar to the human form, so this is a really relevant system for the testing of the quantum dot imaging approach. Another feature of these pigs that is indirectly useful is that they have highly pigmented skin and dark hair, which is a little bit unusual for a pig, but that's what these guys have, and this makes it more of a challenge to detect the light being given off by the quantum dots in the lymph nodes, and so getting proof-of-principle even in this system makes it that much more likely that it would work in humans.

This use of nanomaterials to find lymph nodes is likely several years away from being used in humans, but the potential for impact on surgical outcomes is significant. Lymph node resection is one of the most difficult things for surgeons to learn when they using existing techniques for visualization. It can take new surgeons over 60 surgeries to achieve technical proficiency leaving all of the patients with incomplete resections unless somebody more experienced is looking over the shoulder of the inexperienced surgeon. Being able to use nanoparticles to illuminate lymph nodes should make the learning curve much less steep.

What if someday we were able to teach robots to perform surgery rather than relying on people? This may seem kind of far out, but it turns out that robotic surgery is something that's already being used today. The most common types of robotic surgeries actually have a human being controlling the robotics, but using the robot as an interface to the patient helps eliminate tremors and it allows finer manipulations to be made. It also allows surgery to be done remotely, as already happened in 2001, when a surgeon in New York removed a gall bladder in a patient in France. But one thing that robots really lack is a sense of touch—and for most types of surgery it turns out that this is quite important—a fine sense of touch allows a surgeon to know how much force to use, and it may also give them information about the health of the tissue.

A really neat nano device may provide a solution here and give robots a sense of touch. This device is basically a nanoparticle sandwich—there are two layers of gold nanoparticles on the outside of the sandwich, and a layer of cadmium sulfide nanoparticles on the inside of the sandwich. The two kinds of particles are separated by a layer of squishy plastic. When stress is placed on the gold nanoparticles on the outside, this causes them to get closer to the cadmium sulfide and then the coupling between the two types of nanoparticles causes light to be emitted. By coupling, I mean electronic coupling, or the extent to which the particles can feel the presence of the others.

Now that we've seen how nanotechnology can be used to visualize or feel tumors and also to visualize the spread of cancer cells, let's talk about some other promising approaches to the development of nanoscale surgical tools. The better we get at seeing cancer cells, the better able we'll be to take only the diseased cells during surgery and leave the healthy cells behind. But in order to be able to cut out a single cell, a very small scalpel would obviously be required. Throughout this course, we've looked at nanomaterials that certainly should be able to achieve this kind of resolution but only if they could be manipulated at the macroscale. But this is the tricky part—we can't hold a single nanotube in our hand, so how could this type of material be used?

Well, a study reported in the journal *Science* in 1999 described a really clever approach that gives us some leads on this. What was done here is that a 1000 nanometer glass rod was attached to 2 carbon nanotubes, and the attachment sites were made of metal so that they could serve as electrodes. When there was no potential applied to the electrodes, the carbon nanotubes remained apart. But when 8 volts were applied, the tips of the two carbon nanotubes were drawn together. This amazing set of images shows exactly what happens. You can see that as the applied voltage increases, the carbon nanotube tips get closer and closer until they're touching. This device acts just like a pair of tweezers, and could be able to pick up a single cell. This hasn't actually been tested yet, but the researchers working with the nanotube nanotweezers did show that they could pick up a single plastic particle with a diameter of 500 nanometers. You're looking at an image that shows the tweezers grabbing the particle and keeping a firm grip on it.

Another way that increased precision could be achieved during surgery is through the use of nanolasers. Very fast and focused laser pulses are able to target single cells, or even substructures within cells. This type of approach has been used to cut single nerves in tiny worms—these worms are just 1 millimeter in length. Now why is it useful to practice surgery on worms that may not seem obvious? Well, this is a good model system where the amount of precision needed to cut a single nerve measuring just a few microns could be validated, and it also provides the opportunity to be able to watch the re-growth of the nerve in real time. This will help us understand how nerves can regenerate themselves.

What we've looked at so far are different tools that can assist the precision of surgery. Now let's look at an interesting material that can help in a different way. One of the most difficult things to deal with during surgery is excessive bleeding. During a surgery a cut is made and perhaps it nicks a blood vessel and this can produce a lot of blood. I'm sure you've seen medical dramas where a surgeon is yelling, "Clamp!" and a nurse whips out a pair of arterial forceps, also known as a hemostat, and these things you probably have seen; they look almost like a pair of scissors, but they're really clamping a blood vessel shut.

In addition, there are chemicals that can be used to stop bleeding, but they're not very fast acting. But now brain researchers have discovered a new nanomaterial that could be very effective at stopping bleeding during neurosurgical procedures and other types of surgery. They were working with a peptide that self assembles into a nanofiber, and these researchers were initially studying whether it could be used as a drug to repair brain damage. What they discovered instead was that the peptide was really good at stopping bleeding really fast. In addition to being a very useful material to have on hand during surgery, this could also be an important tool for treating acute trauma where there's lots and lots of bleeding.

Maybe someday a peptide that self assembles into a nanofiber, well it could even replace the Band-Aid. In my house, we have two little boys running around and Band-Aids are always being used to deal with scratches and scrapes. Both kids usually have a few somewhere on their body at any given time, but as you know, especially for little boys who love dirt, Band-Aids get dirty and they're not great when it comes to keeping a cut clean. So maybe someday, we'll have in our kitchens a little tube of this material that could be used as artificial "skin" while a cut heals.

Nanomaterials can also be used to speed wound healing and limit infection. Silver nanoparticles are particularly promising for this application. It's been known for some time that silver nanoparticles can kill bacteria and so they're a good way to keep bacteria from infecting a wound. But studies investigating this in rats showed something remarkable—the particles also made the wounds heal faster. This was a study where they were comparing silver nanoparticles with antibiotics and it was discovered that burn wounds were completely healed four days earlier when silver nanoparticles were used. In addition, the amount of scarring was reduced.

If you look at these images, you're looking at rats that have burn wounds on their backs. If the wounds are treated with silver nanoparticles, the rats have totally healed and regrown their fur in 25 days. Without the silver nanoparticles, you can see that the rats are still in pretty tough shape.

But it's not just the presence of silver—studies were also done with non-nanostructured silver, and it really didn't have any effect. Silver sulfadiazine is actually used clinically for burn treatment, but its effectiveness is pretty limited. Here, having silver present as a nanoparticle really seems to pump up the effect of the metal. We think that the nanoparticles fool the immune system into not overdoing the immune response, which then cuts down on inflammation. Since the nanoparticles kill any bacteria that might find their way into to a wound, this is good.

Now in addition to promoting healing, nanoparticles can also be used to solder a cut shut. We've all had the unpleasant experience of getting stitches and then getting them removed—and using a nanoparticle glue may present a more pleasant alternative. A study that was recently done at Rice University in 2005 showed that this is indeed possible. Using rats as model patients, they applied gold nanoparticles to cuts and then hit the nanoparticles with 800 nanometer near-infrared light and heat soldered the wound shut.

They also generated a control group that had conventional stitches. In these images, you're looking at a comparison of two cuts—the top one had stitches, and the bottom one had the nanoparticle solder. You can see that the stitched wound actually heals faster, but both eventually heal. The discomfort to a patient would really be minimized for the nanoparticle approach so this really seems worth pursuing. The researchers also looked at the skin cells after the wound was healed and they made sure that the cells were normal, and they really looked fine. This seems like a promising way to repair cuts. It's also been shown to work with muscle. There may also be the potential to use a similar approach to repair nerves or blood vessels—so we'll have to stay tuned to see where this goes.

I think it's really clear from the material that we've covered that there is huge potential for nanotechnology to improve what happens before, during, and after surgery. There are many types of tools becoming available that make it easier for surgeons to be more precise, and that will also allow robots to acquire and enhance the capabilities that humans have. There is also the potential to make recovery from surgery faster using better agents for wound healing and treatment. While we've focused in this lecture on cancers, similar kinds of techniques have also begun to make progress for cardiovascular diseases as well, such as atherosclerosis, thrombosis, and myocardial infarction.

In discussing how nanotechnology can be used in surgery, we've thought lots about how to repair damage or take diseased cells away. What we haven't considered yet is how to bring healthy cells back. In the case of spinal cord damage or brain damage, the damage is almost always irreversible. This is because we don't know how to coerce new cells to grow, and our bodies aren't very good at getting this done either.

In the next lecture, we'll look at the role that nanomaterials are playing in a really interesting area—regenerative medicine. In this field, scientists are figuring out how to use nanomaterials to get new cells to grow where there's been damage and replacing not just cells but entire tissues, and progress is even being made on generating artificial organs outside of the body to help us with organ transplants. Even though cells aren't truly nanoscale, we are learning how to get them to form tissues using nanomaterials by providing the same cues as cells get in natural tissues. This is a very interesting and fast-moving field, and I think you'll find learning about it to be fascinating. See you next time.

Nanomaterials for Artificial Tissue
Lecture 15

The field of regenerative medicine, or tissue engineering, focuses on producing artificial substitutes that could restore or replace damaged tissues or organs. We've known how to transplant organs for decades, but transplants are extremely difficult, and a limited supply prevents all who need new organs from receiving them. In this lecture, we'll review a collection of promising discoveries demonstrating that the future of medicine for damaged tissues and organs could be very different from the present.

Natural Tissues and Organs

- Simple kinds of tissues, such as skin and cartilage, are readily made using methods analogous to those for culturing cells in the laboratory for research. Although we can grow cells and layers of cells, we're still not good at putting cells together into more complicated structures.

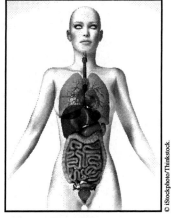

- The building blocks of tissues and organs must be organized. In other words, the cells must be oriented in specific directions, and certain types of cells need to be interfaced in a particular way. Further, tissues and organs need blood vessels and nerves. It's difficult to build up a structure made of 1 kind of cell, but it's even more difficult to build up structures in which the components are made of many different kinds of cells.

Demand for organ transplants can exceed the supply from donors by more than 300%, but nanoscience is being used to advance the field of tissue engineering so that we may one day be able to generate artificial organs.

© iStockphoto/Thinkstock.

- To self-organize in the body, organs and tissues take advantage of cues in their environment to "know" which direction to spread out in. To generate artificial tissues, it's necessary to provide scaffolds that will bring cells together and allow them to interact in such a way that functional tissue will grow.

- In human beings, the scaffold is a complex network of proteins that provides an environment conducive to cell growth. This scaffold is called the extracellular matrix. Collagen is a major component of the matrix.
  - The extracellular matrix looks somewhat disorganized, but it's actually a highly organized structure. Each protein is in a precise location so that it can guide a cell to grow in a certain direction.

  - This matrix also binds factors that may stimulate and provide instructions for directional growth.

  - In recent years, scientists have been able to separate all the cells of an organ from its extracellular matrix. Incredibly, cells can be regrown using the matrix as a scaffold, and the functionality of the organ will return. In 2010, a lung regenerated in this way was transplanted in a rat.

- It seems that if we could re-create the extracellular matrix from synthetic components, we would be able to generate new organs. The formation of this matrix, however, is a precise, programmed biological process, and unfortunately, we do not yet know how to re-create it.

Nanostructuring

- One approach to engineering nanomaterials to create the extracellular matrix is to use different nanopatterns on surfaces to grow cells oriented in specific ways. Just a few years ago, a team at MIT showed that nanopatterning on a hard surface could have a dramatic effect on cell orientation.
  - This group compared cell growth on nanostructured and non-nanostructured substrates and found that cells on the

nanostructured substrates seemed to "know" that they should stretch in the same direction as the nanoscale pattern.

  o In nature, the fibers in collagen line up in a pattern that looks very much like the nanograting used by the team at MIT.

• The same group at MIT also studied how the growth of endothelial progenitor cells (EPCs) was affected by the presence of a nanopattern. EPCs are the precursor cells that form the inside of a blood vessel. When grown on a flat surface, these cells were unable to organize into useful vessels, but on the nanograting, long vessels were formed.

• Researchers at Seoul National University in Korea have shown that nanoposts work well for this application, too. In this study, cells called fibroblasts threaded themselves through a nanograting with posts that had a particular spacing. Fibroblasts are cells in the body that produce collagen, a material important to the extracellular matrix.

Self-Assembling Nanomaterials

• One example of a self-assembling nanomaterial that could be relevant to regenerative medicine is a peptide nanofiber that forms a gel made up of long fibers. The nanoscopic structure of this gel closely resembles the extracellular matrix.

• Among the first cell types tested for growth on this artificial version of the extracellular matrix were neural progenitor cells (NPCs), which mature into neural cells. If it was possible to get NPCs to grow into a precise structure, they could be used to repair central nervous system damage.

  o Nerve cells are not good at regrowing; thus, the gaps that are formed during injury, for example, in the spinal cord, persist, causing breaks in the communication that is essential for the function of the nervous system.

  o Nervous system tissue is a complicated network of fibers and neurons that send electrochemical signals over long distances. As a result, neurons have a much more complex structure than most other cell types and are difficult to grow in the lab or into the fibers found in the human body.

- To test whether a peptide nanofiber could assist with generating artificial nerves, a group at Northwestern University mixed the peptide with a solution of NPCs and allowed the peptide nanofibers to self-assemble around the neural cells. This environment enabled the researchers to grow NPCs much more efficiently.

- With this promising result, the same group then tested whether this material could repair spinal cord injury in mice. Mice who received a treatment of peptide nanofiber after spinal cord injury recovered about 90% of their normal functions, and scarring—which is a significant problem in spinal cord injury—was minimized.

- Another study done as a collaboration between a group at MIT and a group in Hong Kong used an analogous peptide-based material to look at the possibilities for restoration of vision.
  - This study involved cutting a specific nerve axon in mice that's essential for vision, then treating them with the peptide nanofiber and measuring their responses to visual stimuli.

  - In a control group, the mice got back only about 10% of their vision, but the group treated with the nanofiber got back 80%.

Synthetic Organs
- The liver is an essential organ that detoxifies blood, produces proteins and hormones, and provides molecules needed for digestion. About 80% of the cells in the liver are hepatocytes, which synthesize essential proteins and hormones and break down chemicals, such as drugs.

- In order for hepatocytes to do their work on all of the blood in our bodies, the cells must be in close contact with the blood running through the circulatory system; thus, the liver has as an intricate system of vessels running through it.

- The vessels are organized into repeating hexagonal columns that have a central vein running through the center of each column. Then, the arteries are located at the junctions between the columns. There are also ducts that run through the liver that transport bile, one of the most important molecules made in the liver.

- One of the first attempts to make an artificial liver involved a device that had a collection of tiny channels that could pump blood. The channels were made of a porous material, with liver cells grown on top. The liver cells weren't given any external sources of food, but they were clearly able to extract nutrients from the blood. The hepatocytes also excreted proteins into the blood; in other words, the basic level of functionality was present.

  o The researchers then increased the throughput of this device by stacking many of these blood vessel chips with layers of hepatocytes. The resulting device could basically handle the amount of blood that is processed by a human in a single day.

  o So far, this device has been designed to function more like a dialysis instrument than a replacement organ. But there's a good chance that we will be able to engineer some kind of coating so that the device could be implanted into patients without risk of rejection by the body's immune system.

  o One way to get around the compatibility problem would be to use a portion of a recipient's damaged organ to begin growing a new organ. This has been done for some simpler organs, such as the bladder, and the transplants of these semi-synthetic organs have been successful.

Biology and Medicine Transformed

- As we've seen, the fields of biology and medicine are being transformed by increases in our ability to understand biology and intervene at the nanoscale level. The fact that biology operates at the nanoscale, with tiny messenger molecules carrying out all the work of cells and giving cells clues about how to grow, means that working at the nanoscale is quite important.

- We now have materials that allow cells to grow with defined orientations and allow them to assemble into the kinds of complex structures that are found in humans. We've also seen other advances in nanomedicine, such as improved drug delivery, earlier disease diagnosis, and better tools for surgery. These are materials that simply did not exist before nanotechnology enabled us to manipulate matter at such a fine length scale.

Suggested Reading

Atala, Lanza, Thomson, and Nerem, *Principles of Regenerative Medicine.*

Dvir, Timko, Kohane, and Langer, "Nanotechnological Strategies for Engineering Complex Tissue."

Pearson, "Being Bob Langer."

Webber, Kessler, and Stupp, "Emerging Peptide Nanomedicine to Regenerate Tissues and Organs."

Questions to Consider

1. Why do we need regenerative medicine? Cells know how to grow—why is there a pressing need for nanomaterials to help them along?

2. What health problems could be eliminated once routine *de novo* organ fabrication is available?

Nanomaterials for Artificial Tissue
Lecture 15—Transcript

Shana Kelley: The field of regenerative medicine focuses on producing artificial substitutes that could restore or replace damaged tissues or organs. It's also referred to as tissue engineering. We've known how to transplant organs for decades, but transplants are extremely difficult and a limited supply prevents some who need new organs from receiving them. Demand for organ transplants can exceed the supply from donors by over 300%, and in many cases, transplants are the only treatment available that will save a patient's life.

What if we were not reliant on the supply of donated organs coming from humans, but could instead generate them artificially? That might sound even more difficult: if transplanting an existing organ is hard, wouldn't transplanting an artificial organ be even more difficult? Well, what we'll talk about today is how nanoscience is being used to advance this field, and we'll walk through a collection of very promising discoveries that demonstrate that the future of medicine for damaged tissues and organs should be very different from the present.

Let's start with artificial tissues and work our way up to artificial organs. We've talked about study after study during our lectures where cells cultured in the lab are used to study all kinds of things. Labs are really quite good by now at growing almost any kind of cell you can think of in a Petri dish. And simple kinds of materials, like skin and cartilage, can be made using analogous methods to the ones that we used just to culture cells in the lab for research. There are actually already forms of these tissues on the market and they are used to treat burn victims. So while we can grow cells and layers of cells, what we're still not good at is putting cells together into more complicated structures.

You can think of tissues and organs kind of like buildings. In order to build something functional, the building blocks or bricks need to be organized. Same goes for the tissues of human organs. The cells have to be oriented in specific directions and certain types of cells need to be interfaced in a particular way. Just like buildings need plumbing and electricity running throughout in very specific locations, tissues and organs need blood vessels and they need nerves. It's difficult—but not impossible—to build up a structure made of one kind of cell, but it's really difficult to build up structures where components need to come together that are made of many different kinds of cells.

This is where nanotechnology can make a difference. One of the reasons that organs and tissues know how to self-organize in the body is that they are able to take advantage of cues provided by their environment to know which direction to spread out in. You now appreciate that nanotechnology's main aim is to manipulate matter at the nanoscale, and it turns out that this is exactly what needs to be done in order to provide scaffolds that will bring cells together and allow them to interact in such a way that functional tissue will grow.

Before we turn to artificial scaffolds made with nanotechnology, let's look at the actual scaffolds used by nature. In human beings, the scaffold is a very complex network of proteins that come together and provide an environment that cells really like to grow in. This scaffold is called the extracellular matrix, and the image that you're looking at shows how all the strands of protein come together to make this matrix. It takes billions of protein molecules to come together and form the fibers that then interconnect to form this structure. One of the proteins that's involved here—collagen—may be familiar to you. We touched on the function of collagen a few lectures ago, and talked about the fact that it's good at giving tissue structure.

It turns out that collagen is a major component of the extracellular matrix and its fibrous structure is a key structural feature. Now, this extracellular matrix may look somewhat disorganized—but it's actually really a complex structure with a high level of organization. Each protein is in a precise location so that it can guide a cell to grow in a certain direction. This matrix also binds factors that may stimulate directional growth and tell a cell what direction to head in.

It's now known that the extracellular matrix gives an organ its overall structure and it's a very robust entity. Just in the last few years, scientists have learned that they can take an organ, and they can gently separate all of the cells from the extracellular matrix by soaking the organ in a bit of detergent. Once they do this, they have an organ that is primarily the extracellular matrix. This has been done with livers, with lungs, with arteries, and other types of organs. In this state, these organs are not functional, because they don't have the cells there and so that takes away the functionality of the organ.

But incredibly enough, they can then regrow cells using the extracellular matrix as a scaffold, and the functionality of the organ returns. This is really incredible. I mentioned that this has been done with a variety of organ types, and in a recent study reported in the journal *Science* in 2010, a landmark study was reported showing that a regenerated lung could be transplanted into a rat. You're looking at images of a rat lung before it's treated to remove the cells, and then after the cells have been dissolved. It's white because the only thing left behind was the extracellular matrix. You can see that the color comes back once the cells are regrown. If we zoom in using electron microscopy, you can actually see the cells on the matrix that then disappear after the lung has been removed. So this procedure is really good at just removing the cells and leaving everything else intact—you can see that the extracellular matrix basically stays unperturbed.

Even more amazingly, the lung not only had newly grown cells, this lung was actually functional. It was a little bit leaky, and there were a few blood cells in places that they were not supposed to be, but the rats that received the transplants could do everything that rats with two normal lungs could do. This work demonstrates how robust the extracellular matrix really is. It's strong, and that allows us to reuse organs by growing new cells using the matrix as a scaffold. But this doesn't really help us with the organ transplant problem—it may increase the number of useable organs that could be regenerated, but it doesn't help us make new ones from scratch.

What if we could recreate the extracellular matrix from synthetic components—that would solve the problem. Given that the matrix is just a collection of proteins, and we know how to synthesize proteins in large quantities in the lab, this should be doable, right? Well, it turns out that it's not that simple. The formation of the extracellular matrix is a very precise programmed process that biology knows how to organize, but unfortunately, we don't know yet how to recreate. We need find solutions that will allow us to recreate the features of the matrix in a form that we can work with to grow new organs. This is where nanotechnology can play a role—we've seen a variety of nanomaterials that might be able to provide the right type of scaffold, and so the rationale here is that engineering the right material might be a way to recreate the extracellular matrix.

One approach to this is to use different nanopatterns on surfaces to grow cells oriented in specific ways. Just a few years ago, a team led by Dr. Bob Langer at MIT showed that nanopatterning a hard surface could have a dramatic effect on cell orientation. Langer is a pioneer in this field and he's an amazing scientist. He has a research group of about 100 people, he's obtained over 200 patents and has started 25 different biotech companies— he's a chemical engineer who has learned to use nanotechnology to solve a number of important problems including some very pertinent to today's topic of tissue engineering.

Here you're looking at a comparison of cell growth happening on a nanograting made by Langer's group that has a spacing of just a few hundred nanometers versus a flat substrate. It's made using a technique called replica molding that involves making a master mold and for this you use a hard material like silicon that has the features that are desired in the final product. Then a type of polymer can be poured into the master and then it's cured. This process allows lots of substrates to be produced from one master.

As you can see from these images, on the non-nanostructured substrate, the cell doesn't really know what direction to go and it just balls up. With the nanograting, it seems to know that it should stretch in the same direction as the nanoscale pattern. This is really incredible. Now why does this happen? Well, it's related to what happens in nature. In the extracellular matrix, there are fibers of materials like collagen that form oriented fibers. In this image of collagen, you can see that in the yellow portion of the image, there are fibers lined up in a pattern that look very much like the nanograting—the spacing is even the same. So then what has been created using nanotechnology is a material that's a pretty good mimic of oriented collagen—so that's a start!

We've looked at a single cell, and it's clear that nanostructuring influences directionality of cell growth. But can we engineer something more complex, not involving just a single cell but a collection of cells that could eventually be used in the body? Well the same group looked at a type of cells called endothelial progenitor cells—we'll call these EPCs for short—and they looked at how their growth was affected by the presence of a nanopattern. EPCs are the precursor cells that form the inside of a blood vessel, so this is a great system to look at to evaluate whether artificial vessels could be grown.

The difference in how these cells grew on flat surfaces versus a nanograting is really amazing. On the flat surface, the cells grow well and you can see them trying to organize into vessels—but they are not organized enough and all of the interconnectedness of the short vessels that are formed makes them useless. But now on the nanograting, you can see that nice long vessels are instead formed. It's clear that here, too, the cells are really taking a cue from the grating, and they're heading in a certain direction in response.

Gratings are not the only nanomaterials that can be used for this type of application. Nanoposts work really well here too. A group working at the School of Mechanical and Aerospace Engineering at the Seoul National University in Korea was able to show that they could get cells called fibroblasts to thread themselves through a nanograting if the posts had the right spacing. Now, fibroblasts are cells in the body that produce lots of collagen—a material important to the extracellular matrix, so they're working with an interesting cell type that's very relevant for regenerative medicine. We could imagine that if we could generate the right starting scaffold with nanotechnology and then coerce fibroblasts to grow in the right directions, perhaps we could then get an extracellular matrix to grow on a substrate as the starting place for an artificial organ.

We've looked at how cells can be grown on different types of nanopatterned surfaces. These types of nanostructures are made with what we refer to as "top-down" fabrication. That means that you come in from the top with some way to create the nanopattern yourself. But that's not the only way to do this. Let's look at a group of nanostructures very relevant to regenerative medicine that are made using what we call "bottom-up" methods. This means that the materials basically self assemble to perform a desired role and they don't require any top-down processing.

One example of this is a peptide nanofiber that self-assembles into a very powerful type of material. This peptide has a hydrophobic region that—when it gets put in water it wants to huddle together with other peptides so that it doesn't come into contact with the water. This is like grease in water would act. This peptide then ends up forming long fibers that then self-assemble into a gel.

If we zoom in and look at the nanoscopic structure of this gel, we can see that—wow—it looks an awful lot like the extracellular matrix. The scientists who invented this material recognized right away that they had something really special in hand when they first saw this structure. We actually already touched on another application of this peptide gel in the last lecture when we discussed a gel that could stop bleeding during surgery. When this peptide was sprayed on a wound, it acted like a hemostat and it quickly stopped bleeding. It's probably the case that the matrix formed stopped blood cells from leaving the vessel. Here, we're talking about this peptide nanofiber because the idea is that this artificial matrix made of peptide nanofiber could act as a mimic of the extracellular matrix. Let's see what it's able to do when it comes to growing cells.

One of the first cell types that was tested with this material was neural progenitor cells, or NPCs. Like the epithelial progenitor cells we talked about before, these neural progenitors are precursor cells: the NPCs, in this case, will mature into neural cells. Now a neural progenitor cell is precisely the type of cell that—if we could get it to grow into a precise structure, and could control that process, we could use these to repair central nervous system damage. Neural damage, as I'm sure you know, can be devastating. We're all familiar with how falls and accidents can cause spinal cord injury—like the incident in which Christopher Reeve was thrown from a horse and left a quadriplegic. And unfortunately this type of injury is almost impossible to recover from because the damage can't be reversed. Nerve cells are just not good at re-growing, and so the gaps that are formed, for example, in the spinal cord during injury persist and they basically cause gaps in the communication that is essential for the function of the nervous system. The development of methods that would allow us to regenerate nervous system tissue would have a tremendous impact.

Why is neural damage so difficult to repair? Well, the nervous system contains a complicated type of tissue. It's a network of fibers and neurons that send electrochemical signals over long distances. Neurons, or nerve cells, have a much more complicated structure than most other cell types because of the electrical communication that they participate in. The structures that you see protruding from this nerve cell are called dendrites, and they help to extend the reach of the cell's communication range. These cells are actually pretty difficult to grow in the lab, and it's even more difficult to get them to grow into the fibers that are found in the human body.

Can a peptide nanofiber assist with the generation of artificial nerves? To test this, the group at Northwestern University who originally developed this material mixed the peptide with a solution of NPCs, and they allowed the peptide nanofibers to self-assemble around the neural cells. That's what makes the generation of this material "bottom-up" rather than top-down: the nanomaterial makes its structure spontaneously and it knows just how to self assemble around the progenitor cells—and then these encapsulate progenitor cells can get their cues from the newly-formed nanomaterial. What the researchers then observed is that growing the NPCs in this environment allowed them to grow much more efficiently—you can see in this image that there are dendrites coming off of the cell and this is somewhat unusual to see in a cultured neural cell.

With this promising result in hand, this group then went on to test whether this material could repair spinal cord injury in mice. Mice who received a treatment of peptide nanofiber after spinal cord injury recovered about 90% of their normal functions and they fared much better than a control group. Interestingly, the researchers who did the study found not only that neural re-growth improved significantly, but also that scarring—which causes big problems in the event of spinal cord injury—was minimized and this is really a complicating effect in spinal cord injury so you have the actual injury, you have the cells that get damaged, and that gap that happens, and then at the junctions where the injury occurs you can have scarring that prevents any further growth. This was a really exciting result to see and at the time they didn't really understand the origin of this effect and we still don't understand exactly why the nanofiber is able to limit scarring, but it's a really encouraging type of behavior to see out of this compound.

Another study that was done as a collaboration between a group at MIT and a group in Hong Kong used an analogous peptide-based material, and they looked at a similar phenomenon but they used a slightly different readout. Here they're going to be looking specifically at vision and the restoration of vision. What they did is they used a mouse model and then they cut a specific nerve axon that's essential for vision, and then they looked at these mice, again a control group with no treatment and a group that had the peptide as a treatment, and then watched how their sight could come back. This is something that you can do very quantitatively with mice. What you do is you give them a visual stimulus and you watch to see whether they respond and so you can tabulate the statistics around how many times they respond to the stimulus and get good specific quantitation on how much of their vision has come back.

This is a really great way to determine whether a peptide nanofiber can promote nerve growth. In a control group that didn't get any treatment, the mice only got back about 10% of their vision, so this is basically just the natural levels of neural re-growth. But the group treated with the nanofiber got back 80%—that is really incredible. And it's somewhat comparable to what was seen in the last study, but that was much more qualitative, whereas this is a quantitative measure of vision. It indicates that this type of approach could bring back high levels of other functions, like speech and motor skills and all the things that we want to bring back to people that have had spinal cord damage.

So far, we've looked at some very promising examples of nanomaterials that can support cell growth that have very exciting potential for regenerative medicine. But, we still haven't seen an actual example of an artificial organ. Let's take a look at an example of a tissue engineering project more advanced than what I've just shown you—an astonishing first step toward an artificial liver.

The liver is an essential organ that detoxifies our blood, produces proteins and hormones, and provides molecules that we need for digestion. About 80% of the cells in the liver are what we call hepatocytes—they're really good at synthesizing essential proteins and hormones and they're really good at breaking down chemicals like drugs. In order for hepatocytes to do their work on all of the blood in our bodies, the cells needs to be in close contact with the blood running through the circulatory system, and so the liver has as a very intricate system of vessels running through it. It's like a building with lots of plumbing in every room.

The vessels are organized into repeating hexagonal columns that have a central vein running through the center of each column. Then the arteries are located at the junctions between the columns. There are also ducts that run through the liver that transport bile—one of the most important molecules that the liver makes and these ducts take it out of the liver. You can see that this is a very complicated set of structures to think about reproducing in an artificial organ.

One of the first attempts to make an artificial liver involved the fabrication of a device that had a collection of tiny channels that could pump blood. The channels were made of a porous material, and then liver cells were grown on top of the channels. The group that made this device showed that the liver cells were really happy and healthy. They weren't being given any external sources of food, so they were clearly able to extract nutrients from the blood that was flowing by.

The levels of a particular protein that the liver produces were also measured, and it was clear that the hepatocytes were doing their thing and they were excreting proteins into the blood. So the basic level of functionality was there. What they did next was to increase the throughput of the device so that it could be used to substitute for a human liver. They increased the throughput by creating a stacked device that brought together many of these blood vessel chips with layers of hepatocytes. This device could basically handle the amount of blood that needs to be processed by a human in a single day.

But with that said, we're probably not going to see these types of devices being implanted into patients really soon. So far, these devices have been designed to function more like dialysis instruments rather than organ replacements. In order for an organ to be successfully implanted, its surface needs to be covered in cells that the transplant recipient's immune system will recognize, otherwise the body will try to "reject' the organ and serious inflammation will result. This is a different type of problem, kind of a second generation problem, that needs to be solved, but it's one that's actually already been sorted out for devices that are used already like artificial joints, and corneas and the other types of tissues that we have learned to implant. So there's definitely a good chance that we'll eventually be able to engineer some kind of coating for this device so that it can be used in vivo.

One way, a separate approach, and this get around the compatibility problem is to use a portion of a recipient's damaged organ to begin building or growing a new organ. This has been done for some simpler organs, like the bladder, and the transplants of these semi-synthetic organs have been successful. This type of approach could be effective for organs that really only have partial damage, and it likely won't be feasible for organs that have a complex blood supply. There clearly is still a need for the de novo organ fabrication that nanoregenerative medicine researchers are working towards. We'll have to stay tuned to see where this field is headed. It's clear that the potential for impact is huge given that the problems being solved are really intractable by any other means.

The fields of biology and medicine are really being transformed by increases in our ability to understand biology and intervene at the nanoscale level. As you've just seen, cells, which are a little too large to be considered nanoscale, can still be manipulated using the cues that nanomaterials can give them. The fact that biology operates at the nanoscale, with tiny messenger molecules carrying out all the work that cells do and giving cells clues about how to grow, means that working at the nanoscale is quite important.

With the advances that I've described to you today, we now have materials that allow cells to grow with defined orientations and allow them to assemble into the kinds of complex structures that are found in humans. You now know that there are nanomaterials that are really good at helping cells regrow after an injury. This adds to the other advances we've looked at in nanomedicine like improved drug delivery, earlier disease diagnosis, and better tools for surgery.

And these are all materials that simply did not exist before nanotechnology enabled us to manipulate matter at such a fine length scale. The many examples of nanotechnology in medicine that we've looked at really illustrate why nanoscale precision is so important for applications in medicine—without it we just can't recreate the same types of materials and structures that nature uses to build our tissues and organs, and we can't get the precision needed for effective drug delivery or surgery.

In the first half of the next lecture, I'll conclude our discussion of nanomedicine by talking about how nanotechnology research actually gets done. Ted Sargent will be taking the second half of this lecture and together, we'll take a dive into what it takes to build a successful team of nanotechnology researchers, and how they pull together to make the kinds of exciting discoveries we've covered so far. See you next time.

How Nano Research Gets Done
Lecture 16

This lecture is devoted to discussing the research process in nanotechnology—the kinds of people that are involved in this research, how it's funded, and how discoveries are moved out of the laboratory and into commercial products. There are thousands of academic labs across the world that are working on nanotechnology-related projects, and hundreds more research labs at companies, in the government, and at research institutes. This is a large community of people, all working toward realizing the applications of nanotechnology that we've discussed in this course.

Interdisciplinary Teams

- The teams that perform nanotechnology research are highly interdisciplinary. In order to move projects forward, it's often necessary to have people with backgrounds in chemistry, physics, biology, and engineering.

- Researchers join these teams at a variety of levels: Some are graduate students, some are postdoctoral researchers, and some are research associates who hold undergraduate degrees.

© iStockphoto/Thinkstock.

- On a project at the University of Toronto that focuses on the development of a new type of DNA-modified quantum dot, the project lead is a chemist, who works closely with a master's level student in engineering physics. Students and researchers with backgrounds in mechanical

People with backgrounds in almost any area of basic science—chemistry, biology, physics—can find a place on a nanotechnology research team.

engineering, biochemistry, biology, and chemistry also contribute to the project.

- Team members in nanotechnology research must be versatile and constantly willing to learn aspects of many different fields that may be involved in a particular project.

Research Funding
- Funding for nanotechnology projects comes from a variety of sources: the government, private foundations, and companies.

- A healthy budget for a group of 20 researchers is about $1 million a year; this money is split fairly evenly between personnel costs and supplies and equipment. Nanotechnology research is a bit more expensive than other types of scientific research because the equipment needed is sophisticated and the teams tend to require many different types of expertise.

- Such organizations as the National Institutes of Health, the National Science Foundation, and the Department of Defense provide research funding.
  o In order to obtain this funding, teams prepare detailed proposals describing their projects that are then subject to rigorous peer review.

  o It's not uncommon for a proposal to be turned down several times before it is funded, but the system works in that it prioritizes high-quality, high-impact research.

Dissemination of Results
- Research results are disseminated in a number of ways, such as by publishing papers, applying for patents, or reporting on results at conferences.

- If the research is basic in nature, such as work done to develop a new material or imaging technique, the outcomes may take quite some time to materialize. Basic research serves as the foundation for work focused on different applications. For this reason, follow-up work is often needed before new materials can be commercialized.

- Still, basic research is often where game-changing discoveries are made because it is usually curiosity-driven and can take a project in unexpected directions. For example, a project that started as an exploration of the properties of some basic materials based on peptides has led to the engineering of these materials as powerful drug delivery agents.

- With applied nanotechnology research, patents may be generated from the work, and an existing company may be interested in licensing these patents.
  o This company would turn the research into a product, and once it's commercialized, the company would pay royalties to the inventors and the university where the patents were generated. This is the typical process that takes place when new drugs are created.

  o For certain types of inventions, it may make more sense for a new company to be created—a spin-off or start-up. This approach is often used in creating new technology, because the kind of work required to mature a technology to the commercialization stage cannot usually be done in a university lab.

  o One of the best funding channels for start-ups based on nanotechnology research is venture capital. The advantage of giving venture capitalists equity in a company in return for an investment is that in addition to getting funding, the company also gets access to the contacts and experience of the investors.

A Case Study in Commercialization
- As mentioned earlier in the course, colloidal quantum dots represent an exciting development in nanomaterials. These materials can be synthesized in solution, essentially making a

paintable semiconductor, and they can be tuned—customized to certain applications.

• Devices made with colloidal quantum dots are extremely good photodetectors, and the dots themselves can be engineered to see in the infrared. Thus, they offer the potential to create an image sensor with capabilities that go far beyond conventional imaging.

• In 2005–2006, the company InVisage was formed to commercialize these very sensitive photodetectors. Since that time, the company has built prototypes that improve the capability of these materials to enhance the sensitivity of image sensors in cell phones.

• New functions have also been incorporated into these chips. For example, a true electronic shutter has been developed that eliminates the jitter present in cameras.

• Although it seems as if working with these remarkable materials and exotic ideas might translate into high costs, it's possible to achieve low cost and high performance simultaneously with nanomaterials.

• It's also true that commercialization offers the possibility of marrying new developments with established technologies. In the case of InVisage, the firm has combined a new light-sensing capability with a platform of microelectronics that is cost-effective and manufacturable.

Research Leaders in Nanoscience
• Paul Weiss is the director of the California NanoSystems Institute. His work is involved with gaining an atom-scale understanding and control over the properties of materials, and he is quite talented in the use of scanning tunneling microscopes.
  ○ Weiss insists that science gets interesting when he's exploring the ground rules of phenomena that are distinct as a result of being at the nanoscale.

o In addition to directing a large program, Weiss also founded a journal for the dissemination of nanotechnology research, *ACS Nano*. The journal has been active in disseminating research through social media and in attracting contributions from top scientists in the field.

- John Polanyi is a professor at the University of Toronto and winner of a Nobel Prize in 1986 for his work in the field of reaction dynamics, which looks to understand how chemical reactions occur. In particular, Polanyi advanced the method of infrared chemiluminescence, enabling people to see the energy coming out of chemical reactions in real time.
  o Polanyi is now working in surface-aligned photochemistry, studying the chemical reactions that result from the interactions of molecules at specific angles.

  o In addition, Polanyi is what we might call a scientist for peace. He has spoken out internationally on such topics as nuclear armaments and nuclear energy. He seems to believe that scientists should use their deep understanding of technical issues to address important questions in public policy.

- Michael Graetzel is a professor at the École Polytechnique Fédérale de Lausanne in Switzerland and is acknowledged as the inventor of the first efficient dye-sensitized solar cells, essentially the first solar cells that showed promise for being very low in cost. Like the other scientists mentioned here, Graetzel is distinguished on the world stage, yet he continues to study every element of the system that he invented and teams with other researchers around the world.

Corporate Research Activity
- A great deal of exciting research activity is also performed in the corporate world. A group at DuPont, for example, published a prestigious paper on sorting carbon nanotubes with the aid of DNA. This work had a direct impact on DuPont's realization of flexible substrates for photovoltaics, enabling the printing of solar cells based on roll-to-roll processing.

- Researchers at IBM developed the scanning tunneling microscope and have done important work on carbon nanotubes and graphene in the context of electronics. The company has recently shown some striking results in integrating these new classes of materials onto silicon. IBM has also shown leadership in the field of photovoltaics, with researchers looking at Earth-abundant materials that can be turned into energy-harvesting materials.

- Researchers at Intel have done work on figuring out how to wrap the gate electrode around the channel of a transistor in order to allow scaling to smaller dimensions. In fact, Intel has always been very much in the lead in downward scaling.

- Research and the transformation of research into products can be thought of as an ecosystem, and it's because of the existence of this ecosystem that nanotechnology is having a growing impact on our lives every day.

Suggested Reading

Christensen, *The Innovator's Dilemma.*

DuPont, "Science and Technology at DuPont."

IBM, "IBM Research."

Intel, "Intel Labs Research Areas Overview."

InVisage, "Technology."

Mouttet, "Nanotechnology and U.S. Patents."

Questions to Consider

1. What challenges related to bringing a product to market are specific to nanotechnology, as opposed to being general to all technology commercialization endeavors?

2. Everything is made from atoms and molecules, yet not every product is a nanotechnology innovation. How would you define a nanotechnology product?

How Nano Research Gets Done
Lecture 16—Transcript

Shana Kelley: As you've listened to our lectures, I'm sure you've wondered about how nanotechnology discoveries are actually made and how the research gets done. We decided to devote this lecture to telling you about the research process in nanotechnology so that you have a clearer idea about what kinds of people are involved, how it's funded, and how we move discoveries out of research labs and into commercial products. There are thousands of academic labs across the world that are working on nanotechnology related projects, and 100s more research labs at companies, government labs and research institutes. This is a very large community of people all working towards realizing the applications of nanotechnology that we've discussed in this course.

You might wonder what kind of training is required for nanotechnology researchers. Well you'll find that almost anything goes, people with some type of background in almost any area of basic science can find a place on a nanotechnology research team and make that important contribution. What's really unique about the teams that work on nanotechnology research is that they're highly interdisciplinary. In order to move projects forward, it's often necessary to have people with chemistry, physics, and biology in their background, and it's also important to have people with engineering training involved.

The chemists can help us generate new materials. The physicists can help us understand the properties of new materials, and biologists can help us put biomolecules and nanomaterials together. The engineers help us turn basic discoveries into devices—an important step in getting new science turned into solutions for medicine, computing, or energy.

To make this more tangible for you, I thought I would introduce you to some of the members of my research group so that you can get an idea of how people work together. I serve as the principal investigator leading a team of about 20 researchers from a variety of different backgrounds—we are a cross faculty group and we draw people from the Faculty of Medicine, Faculty of Pharmacy, Faculty of Arts and Sciences, and the Faculty of

Engineering. In addition to having people with different backgrounds, people come into the group and join the team at a variety of levels—some are graduate students earning a Masters or Ph.D. degree, some are postdoctoral researchers who are getting more experience after their Ph.D., and then some of our team members join us as research associates after getting their undergraduate degree.

One of my projects focuses on the development of a new type of DNA-modified quantum dot that can form really neat three-dimensional networks. The lead on this project is Paul Lee. Paul is a chemist and he got his Ph.D. at Caltech—he actually worked in the same lab I did as a graduate student. Paul has really helped us really perfect the chemistry that makes our materials functional and highly luminescent. You'll see Paul holding a tube of material that's really glowing and it's glowing so brightly because of all the chemistry that he's use to optimize it. Paul's deep expertise in understanding chemical reactions makes all the difference here.

Paul works closely with a Masters student named Davis Holmes. Davis has an undergraduate degree in Engineering Physics, and so he comes at the same project from a totally different perspective. Davis can help us think about the behavior of the quantum dots we make and why their electronic properties change in the presence of DNA. Having someone with this skill set on the project is really critical so that we understand how to give our quantum dots the highest level of performance possible.

As you know, we also work on making nanomaterials-based sensor chips in my lab. Here we also need lots of different kinds of expertise. This is Mario Moscovici and Mario is a Masters student with a mechanical engineering background. Mario is working on developing a device that will capture circulating tumor cells out of blood samples for early cancer detection. His mechanical engineering experience helped us figure out how to flow solutions around our chips and this is a really essential capability.

We also need Biology and Biochemistry expertise on this project in order to understand how to work with the DNA and RNA molecules that we're trying to sense. This is Sean Guo—Sean has an undergraduate degree in Biochemistry and he's now a Masters student with us and he's working on getting our chips to detect viruses. Sean came in with the expertise to help us with the biochemical aspects of this project, but as you can see, he now works with pretty sophisticated electronic equipment. This is a workstation where Sean is figuring out how to break up the viral particles up with an electric field so that we can analyze them. Sean has really had to stretch beyond what he learned as a graduate student and actually learn some electrical engineering and this is very typical for members of a nanotechnology team— they're always learning something new.

Alex Zaragoza brings a background in biology to our chip sensor project. Alex has an understanding of the markers within cells that can tell us that a cell is cancerous. He's engineering a chip to make it pick up on leukemia biomarkers. Since he's been with us, he's learned all kinds of things outside of the biology that he came in with, so he's learned aspects of electrochemistry, chip engineering, bioanalysis—all new skills. You heard in a previous lecture about the results of his work—a really powerful new diagnostic tool for leukemia.

On the chemistry side of the project, we have Brian Lam, who is working on a Ph.D. in Chemistry. Brian is really good at developing new types of materials chemistry. Here he is sitting at our scanning electron microscope and imaging one of the chips he made. While he waits for the image to come up, he's actually giving Davis Holmes a tutorial on how SEM works—this is a common occurrence on our team—one member with a certain expertise can help another fill the gaps in their background. This is one of the ways that these team members are able to learn about all the different areas that are involved in nanotechnology—by educating one another.

You can see Brian zooming in on the surface of his chip—you can see the nanomaterials he deposited on the chip now coming into focus in real time. SEM is just one of the techniques that Brian uses everyday—he moves back and forth between our clean room where he fabricates devices, sometimes over to our workstation where he makes DNA molecules, then he does some electrochemical measurements and it just goes on and on. Nanotechnology researchers have to be incredibly versatile—they're always changing gears and they usually never do the same thing two days in a row!

I think you can see that people that work on these types of nanotechnology teams, they all have their own specialization, but at the same time they really have to become broader and broader as they work and this is a very unique aspect of nanotechnology research. The team members need to be willing to be very versatile, to go back and forth between different techniques, and they're constantly teaching themselves something new. That's quite different from more traditional areas of science, where you typically learn one thing, really deeply and that's your area of specialization. Nanotechnology researchers tend to be much, much broader and they're exposed to all sorts of things during their careers. I think this is why many are attracted to the field—it has a unique set of challenges that really appeal to people that are curious and like learning new things.

You might wonder—how do we pay all these people and how do we buy all of the instrumentation that you've seen? We get our funding from a variety of sources—the government, private foundations, and companies. In Canada, we get funding from both the provincial and the federal government, and in the U.S., most of the funding comes from the federal government. A healthy budget for a group of about 20 is close to about a million dollars a year, and the money gets split pretty evenly between personnel costs and supplies and equipment. Nanotechnology research is actually a bit more expensive than other types of scientific research—we need lots of sophisticated equipment, and our teams are big because we need so many different types of expertise.

It's a pretty major undertaking actually to raise this kind of money and getting money from the government, whether it be the National Institute of Health, the National Science Foundation, or the Department of Defense involves writing very long, detailed proposals that describe a project we want to work on, and once we assemble the proposal and send it off it undergoes very rigorous peer review. Unfortunately it's not uncommon for a proposal to get turned down several times before it gets funded, so we also spend quite a bit of time iterating on and improving proposals. But the system really works in that it prioritizes high quality high impact research.

What are the tangible outcomes that come from this kind of investment? We disseminate the results of research in many different ways, and then the ways the results get used differ depending on what the application is. To get the word out about what we've discovered, we write papers and patents, and we attend conferences where new results get reported.

If the research that we do is quite basic in nature, like work done to develop a new material or imaging technique, the outcomes may take a while to materialize. Basic research serves as the foundation for more applied research focused on different applications, so very often more follow-up work is needed before anything can be brought to the marketplace or commercialized. But basic research is really important—this is where the most game-changing discoveries are often made. That's because it's usually curiosity driven and it can take a project in unexpected directions.

For example, a few years ago my group started working on a project where we were studying some very basic materials that were based on peptides. When we started, we were mainly just curious about what the properties of the materials would be and we didn't really have any particular application in mind. But after working with them for a few years, we've learned how to make them into powerful drug delivery agents and we found that they can attack even the most resistant cancer cells. So clearly, it's really important for researchers to pursue sound basic ideas even if the immediate impact is not clear.

For nanotechnology research that is more applied, a few different things can happen. If patents were generated from the work, an existing company may be interested in licensing them. They would then turn the research into a product, and once it's commercialized, they would pay the inventors and the universities where the patents were generated a royalty. This very often happens when new drugs are created. It takes lots of money to develop drugs and put them through FDA trials. We've talked a little bit about that and so typically those patents are licensed by companies with pretty deep pockets so that they can take it all the way through all the clinical trials that are needed.

For certain types of inventions, it actually makes more sense for a new company to be created—we refer to these companies as spin-offs or startups. When is this the best route? Well, in some industries, and the diagnostics industry is one example, a new technology actually needs to be very mature before it can be licensed. But it's not really possible to do the kind of work that is needed to mature a technology to this stage in a university lab—it needs to be done in a regulated environment so that the technology can get FDA approval eventually, and the optimization that needs to be done is not really suitable for students earning a degree. So here, if a company can be created and funded, it's a good way to get a technology to market.

How do you fund a company to take those next steps? Well there are many different channels, but one of the best for nanotechnology research is raising venture capital. The advantage of working with venture capitalists and giving them equity in a company in return for an investment is that in addition to getting their money, you also get to access their network of contacts and their experience that they've gotten working with other companies. It's not easy, the amount of venture capital is shrinking, and it's becoming more and more competitive to raise this kind of money.

I've actually been involved with 2 start-up companies. One that I co-founded after my Ph.D. studies was called GeneOhm Sciences. This company was set up in 2000, right when the idea of using genomics for medicine was getting really hot. We developed a variety of tools for genetic analysis, and eventually commercialized a series of tests for antibiotic resistant bacteria. This company was backed by a variety of venture capitalists and it was eventually sold for $250 million dollars in 2005.

Ted Sargent and I recently co-founded a company called Xagenic. Xagenic is commercializing the chip based diagnostic technology that our groups have co-developed and Xagenic will produce a variety of tests that will enable more rapid diagnosis of infectious disease relative to the tools that we currently have available. It's just the early days at Xagenic, so I can't tell you when the products will hit the markets, but we hope to be successful with getting our nanomaterials-based chips commercialized quickly.

These are just two examples from my own experience of how academic nanomaterials research can get commercialized. I think they are pretty representative, though, of how discoveries move out of academic labs and eventually are turned into products. So now I'm going to hand things over to Ted, who will tell you about a few experiences he's had commercializing nanotechnology research, and he'll also tell you about some other aspects of how nanotechnology research gets done.

Ted Sargent: Just like Shana, I've been very interested in commercializing the fruits of research that happened within my group at the University of Toronto and I've gotten to do that in the last couple of years. It's been incredibly exciting. Well before we started this company, which is called InVisage, for about four years leading up to that I'd been working in the field of colloidal quantum dots which we've spoken about in this course earlier. What's so exciting about these materials is twofold, first that you can synthesize them in solution and so you can simply coat them onto things, you can essentially make a paintable or a sprayable semiconductor and that in addition to that you can tune them; we talked about the quantum size effect, the fact that you have a material that you can really customize towards certain applications. We've been working with them for awhile and really what we were trying to do is to understand the potential of these materials.

There's various ways you could see using them and light emission which is very relevant to displace or in energy capture very relevant to solar energy harvesting. But, we ended up discovering that our devices made extremely good photodetectors, extremely sensitive detectors for light and that,, of course, turned out to be very useful when you combine it with the spectral feasibility of these materials, the fact that we could engineer a set materials such that they were visible light sensors, very useful in visible imaging that we all do every day, but we could also engineer them to see in the infrared, to see wavelengths that we can't see with our own eyes and therefore potentially to create an image sensor that gave entirely new capabilities that went beyond conventional vision and imaging.

In about 2005, we made the discovery that it was possible to make these very, very sensitive photodetectors and I had always wanted to commercialize some of the fruits of our research. I was really looking for a time when we said wow we've got something that nobody else has. We got their first, we invented it, we patented it, and we've got a really special advantage in going out there and building a company, building products, taking them all the way to the market. That's what we did in 2005–2006; we managed to attract investors into InVisage. In the past couple of years, we've built prototypes that improve the capability of these materials to enhance the sensitivity of image sensors, the kinds of image sensors that are inside your cell phone, inside your mobile phone, we've shown that it enhances them in many ways. It allows us to take them out into spectral regimes that have previously been unheralded when silicon was the basis for image sensing.

It has allowed us to put new functions into these chips. Because of the way that silicon chips where they utilize silicon for the light sensing function as well as for the electronics that drives the chip, they've been limited in how complex they could make the electronics because the real estate was scarce since they were sharing it between the light sensing and the circuit function. We realized within InVisage once we brought together a team of amazing circuit designers and experts in material science, we realized that we were able to break those compromises and make image sensor circuits that delivered new functions like a true electronic shutter that gets rid of the jitter that you see in cameras today.

This has been a very exciting part of the work and it has been incredibly gratifying to see that we can do more than just build materials, build devices that evince the potential of work on the nanoscale and that we've actually been able to turn them into real prototypes, ultimately into products that evince what we're talking about when we talk about how excited we are about engineering at the nanoscale. You know, I've actually learned a lot not just about commercialization, but also about nanotechnology through this experience in nanotechnology commercialization. For example, you might think with these remarkable materials with these very special properties that all these exotic ideas would have to mean high cost, but in fact the work that we do and Shana's commercial activities as well are all about using nanomaterials for these very specific purposes where they're really needed in order to achieve our technical objectives, but in a way that doesn't have to mean high cost, in fact it can mean low cost and it has in both of our cases. It doesn't have to be a compromise if you like. We can have a low cost and high performance simultaneously.

Another thing that I've learned through the course of this, I had this idea before getting the company going, but this became so much more tangible as we built it that nanotechnology doesn't have to stand alone. We don't have to be interested in nanoparticles or nanotubes for their own sake or in isolation, but that it can be very compelling to take a new technology, a new capability, and marry it with an established one. In the case of InVisage, it's that we're taking a new light sensing capability and we're putting it onto the platform of microelectronics, a platform that has been developed, rendered robust, rendered cost effective, rendered manufacturable over decades and it's really a synergy between this new element that the nanomaterials bring, but this very sound and stable platform of microelectronics that is enabled to build something rapidly that's been very compelling.

I tell a couple of stories about three examples of people that have inspired me in the field, people who are through leaders, they've made huge technical and scientific contributions, but I think as often in the case for the people one really admires, they even go beyond that as well. My first example is that of Paul Weiss and Paul fairly recently moved from Penn State to UCLA where he directs the California Nanoscience Institute. Paul does some incredibly beautiful science, science that pertains to really gaining an atom scale understanding and control over the properties of materials. He is very talented in the use of scanning tunneling microscopes to do this. In fact, he notes that one of the almost magical elements of the scanning tunneling microscope is that you can both sense and you can also move matter, you can displace atoms, you can control where they end up using your scanning tunneling microscope. It's a very powerful tool.

What I find so compelling about the way Paul does science is that he really insists that when it gets interesting is when he's exploring phenomena ground rules limits that are different, they're really distinct as a result of being at the nanoscale and so his curiosity really focuses on understanding what it is about engineering or doing science at the nanoscale that confers entirely new properties. Another thing about Paul that's so remarkable is that with a huge group, a very compelling program that's known internationally, at the same time he took it upon himself to found a new journal for the dissemination of the very best nanotechnology research and it's known as ACS nano. ACS is the American Chemical Society which publishes a lot of the top journals in the field. This was a new journal that Paul was involved in from the very beginning.

You know, academics and especially in the field of nanotechnology, but academics, generally they're always looking out for the very strongest journal, the one with the great reputation one where by being able to publish in one of the journals, the glory of that journal was kind of showering down on the scientists for their capacity to publish in such a great venue. It's very difficult to build a journal from scratch, in fact your reach, the extent to which people notice inside the work center, this inevitably is going to be less when you get it going. Paul took what I thought was a very innovative approach. First, right when we were getting into social networking and social media, Paul started to use the tools of disseminating information in a very accessible way over the internet, in fact, the little video clips that he did were called nanotube in which you could watch scientists talking about the work that was being published in his journal that month.

The other approach that he took that was sort of a fostering or nurturing approach is that instead of his technique for raising the stature of his journal being to say no to a lot of people, which is one way to do it, is just to be extremely discriminating. Paul did that and he had to do it, but it really felt like the way he drove it forward was by going out and attracting the people who he thought were doing the most exciting work and saying to them listen you should publish in my journal. We know each other, everybody likes Paul, he's everybody's friend. So come publish in my journal, it would be great for you; it'll be good for the journal. People did it, they responded to them, and as a result he's doubled the impact factor over a couple of years which means that he's taken his journal from being one that people cited at a reasonable level to being one of the strongest journals in the field all through this positive force of attracting the best scientists to work with him.

Another person who has been a real inspiration in fact to, I think, pretty much everybody born in Canada, he's kind of a model, is john Polanyi who's a professor at the University of Toronto. John won the Nobel Prize in 1986 for his really invention of a new field in concert with a few others is a field of research and chemistry called reaction dynamics and essentially John and a few other colleagues who shared the 1986 Nobel Prize with them won it for providing a much more detailed understanding of how chemical reactions occur and John in particular advanced the method of infrared chemiluminescence where he's able to essentially see the energy that was coming out of a chemical reaction in real time and use it's spectral properties to see where the energy was going, to do kind of a complete balance, or a complete accounting for these reactions.

Since then, because that was in 1956 that John made those discoveries though the Nobel Prize didn't come until 1986, but since then and prior to then as well he's started new efforts and new fields and new endeavors entirely. One of the most exciting things that he does now is surface aligned photochemistry where he recognizes that the angle with which two molecules interact with each other will drive the kind of chemical reaction that occurs, what the products will be. So he takes advantage of having a surface of atoms that's extremely well-controlled, the kinds of things that you can measure with your scanning tunneling microscope, the kind of things on which you can move around molecules using your scanning tunneling microscope tip, and he uses it to poise molecules in specific orientations and then bring in other molecules at specific angles and so he's able to discover and understand better the influence of the geometry, the relationship between molecules and space at an angle and how that actually drives reactions, and so some incredibly deep science that says we want to understand these reactions at the deepest level.

Another way in which he's really been inspiring though that goes beyond the science that he does, he was, as I was saying, a hero to school children growing up in Canada, so a somewhat small country in terms of population, a countable number of Canadians to have won the Nobel Prize, who is still working in Canada today of whom John is one, and John decided to use this well-earned platform to be very vocal in other subjects as well as to influence public policy and really public thinking. He's really a scientist for peace, somebody who has spoken out and who has a resonance naturally internationally on the subjects of peace on how we should think about nuclear armaments, nuclear energy, and I think he really takes the approach that, it's certainly that scientists are entitled to do, in fact, it's almost something that scientists are required to do, is to use their platform and their deep understanding of the technical or scientific issues that underlie what they're speaking about, that underlie a lot of important questions in public policy and to be vocal about them. That is really their duty and John inspires a lot of people that way.

Another scientist who has inspired many in the field of nanotechnology, including those particularly passionate about working on problems in energy is Michael Graetzel who's at École Polytechnique Fédérale de Lausanne in Switzerland. Michael is acknowledged as the inventor of the first efficient dye-sensitized solar cells. These are essentially the first solar cells that showed promise for being very low in cost and therefore got people excited about the concept of integrating solar cells into somebody's backpack.

There's some fascinating chemistry at work, some fascinating inorganic chemistry, and Michael managed to make that field in adding photons into it and harvesting energy with it, into an incredibly exciting one. What I find so striking about Michael Graetzel's work today is that like the other people that I've mentioned, I mean he's so distinguished on the world stage, he's won the Millennium Prize for Finland, and he could easily rest on his laurels if he wanted to, but in fact he has exactly the opposite approach. The science that he does today, for one thing it's prolific, but he just studies an incredible depth in detail every element of this system that he invented. He's had these large impact papers that have really influenced people and then by teaming with researchers all around the world in Israel and Japan and Korea, and we collaborate with him, my group, people in the U.S., people around the world get to participate in this community of research surrounding understanding the fascinating chemistry and physics that underlie this new class of devices that Michael and his team invented.

Of course, I've spoken about commercialization of nanotechnology, Shana's spoken quite a bit about how nanotechnology actually gets done within universities, but within large companies there's a great deal of very exciting activity. In fact, in many respects large companies have an advantage. They are already product companies today, they already know how to manufacture a chip, and even be profitable one hopes, but in addition to that in their research arms, they have the potential to look down the road 5, 10, 15 years into the future, figure out where they have strengths and where there are needs available. DuPont, for example, is one company that's done some fascinating work. There was actually academically a very prestigious paper published by a DuPont group on sorting carbon nanotubes with the aid of DNA where different sequences of DNA could essentially recognize different classes of carbon nanotubes, something that has since had a lot of direct impact and of practical importance is DuPont's realization of flexible substrates for photovoltaics, the real promise of solar cells based on roll-to-roll processing, essentially printing solar cells the way we print newspaper is to be achieved, and it will be on flexible substrates that are reliable, cost effective, in some cases optically transparent, and people at DuPont have really shown leadership in that very important field.

IBM research is a fascinating place where many discoveries from the last decades have occurred. Of course, the researchers who developed the scanning tunneling microscope, Binning and Rohrer were at IBM Zurich, there has been some of the most important work on carbon nanotubes and graphene essentially in the context of electronics, the electronic properties of these materials have been advanced by Phaedon Avouris at IBM Research. This is where one of IBMs great advantages is so obvious that especially in the field of electronics there's a pathway there to figure out how to take these upstream discoveries, this R&D, and transform it into reliable robust manufactural devices, which is really one of the central challenges of that area and scenario where IBM has just recently shown some very striking results and really integrating these new classes of materials, these new concepts onto silicon.

In the field of photovoltaics, they've also shown leadership with David Mitzi's work on looking at new earth abundant materials that can be processed in a very cost effective way and turned into energy harvesting materials. As we've discussed throughout the course, Chris Murray's work on the colloidal quantum dots in building superlattice materials and devices out of them has come out of IBM research, as has Yuri Vlasov's work that we discussed in the context of silicon photonics, trying to put light onto a chip. Intel is kind of another animal entirely there. There's this very well-defined, very focused enterprise within Intel on just bringing us the next generation of integrated circuits as they've done so successfully for decades.

The FinFET that we spoke about earlier came directly out of Intel, out of research done there, in figuring out how to wrap the gate electrode around the channel eventually of a transistor in order to allow scaling to smaller and smaller dimensions. Speaking of which, that scaling itself is something in which Intel has always been very much in the lead in figuring out how we will get to that next lithographic node, figuring out how we can extend the incredibly long lifetime of photolithography down to smaller and smaller length scales. I know that you've enjoyed this kind of perspective on how research gets done, research that happens in university labs, research that gets spun out from there, how academics make an impression on each other through their publications and interdisciplinary journals, how they talk to each other through those venues, and how research happens within big companies.

You can see that the research and the transformation into innovation into products, it's really an ecosystem, it's got the incredibly important foundations of basic research without which we would not understand how to talk to the nanoworld, how to measure the nanoworld, how to think about what materials we can build, what's possible. Then it has researchers who kind of reach upstream and who find new materials, new concepts, and try to translate them into things that are practical, and then those that are willing to take that even further, take it into companies and transform it robustly into products. It's because this ecosystem exists is because there are researchers who are passionate at every stage within that ecosystem that nanotechnology really is starting to have an impact on our lives, a growing impact with every day.

Nanomotifs—Building Blocks, Complex Structures
Lecture 17

Throughout much of this course, we've concerned ourselves with nanotechnology from the point of view of its applications, but it's also fascinating to view nanotechnology through the lens of design or architecture. In this lecture, we'll look at the incredibly diverse building blocks of nanotechnology and the capability of crystal facet engineering these building blocks give us to create beautiful structures.

Building Blocks of Nanostructures
- A nanoparticle is approximately a sphere, but because such particles are crystalline arrays, they possess facets. The constructions we build on top of nanoparticles are called core shell structures.

- The term "epitaxy" is used to describe the growth of crystals on top of other crystals. The key to this term is the idea that the spacing among the atoms in the first material is perfectly mimicked in the second material that lies on top of it.

- The term "heteroepitaxy" is used to describe the growth of a shell of a second type of material on top of a first material. Such heteroepitaxial core-shell nanoparticles have properties that go well beyond those that are embedded in the cores alone.
  - We've already discussed the fact that we can change quantum confinement at the core. We can also wrap a core within a shell to achieve a decrease in the degree of overlap between more and less excited energy states.

  - As a result, the transitions that occur within a core-shell nanoparticle can be different. If the overlaps are weak between the two states—the initial and the final state—we'll have a weak transition, and we may have poor luminescence from the materials. If we engineer a shell that's efficient at cramming the electron and all of its possible states tightly inside the core, we can achieve a much more strongly luminescent structure.

o This is an example of what can be accomplished by engineering on just one more length scale beyond the core itself. In fact, we can build structures that embed many layers of shells, in which each of those layers is used to manipulate the structure of the material within.

Crystal Facet Engineering

- As we said, a nanoparticle is approximately spherical, but it still has facets, regions where certain atoms of 1 type are exposed and others where certain atoms of another type are exposed.

- As an example, let's consider a binary material that consists of tin and sulfur. If we were to slice it along certain axes, we could see tin and sulfur atoms in equal ratios, 1:1. There are other axes on which we could slice it where we would see only tin atoms or axes where we would see only sulfur atoms.

- We can engineer the propensity for these facets to react and, thus, differentiate certain facets from others. For example, we might want to grow an "arm" off 1 facet while protecting the other facets that don't have the same degree of reactivity. The ability to control these facets leads to the capacity to build things that are directional.

o Quantum dots can be thought of as 3-dimensionally confined systems, in which electrons are confined in both horizontal planes and the vertical plane. They can also be thought of as 0-dimensional from the point of view of the number of dimensions on which the electronic states are extended.

o We can use that same concept to talk of materials that extend the electron along 1 axis but confine it along 2. These we call 1-dimensional materials, where there's a propagation in 1 direction.

o We also have what are called quantum wells, where the electron can swim around freely within the plane and is confined along only 1 axis.

o Nanotubes, rolled up sheets of graphene, allow propagation along their axis and confinement in the other 2 dimensions. If we unroll a carbon nanotube, we produce a graphene sheet. Electrons can skirt around within the plane, but because they are confined to reside within that plane, they function more like quantum wells.

• The traditional inorganic semiconductor materials, such as silicon and germanium, with which we are able to grow various types of nanoparticles, and the carbon-based organic materials, such as buckyballs, nanotubes, and graphene, all have analogs of one another. They all can see different degrees of confinement and propagation engineered at the nanoscale.

Supercrystals and Superlattices

• The easiest kind of structure we could build with nanoparticles would be another crystal. We might think of it as a supercrystal, a periodic array of nanoparticles, in which each nanoparticle is itself internally a crystal.

• To make a perfectly ordered structure of nanoparticles—a perfectly regular array—all the building blocks must be the same. This property is known as monodispersity.

• The other ingredient needed to build a supercrystal is a strategy to allow every constituent nanoparticle to find its place in the lattice. This typically involves a slow growth, similar to allowing a solution of salt and water to evaporate slowly to give every atom time to find its place in the resulting crystal.

• Superlattices can be made not just out of a single particle but from multiple types of particles. This tiling idea has led to binary superlattices, which allow the fusing of the properties of their constituents and the development of super-semiconductor materials.

- The ideas of oriented attachment have been extended beyond making 3-dimensional crystals to attaching nanoparticles along a 1-dimensional axis to form a string. These long wires are prone to carry electronic charge along their length, while still maintaining quantum confinement along the direction that's perpendicular to the length axis of the wire.

Tetrapods

- A tetrapod is a structure that has a number of legs pointing downward and 1 arm pointing upward. Electron propagation is achieved along the component that points upward.

- This is a useful architecture. The problem with wires on their own is that they are naturally prone to lie down on a surface. The fact that tetrapods plant their legs on the surface and point an extension upward means that they have conduction in the vertical direction.

- To build these structures, crystals that form tetrahedral structures are used. The 4 exposed facets are all equally prone toward growth. Thus, we can create 4 substrates at various angles to one another, off of which growth of the rods can occur. Typically, 1 material is used to form the body and another forms the basis for the arms.

- These materials have applications in making more controlled electronic structures. We can combine materials into a single nanoparticle, enabling the inclusion of a metal and a semiconductor, for example. We're also able to create a sense of orientation or a polarization, a propensity for charge to flow in a certain direction.

From Building Blocks to Architectures

- The fact that DNA acts as a powerful type of Velcro® offers a technique for the controllable construction of structures that combine many different nanomaterials.

- One simple structure involves a series of nanowires that are grown from the bottom up. Attached to the nanowires are single-stranded pieces of DNA. In a separate reaction vessel are nanoparticles with complementary strands of DNA attached. The fusing of these two different classes of nanostructures forms a new nanostructured material.

- This concept leads to the idea of combining nanoparticle types with different colors. Each of these could be labeled with a different sequence of DNA, and the number of DNA strands that would adhere to each could be controlled.
  - The DNA concept, putting a programmable number of strands on a surface, is analogous to the valency idea in the periodic table. We could start with a large inner nanoparticle, having, say, 4 pieces of DNA on it that displayed a certain sequence. We could then couple that to a green class of nanoparticles having the complementary sequence and, thus, ensure that the center nanoparticle had exactly 4 green nanoparticles bound to it.

  - Extending this idea even further, a third class of nanoparticles could be introduced that would bind to the second class. In this way, crosses and triangular structures could be built from an inner-core nanoparticle.

  - With this process, nanostructured materials could be designed in a controlled fashion by simply combining ingredients.

- In research at the University of Toronto, we used this process to build a structure in which the outermost set of nanoparticles possessed excited electrons when it was illuminated at the highest available energy state; the inner ring had a sort of middling energy excited-state level; and the heart of the structure had the lowest energy.
  - When we photoexcited the outer ring, energy was inclined to trickle downhill; the energy would pour into the inner shell, then to the center nanoparticle. We built, in essence, an energy

funnel. We could have an absorption from this complex that was proportional to the number of nanoparticles.

o This funnel is an analogy to the way in which the photosynthetic apparatus acts in plants. Plants have evolved systems that function like antennae to harvest light. They actually extend their reach for light absorption and then funnel energy down toward a reaction center.

o We did the same thing with our multi–length scale structured molecular complexes, and we showed that the efficiency with which we were able to capture and transfer energy toward the virtual reaction center was extremely high.

o Interestingly, we were also able to turn this phenomenon on and off by changing the pH within the structures or within the solution.

Virus-Shaped Nanoparticles

• Angela Belcher at MIT is working to merge the world of the biological with the world of nanoparticles. She has been able to engineer materials that take on the shape of viruses by growing semiconductor nanoparticles off the surfaces of viruses.

• Belcher has further combined the field of semiconductors and material science with the field of genetic engineering in that she's been able to find which proteins displayed on the surface of these viruses allow growth with particular success, that is, with particularly high yields of nanostructured materials.

• This work illustrates the idea that when we think about nanomotifs, we don't have to limit ourselves to thinking only about inorganic semiconductors or only about organic materials; we can get biological entities and even life forms into the game for engineering on many length scales.

Suggested Reading

Lee, Mao, Flynn, and Belcher, "Ordering of Quantum Dots Using Genetically Engineered Viruses."

Ozin and Arsenault, *Nanochemistry*.

Whaley, et al., "Selection of Peptides with Semiconductor Binding Specificity for Directed Nanocrystal Assembly."

Questions to Consider

1. The existence and structures of many types of matter were hypothesized before direct observations were made. Why was it difficult for us to even imagine that such structures as carbon nanotubes and fullerenes (buckyballs) existed before they were characterized?

2. Are there any limitations we can envision for the structures of nanomaterials? Should there be an infinite or discrete number of nanomaterials?

Nanomotifs—Building Blocks, Complex Structures
Lecture 17—Transcript

Ted Sargent: Much of this course, we've concerned ourselves with nanotechnology from the point of view of its applications from the perspective of what it can enable. Why not? I mean so many of us are passionate about this field because of what we can do with it. I think there's another interesting perspective to bring to the field, which is there are so many beautiful things that we can create, such amazing materials, such amazing images. Some of the pictures that people are taking on the nanometer length scale using their transmission electron micrographs or their scanning tunneling microscopes are so beautiful and so fascinating. I think it's interesting to view nanotechnology almost through the lens of art or design or architecture.

We'll start with the building blocks themselves and then we'll think about the buildings. We'll think about what different types of structures we could engineer and then how we can build those into more complex buildings from these building blocks. Here's a couple of examples of some of the more interesting building blocks. Think of it as kind of an artist's portfolio of what they can do.

We have on the top left a nanoparticle, something we've spent lots of time on throughout this course. It can be kind of approximately a sphere although you can often see hints of it having crystal facets. Since these are crystalline arrays, they do possess facets. Those facets end up being the basis for a lot of the shapes that you see elsewhere here; the pyramids, the cubes, the structures that have a hexagonal cross-section, things that look like die that you might roll, or tetrapods, or pointed objects, or even stars. These structures are ultimately having their origins traceable to the underlying crystallinity that is at their base.

Another thing that we can do, sort of the first thing that you imagine doing once you have a nanoparticle available is that you can build further on top of it and so people call these core shell structures. We can start with a particle having a particular crystal lattice and then we can grow on top of it some kind of shell typically of another material. We use the term epitaxy to describe the growth of crystals on top of other crystals and key to the word epitaxy is the idea that the crystalline periodicity, the spacing amongst the atoms in the first material is perfectly mimicked in the second material that lies on top of it.

We use the term heteroepitaxy to describe the growth of a shell of a second type of material on top of a first material. Now these heteroepitaxial core shell nanoparticles have properties that go well beyond those that are embedded in the cores alone. We've talked already about how at the core size we can change quantum confinement; we can change the band gap of the structure. With the shell of example, we can wrap a core within a shell where the shell is prone to attract excited electrons into it, but it's prone to repel the low energy electrons. It decreases the degree of overlap between excited and less-excited states. As a result, the transitions that can occur within a core shell nanoparticle can be different. If those overlaps are weak between the two states, the initial and the final state, we'll have a weak transition. We may have very poor luminescence from the materials.

On the other hand, if we engineer a shell that's great at just cramming the electron and all of its possible states tightly inside the core, we can achieve a much more strongly luminescent structure. This is an example of something that we can do by engineering just on one more length scale beyond just the core itself by building these shells. In fact, we can build a quantum gobstopper. We can build structures that embed many, many layers of shells growing out of them where each one of those layers is used to manipulate the structure of the material within.

When we talk about epitaxy and we talk about growth of crystals on other crystals, there we really need to think about these facets, these planes of atoms that exist. In fact, when you look at a nanoparticle and you think it's spherical, it really isn't. It may have many, many planes shaved off to look almost spherical, but it still has some structure, it still has regions where certain atoms of one type are exposed, certain atoms of another type are exposed. Let's take as an example a binary material, one that consists of tin and sulfur. If you were to slice it along certain axes, you could see tin and sulfur atoms in equal ratios, 1:1 ration. There are other axes on which you could slice it; the way you might imagine cleaving a diamond face, there are other axes where you would only see tin atoms or axes where you would see only sulfur atoms.

This in turn allows us to engineer the propensity for these materials, or for these facets, to react. This gives us the ability to differentiate certain facets from others and so if you look at a nanoparticle that has an exposed facet off at some angle, well perhaps we can engineer that facet to be one where we can grow an arm off of it while protecting the other facets that don't have the same degree of reactivity. Perhaps we can use organic molecules such as these ligands that we've spoken about to help us to keep one of those facets well-protected and we can make those organic ligands really pop off of the facet that we want to grow our arm on and so we can further engineer the structural nature of these materials.

What can we do when we can control these facets? This is what really leads to the capacity to build things that are directional. You could say that our quantum dots or we can call them 3-dimensionally confined systems where we've confined electrons in both horizontal planes and also in the vertical plane. We can call these 3-dimensionally confined or 0-dimensional from the point of view of the number of dimensions on which the states, the electronic states are extended. We can use that same concept to talk of materials that extend the electron along one axis, but confine it along two. These we call 1-dimensional materials where there's a propagation direction, one propagation direction.

We also have what are called quantum wells where the electron can swim around freely within the plane and it's confined along only one axis. These are now the kinds of materials that we can grow with the power of controlling directionality through controlling the propensity to grow along certain facets. In fact, these ideas of 0-D, 1-D, 2-D materials, these are really the same forces that are at work when we think about some of the carbon based nanomaterials that are also so beautiful. Bucky balls have a lot in common with quantum dots in the sense that they're confined along all three axes.

Nanotubes, rolled up sheets of graphene, allow propagation along their axis and confinement in the other two dimensions. If you unroll one of those carbon nanotubes you produce a graphene sheet. Electrons can skirt around within the plane, can move freely but they are confined to reside within that plane so they function more like quantum wells. These semiconductors, these traditional inorganic semiconductor materials like silicon and germanium with which we are able to grow various types of nanoparticles and the carbon based organic materials, such as the Bucky balls, nanotubes, and graphene, they all have analogs of one another. They all can see different degrees of confinement and propagation engineered at the nanoscale.

That's one very useful length scale to operate it. It's the building block length scale. It's the particle length scale. I think it's really interesting to think about whether we can build structures out of those particles and the easiest kind of material to think about building would be another periodic structure. It would be another crystal. In fact, you can think of it as a super crystal, a periodic array of nanoparticles where of course each nanoparticle is itself internally a crystal.

Here, Chris Murray, who was at IBM in some of his earlier work and is now at the University of Pennsylvania, has done some incredible work where he's shown how to take the semiconductor nanoparticles and get them to pack into perfectly regular arrays. You might wonder, what are the requirements for doing that? Well there are a couple. The first is to make a perfectly ordered structure; all of your building blocks have to be the same as one another. It's like building a salt crystal. It's because all the sodium's are the same as one another and all the chlorines are the same as the other chlorines that you can get a perfectly regular array. If you were to have a bunch of impurities in there, materials of different sizes included, you would eventually have a pretty big mess.

So building one of these supercrystals or superlattice materials is reliant on making all the nanoparticles the same. We call that property monodispersity. We call the property of having every particle identical to all the others and we've gotten pretty good at carrying out the synthesis of these nanoparticles to make them all identical, but when it's not perfect, even if it's not completely perfect, we have some other options available to us. For example, we're able to ensure that overly big nanoparticles that we don't want in the mix, we're able to cause them to precipitate out of solution. They can be particularly easy to cause to drop down to the bottom of the solution so all we have left are the smaller particles of the right size.

This process known as size-selective precipitation has been used now for two decades in order to produce increasingly pure sets of nanoparticles. The other ingredient that we need in order to build one of the supercrystals, something that's very regular is we need some kind of strategy to allow every atom, every constituent nanoparticle to find its place in the lattice and that typically involves kind of a slow and kneeling or a slow growth. It would be like trying to build a really nice, big, large, very organized crystal by allowing say the liquid in which the precursors were contained, think of salt once again, allowing that solution, say allowing the water to evaporate very slowly to give every atom lots of time to find just the right crucible of where it could reside in the ordered structure.

Well in this case of building nanoparticle superlattice is exactly the same idea is used and there's a very clever way to accelerate that, which is through solvent mixtures. Researchers don't just use one solvent containing all these nanoparticles dispersed in them, drop a drop, let it dry, but instead they use a pair of solvents, the majority solvent, the one which they use a preponderance of is one that evaporates pretty rapidly and then a small fraction, maybe 10%, will be one that evaporates much more slowly. They put a droplet of this onto typically a very smooth substrate, allow the rapidly evaporating one to evaporate and then you're left with this kind of gooey mass where the nanoparticles now are in a very dense concentrated solvent and that solvent is evaporating very slowly.

As a result, every nanoparticle has a chance to kind of look around, feel its way around the growing crystal that's emerging, find its lowest energy site, so find the region which enables it to form an ordered structure. There's another particularly beautiful result that Chris Murray has achieved, which is not just to make these superlattices out of a single particle, but to make them out of multiple different types of particles. This reminds me a little bit of the amazing tiles that you can see often in the Middle East to go see some of the beautiful architecture there. You can see now periodic patterns that aren't just simple repetitions of a single repeat unit, but instead periodic patterns that have embedded within them subpatterns as well.

These kinds of mosaic or tiling ideas have led to what's become known as binary superlattices. Binary superlattices, they add in another ingredient, they add in another degree of freedom. They allow us to make materials that don't just have the properties of a first or a second constituent, but that fuse those properties. Chris Murray and his group have used these ideas to make sort of super semiconductor materials, one's based on two different types of constituents all ordered and where the ability to propagate electrons and the ability to have an abundance of electrons are separately controlled through the two constituents that make up these materials.

Some beautiful work also coming from Murray in collaboration with Dmitri Talapin who was with him at IBM and who now runs his own research group doing very exciting work at the University of Chicago has been to take these ideas of oriented attachment and to extend them not just to making these 3-dimensional crystals, but taking individual nanoparticles and causing them to form a string, causing them to attach along a 1-dimensional axis. As a result, they've made incredibly long wires, micrometers long, out of nanometer sized materials. These are obviously very prone to carry electronic charge along their length while still having the confinement, the quantum confinement, along the direction that's perpendicular to the length axis of the wire.

The concept that they utilized, that enabled them to explain how this work was quite fascinating. It did involve these facets, involved the fact that the constituent materials making up these crystals, they obviously like each other. The reason you make tin-sulfide, the reason it's so naturally easy to make is that tin and sulfur really like each other and so they made these nanoparticles consisting of tin and sulfur in equal concentrations, but where some of the exposed facets were tin based and the others were almost purely sulfur based, and so two nanoparticles would see each other and if they ran into each other in solution and the sulfur facet was facing the tin facet, they would bind and otherwise they wouldn't. They created an avenue towards then kind of a propagating idea where one got this growth of a longer and longer chain, an incredibly long very ordered chains, and epitaxially connected to chains kind of using an idea of complementarity, almost a yin and a yang between the different facets of the nanoparticles being attracted to one another to form these oriented attachment structures.

There are some other really interesting and actually quite powerful materials concepts that have been developed as well. One of them is the idea of engineering tetrapods so these structures have a bunch of legs pointing downwards and then one kind of arm, or if you like a body, pointing upwards. Along that component that points upwards, of course electron propagation is achieved very well. Well this is actually a very useful architecture, the problem with wires on their own or just nanorods is that if you plunk them all onto a surface or if you just sort of coat them down, well they'll naturally be prone to lie down on that surface, very few of them would point up, in fact often none of them can.

With these tetrapods, because of their legs, you can ensure that they all plant three of their legs on the surface and they point their fourth extension upwards. Now they have conduction in the vertical direction and they have this orientation that's enforced by their underlying structure. In fact, you might wonder how does it happen, how is that possible? Well here we use crystals that form tetrahedral structures so where they have four exposed facets, all equally prone towards growth, and then we grow off of those facets so we kind of create four substrates at various angles to each other off of which growth of the rods can occur.

We do it heteroepitaxially typically. We do it with one material to form the body off of which growth can occur and the second material that forms the basis for the arms. So with this, researchers have achieved really incredible control over the formation of these new materials, which have all sorts of applications in making more controlled electronic structures. This is a picture of something that looks like a pencil and it gets called a nanopencil, in fact, you can even see the eraser on one side and the pointy end on the other and what it illustrates, this is an example of a structure that hasn't yet found its utility, the eraser isn't actually used as an eraser.

What it illustrates is the idea that we are able now to combine multiple materials into a single nanoparticle so we're able to include a metal here and a semiconductor over here. We're able to create a sense of orientation as well and so this ends up being a very powerful idea. There's a front and a back to a structure, and so this is what allows things to form chains as a result of having a directionality to them. Another way to think of that is a polarization to it. There's a particular proneness for charge to flow in one direction. One can even imagine making little semiconductor materials, little junctions, little p-n junctions or diodes, but now at the nanoscale and synthesized in solution.

This is one of my favorite pictures; it's from some beautiful work that Jinwoo Cheon in Korea has done. It's one of his nanostars and he's been one of the leaders in figuring out how to build such a diversity of different shapes. He's really able to rationally engineer from a knowledge of the crystal structure that will exist, from a knowledge of the facets that will be exposed, how he can then grow these larger shapes, which extend outwards in all sorts of interesting directions.

I'd like to turn now having spent some time on the building blocks; I'd like to turn to some of the architectures that we're able to create. Here I'd like to bring in DNA. DNA is a very powerful type of Velcro effectively. We know lots already from this course about the specific binding properties of DNA. We know that a single strand of DNA, when it encounters a complementary sequence of DNA having exactly the complementary sequence that they will bind, they will form the duplex, and if there's a lack of a match they will not form that duplex. We have kind of a lock and key recognition system; it's like Velcro, but Velcro that will only stick to a very, very specific complementary piece of Velcro.

I think of this as just an incredibly powerful technique for the controllable construction of structures that combine a bunch of different nanomaterials. It allows us when we kind of label various different nanomaterials with different sequences of our DNA Velcro. It allows us to engineer potentially a diversity of structures this way. Let me start with a simple structure and then I'll go to some more complex ones that have emerged very recently. The simple structure is illustrated here. It involves a series of nanowires that are grown from the bottom up and then it involves attaching a strand of DNA to the nanowires, a single stranded piece of DNA, and that single stranded piece of DNA has a functional group on the end of it that makes it really want to stick to the surface of the nanowires.

We do the same thing in a separate reaction vessel with a bunch of nanoparticles and there though we use a sequence of DNA that of course will bind at its end to the nanoparticles where that sequence is complementary to the one that we stuck on the rods. Then when we combine these two things, when we take the nanoparticles in solution and put them on top of these nanorods there's an opportunity for specific hybridization to occur. This image is showing, and this is actually some of Shana Kelly's beautiful work from a couple of years ago, this image is showing how we were able to sort of take two different classes of nanostructure and fuse them or combine them in a rational way in order to form a new nanostructured material.

You can think of it as forming a nanostructured material building on a higher length scale or a higher degree, a higher order, or a higher hierarchy as a result of combining pre-synthesized nanoparticles in a way that provides a lot of control. This concept, the idea of hybridizing DNA with itself and then using as building blocks nanoparticles that have single strands tethered to one another. This is a concept that Shana and I thought was very interesting and that could allow us to engineer even more complicated structures than what we showed there.

Our concept was this that we could each have a number of different nanoparticle types, perhaps different colors. We could have a red emitter that would emit light around 600 nanometer wavelength, a green emitter that would emit around 500 nanometer wavelength, and a blue emitter and this sort of 400 wavelength range and that we could label each one of these with a different sequence, a very carefully chosen sequence of DNA, and that furthermore we thought that we could introduce the possibility of controlling how many DNA strands would adhere to each one of these nanoparticles, each one of these quantum dots. You can see now already that we're starting to develop a bit of an analogy with the periodic table and the periodic table that we spoke about earlier.

We have this potential for one or two or three or four valence electrons to be available for binding and the kind of marriages that are formed, the kinds of proclivities amongst different atoms in the periodic table. These are all determined by the valency, by the number of electrons available for binding on the outer surface. With this DNA concept we were kind of building an analogy with that valency idea we were putting a programmable number of different strands on the surface. When we started with a large inner nanoparticle having let's say four pieces of DNA on it that displayed a certain sequence, when we then introduced to couple to that say a green class of nanoparticles having the complementary sequence, we were able to ensure that the center nanoparticle had exactly four green nanoparticles bound to it.

Then we were able to extend this idea even further. We were able to introduce a third class of nanoparticles that would bind to the second class of nanoparticles. We were able to build from an inner core nanoparticle, we were able to build crosses or triangular structures, and then we were able to build out from there as well. Once we made these things, initially we did it because it seemed like such a fascinating challenge that you could build designer nanostructured materials, kind of an analogy with building molecules from the atoms in the periodic table that you could design these nanostructured materials in a controlled fashion and all you had to do is kind of combine ingredients. You didn't have to do anything yourself at the nanoscale, you just got all of these materials to organize so it seemed like just a neat thing to do and something that led to some beautiful images, some very aesthetically appealing results.

Nevertheless, once we built these structures we asked ourselves, well what kind of special properties do they have? How do they behave like things that go beyond just kind of mixing together two vats or three vats of materials? How do they actually evince the fact that we've coupled these materials to one another? Where we went looking was on how energy is communicated amongst these nanoparticles. We actually ended up making a structure where the outermost set of nanoparticles possessed excited electrons when you illuminated it at the highest available energy state and that the inner ring had a sort of middling energy excited state level. The very heart of the structure had the lowest energy.

What that meant is that when we photoexcited the outer ring it was very inclined, energy was very inclined to trickle downhill and so the energy would pour into the inner shell and then the energy would further pour all the way into the very center constituent nanoparticle. The way we were able to see this, the way we were able to measure this was that even though we were exciting very brightly luminescent materials in the outer ring, once we coupled them into these called artificial molecules, as we termed them, we were no longer able to see any light coming out of the materials on the outer shell because they transferred it all into the heart of our structure. We'd really built an energy funnel; we kind of build a concentrator where we could illuminate one of these complexes. In fact, we were illuminating many of these complexes at the same time.

We could have an absorption from this complex that was proportional to the number of nanoparticles and these complexes are starting to get quite big so they had quite large absorption. All of the energy would be funneled within the complex because of the architectures that we built; it would all be funneled toward the center material. We realized once we'd done this and once we saw the results which were so striking, I mean the spectra just spoke eloquently to us that we'd really coupled strongly together these nanoparticle structures. We realized that we had really built something that was an analogy with the way in which the photosynthetic apparatus acts in plants. In plants, there exists what are called light harvesting antennas and in these the idea is that if only the regions that actually translated photonic energy into excited states translated at and distorted chemical potential energy if only those reaction centers were present then the efficiency of plants, of leaves, would be very, very low because the absorbance from those centers would be very low.

Instead, plants have evolved systems that function like antennas; they actually kind of extend their reach for light absorption the way an antenna extends its reach for the absorption of electromagnetic radiation and radio waves, they extend this reach and then they all funnel all of that energy down towards the reaction center. We had done the same thing with these multi-length scale structured molecular complexes and we had showed that the efficiency with which we're able to capture and transfer the energy towards our virtual reaction center was extremely high, almost all of the energy ended up right at the heart of these structures.

The other concept that I found very appealing about this work was just that it turned out to be a tunable reaction. This is something that one doesn't find in the photosynthetic apparatus, but we were able to turn on and off this phenomenon. The way we did that is we just changed the pH within these structures or within the solution these structures found themselves in and so at certain pHs the charge on these materials was revealed, it was exposed effectively and because all of the different constituents of these artificial molecules have the same charge they were prone to repel each other. Now we detached them to tightly for them to blow up , but what happened is they took an extended confirmation, they spread out, and so the constituent particles are now far apart and the amount of energy transferred was essentially turned off.

When these were in their extended state that we controlled through the solution conditions, every nanoparticle acted essentially like an independent nanoparticle. There was no energetic coupling, but when we chased the pH in order to enable these structures to collapse or condense into smaller more dense structures, only then did we turn back on this reaction. We made a tunable system, I mean it was always functioning as a light harvester, but we were able to turn on and off its funnel, we were able to turn on and off its propensity to transfer the energy to the reaction center.

Another way to think about it is we made a pretty good sensor for ph. We were able to test the acidity or the basicity of the solution that our nanoparticles were in through the spectral signatures that were coming out of the light that was being emitted from these materials. My final example for this lecture on nanomotifs draws in the work of Angela Belcher, a professor who does incredible stuff at MIT. Professor Belcher has really made her name by merging the world of the biological, including things like viruses with the world of nanoparticles. What she's been able to do is build viruses that have codes that are particularly prone to grow certain nanoparticles on their surfaces and so she's able to engineer materials which take on the shape of the virus because she's able to effectively epitaxially grow semiconductor nanoparticles off of the surfaces of these viruses in a very selective way.

She's further combined that field of semiconductors and material science with the field of genetic engineering in that she's been able to find which proteins displayed on the surface of these viruses allows her to grow with particular success, with particularly high yield these nanostructured materials. It illustrates the fact that when we think about nanomotifs we don't have to limit ourselves to thinking only about say inorganic semiconductors or only about organic materials like Bucky balls and nanotubes, but that we can even get biological entities and even life forms in this case into the game for engineering on many length scales.

To summarize this lecture, we've seen that nanotechnology clearly provides us with this incredible diversity of building blocks. It goes well beyond the quantum dots that we've seen lots of, or rods, but it also through the crystal facet engineering capability it allows us to build structures that are beautiful and fascinating. They remind me a little bit of the shape games that my two year old plays at home where he's able to match his triangle up with the triangle in his puzzle and it's such a diversity of interesting shapes that are beautiful and fascinating to look at. I think we just scratched the surface of what we can do on that front, but we certainly already can do a lot of things.

Once we have these building blocks, the next step in nanotechnology is that we take them, we typically have to functionalize them, we typically have to do something so that they're prone to interact with each other in a certain way. When we do this we're able to make structures that are like tiled mosaics in the case of superlattices or that form extended crystals along a single axis like the oriented attachment wires. Finally, especially when we bring in biology, when we bring in the power of DNA specificity, or when we bring in the capability to build a nanostructure on the code of a virus. We can go higher and higher in the hierarchy of building up these structures. It's really the idea of specificity that enables this remarkable degree of control, all of it engineered from the bottom up.

Using Nanotechnology to Capture Sunlight
Lecture 18

S o far in this course, we've spoken about nanotechnology in relation to information and communication technologies, as well as biology and medicine. But if we think about the biggest challenges facing the world today, another one that immediately comes to mind is energy. How can we capture and store renewable, sustainable, and clean energy? In this first lecture of a series on energy, we'll look at the role of nanotechnology in harnessing and using solar energy.

The Sun and Its Properties

- As you're aware, on the spectrum, the Sun is very hot. That explains the fact that the peak of its emission lies within the visible spectrum. In addition, however, the Sun has a significant spectral signature in the low-energy infrared and near infrared. Opportunity for making more efficient solar cells can be found in making full use of the Sun's broad spectrum.

- Note that the Sun is the opposite of a laser. If it were a laser, we'd have an easier time making solar cells because we could tailor our converters of light energy to 1 specific wavelength.

- It's not true that Earth does not receive sufficient energy from the Sun to meet a significant portion of our energy needs. The total amount of energy reaching the Earth every hour from the Sun is, in fact, enough to meet the world's energy needs for a year. The reason we haven't made fuller use of the solar resource is that we haven't yet found ways to make solar cells that are simultaneously efficient and low cost.

1st- and 2nd-Generation Solar Cells

- Flexible solar cells offer the promise of significant cost reductions as a result of their ease of fabrication. Because they aren't rigid, they can

A significant part of the cost of solar cells—and the impetus for application of nanotechnology to the enhancement of solar cells—is rooftop installation and maintenance.

be made using roll-to-roll processing, similar to the way a newspaper is printed. The flexibility of these cells also facilitates deployment.

- Silicon-based solar cells have their own version of Moore's law, a rate of improvement in the efficiency-to-cost ratio. In this case, the law predicts that it will be many decades before we will be able to transform conventional existing solar technologies into compellingly cost-effective technologies.

- What we need is a new regime, something that will steer us away from merely extrapolative improvement in solar cell efficiency. Neither the 1st generation of solar cells—silicon solar cells—nor the 2nd generation—flexible solar cells—has led to breakthrough improvements in efficiency combined with reductions in cost.

- The opportunity for the 3rd generation of solar cells is to make such better use of the Sun's broad spectrum that we can overcome the limitations of using a solar cell based on a single semiconductor junction.

Absorption inside a Semiconductor

- As we've discussed, when an atom, such as a silicon atom, exists in isolation, it has shells that correspond to the energetic levels that electrons fill up. That accounts for silicon's membership in a particular column of the periodic table. These shells are called discrete energy levels. They are well defined and distinct—only certain energetic transitions are available through each type of atom.

- In a semiconductor material, the behavior of the constituent atoms doesn't matter; what matters is what happens when they come together. When these atoms come together, electrons have some extent; they start to merge and exist over many atoms.
  o Inside a semiconductor, this phenomenon is advantageous. The fact that electrons can propagate as waves along a semiconductor is the basis for good electronic transport.

  o It also leads to the establishment of energy bands. Instead of having discrete steps, there are now ranges of energy where electrons can exist and propagate freely. In between energy bands are chasms that are called band gaps.

- In building a solar cell, the band gap of the semiconductor must match the spectral properties of the Sun reaching the Earth. Silicon has a band gap that is actually very well matched to the emission properties of the Sun.

- It's worth noting that the light sensors we spoke about in an earlier lecture and solar cells have quite a bit in common. Each is responsible for absorbing light, and each typically covers the visible and a bit into the near-infrared wavelengths.

  o Solar cells, however, must work with a preordained intensity—1 sun, the unit of intensity used to describe the brightness of the

Sun. Light sensors typically deal with intensities that are much, much lower.

- o Further, sensors convert information about the physical world into an electronic representation. That means it's acceptable to put a bit of potential across the photodetector. But in solar cells, the goal is to harvest energy—not expend it. We want the device to deliver the Sun's photons to us in the form of an electrical current. Thus, the mode of operation of photovoltaic devices and solar cells is different.

The Heart of a Solar Cell

- In building a solar cell, two materials are brought together that have the same semiconductor band gap but are dissimilar in their affinity for electrons. One of these materials will be rich in electrons, and on the other side of the junction, the other material will be depleted of electrons.

- When we excite a charge on one side of the junction, we now have a propensity for the electrons to go from one side to the other as a result of this built-in cascade, or potential. That asymmetry is one of the crucial conceptual building blocks of any solar cell, because it doesn't involve applying an external electrical bias. The device is one that absorbs light, then funnels the energy that's extracted from that light in a specific direction toward a circuit.

- The existence of the semiconductor band gap means that there will be certain photon energies below which there is no absorption in the semiconductor; these colors of light will simply pass through the solar cell. Others will just barely cross the band gap, leading to absorption. In fact, this is a very efficient region of the spectrum for solar cells because all of the energy in the photon that impinged on the semiconductor is extracted.
  - o As we've said, however, the Sun's spectrum is broad, and there are photons at much shorter wavelengths corresponding to much higher energies where there's an overabundance of energy in each photon.

o   If we could harvest that entire photon energy, we'd be doing well, but the way semiconductors work is that if we excite an electron well into a band, it trickles down to the band edge extremely rapidly.

o   Further, the states within a given band are very well coupled to each other. Thus, at room temperature, we get a rapid loss of energy; photon energy is converted into thermal energy, not something we can harvest inside a photovoltaic device.

- This idea of loss of energy from a given photon is important in understanding the limits on solar cell efficiency. If we were to use a semiconductor with a larger band gap, we'd be able to extract more power, but it would also absorb fewer photons because there would be more photons in the Sun's spectrum that would not be able to breach the band gap.

o   This leads to the choice of a semiconductor band gap that is small enough to enable the harvesting of a good fraction of the Sun's photons but large enough that we don't throw away too much energy.

o   A photovoltaic device based on a single band gap achieves a power conversion efficiency of only about 30%.

Using Nanoscience to Improve Efficiency

- One of the concepts of nanoscience applied to make solar cells more efficient involves a textured solar cell.

- As we've said, silicon is a good absorber of blue photons (the more energetic, visible photons), but it gets much weaker in its absorption of light at longer wavelengths, even those above its band gap. Thus, silicon is called an indirect band gap semiconductor.

- When we try to make an efficient solar cell, we're trying to absorb all of the light across the Sun's spectral region that is above the band gap. With silicon, it's necessary to make a very thick wafer of semiconductor in order to absorb all of the light in the infrared because of silicon's weak optical absorption in the infrared wavelengths. Historically, this has driven up the cost of silicon solar cells.

- But if we roughen the surface of a silicon solar cell, we create the opportunity for multiple passes through this device. Instead of bouncing in and out of the solar cell and losing its chance for absorption, light is typically reflected or scattered in a different direction by the rough surface.

- This phenomenon in which light is trapped inside a semiconductor and given multiple opportunities to bounce around is called light trapping, and there are now low-cost and convenient methods to make nanostructured silicon surfaces that are prone to trapping light.

Suggested Reading

Green, Emery, Hishikawa, and Warta, "Solar Cell Efficiency Tables."

Nelson, *The Physics of Solar Cells.*

Sargent, "Infrared Photovoltaics Made by Solution Processing."

Questions to Consider

1. How abundant is the element silicon? In light of this, what drives the cost of silicon solar cells?

2. How do the time-of-day cycles of the Sun's power incident on a given site on Earth compare with the cycles of our energy consumption? What are the implications of these cycles and their partial alignment on our willingness to pay for solar energy compared to coal-fired plant electricity? What do they mean for the importance of energy transport among jurisdictions in different time zones and climactic zones? What do they mean for the importance of, and our willingness to pay for, electrical energy storage?

Using Nanotechnology to Capture Sunlight
Lecture 18—Transcript

Ted Sargent: We've spoken in the course so far about information and communications technologies and the role that nanotechnology has to play in advancing those. We've spoken of biology, biomolecules, and how nanobiosciences and nanobiotechnology have a real opportunity to play there as well. If you think about some of the big challenges facing the world today another one that comes immediately to mind is the field of energy. How do we find ways to capture energy, store energy? How do we find ways to capture energy in a way that's renewable, that's sustainable, and that's clean?

For the first lecture in this series on energy, we're going to talk about solar energy, in particular how do we harness it, how do we turn it efficiently into electricity, and what role does nanotechnology have to play in that. First let's spend a minute on the Sun and its properties. We need to understand the Sun and its spectrum in order to think about solar energy properly. First on the spectrum, the Sun is very, very hot as you're well aware. That accounts for the fact that the peak of its intensity, the peak of its emission lies within the visible spectrum. We were speaking earlier about thermal imaging and how you can see a warm person against a colder background.

Their wavelengths of emission are much, much, much longer than the Sun's, but it's all based on the same physics called black body emission. In the Sun's case, because it's so hot, about 5- or 6000 degrees centigrade, the Sun peaks its luminescence, its intensity, right in the visible wavelength spectrum. And as we also discussed earlier, that's why our eyes have adapted to see in what we call the visible wavelengths. An important thing to know about the Sun though is that in addition, it has a very significant spectral signature in the infrared and not the very long wavelength, low energy infrared. There's a major portion of Sun energy right up against the visible in what we call the near infrared wavelengths. In fact, only half of the Sun's energy lies in the infrared.

A lot of the opportunity for making more efficient solar cells is going to be to make full use of the Sun's broad spectrum. Another important thing to think about with the Sun is we think about making a good solar cell is the breadth of that spectrum. It's kind of the opposite of a laser. In fact, if the Sun were a laser, which it's not, and it's not going to be, but if the Sun were a laser we'd have an easier time making solar cells because we could tailor our converters of light energy and to electrical energy, we could tailor them to one specific wavelength, we could customize them.

Inevitably this is the source of energy that we have and we have to make good use of all of its spectral components in order to make an efficient solar cell. This will be one of our challenges and I'll call it the broadband challenge. Instead of having a narrow spectrum, we have a broad range of colors, a broad set of bandwidths that we need to deal with.

Let's start by asking kind of the economic question though, the practical question on planet Earth. Far enough from the Sun, is there actually enough energy to meet a significant portion of our energy needs? If you were to look today at the way in which we meet our energy needs and you looked at fossil fuels and look at sources such as coal, look at nuclear, look at hydroelectric, and then you were to look at the portion of energy that's met using solar energy, you'd find it a very, very small percent, much less than 1% of our total energy needs are met today using renewable. You might then ask the question, well is there some fundamental reason for that, is there a lack of sufficient, a gift of solar energy reaching the planet Earth?

The answer to that is very much not. A couple of statistics there, one is if you were to look at the total amount of energy reaching the Earth every hour from the Sun, there's enough energy there to meet all of the world's energy needs for a year. Another way to look at this is if we were to cover the Earth with only a small fraction of the area of Nevada with good solar cells, not perfect, but just good solar cells, we could meet all the world's energy needs. Scaling by time or scaling by area, the same message is given that the solar resource is abundant and the reason why today we're not making fuller use of it relates to the fact that we haven't yet found ways to make solar cells that are simultaneously high in their efficiency and also low in their cost.

That's what we'll talk about much during this pair of lectures is how nanotechnology is enabling us to seek to break compromises between cost and efficiency in solar cells. One more thing just to think about about the Sun before we move into the technology of solar cells is how it's distributed. Obviously at the equator, there's a little bit more intensity of sunlight and then it's also better distributed throughout the year and in some locations at the equator we're also doing better in terms of cloud coverage. The point I want to make with this map of insulation, which is the amount of energy per day or per year reaching different regions of the Earth is that even if you live where I do in Canada, there's actually an abundance of solar energy and if you were to compare us with the amount of solar energy reaching say right at the peak in Saudi Arabia or right near the other locations right near the equator, it turns out that we have maybe 60% as much solar energy as they do at the peak.

Given that there's this huge over-abundance of available solar power, that's a lot. Even those of us who live well into the northern hemisphere have an abundance of solar energy available to us and the challenge is to find the ways to harvest it efficiently and cost effectively. On that point about harvesting it cost effectively, this is where there's been some real advances through nanotechnology in recent years.

Take a look at this picture of a physically flexible solar cell. You can see that it's bent, it's actually on a plastic substrate and one of the great things about this new emerging area of solar cells that aren't rigid, they're not made on panes of glass, but instead they're printed onto flexible backings is that we're able to make them the way you'd print a newspaper. We're able to use roll-to-roll processing in order to make these flexible solar cells in a manner that's very cost effective instead of to being a sequential serial process like the semiconductor industry, you know we talked about these semiconductor wafers that go through lithographic fabrication stepwise. Instead it's a serial process, a continuous process, and these flexible solar cells are offering promise of significant cost reductions as a result of their ease of fabrication.

The other great thing about these being physically flexible is that they're ease of deployment is enhanced as well. A significant part of the cost of getting a solar cells system installed isn't actually in the manufacturing the solar cell or the modules that you put on to your roof, it's in putting it on to your roof. These heavy materials, sometimes there's a need to reinforce the roof as a consequence of trying to install these heavy materials on top of them, so lightweight flexible solar cells that can be readily integrated into a building, in cases even integrated into the building materials themselves offer great promise for reducing this other half of the cost of the solar system, which is often referred to as the balance of systems cost.

Let's take a look at another slice of the kind of Moore's law concept that we spent lot so of time in on technological roadmaps. Silicon based solar cells actually have their own Moore's law as well, a rate of improvement in the efficiency to cost ratio in the solar cells. The challenge though is that if one projects this law, this empirical observation for the rate of improvement of power versus cost in the solar cells. One would predict that it would be many, many decades until we will have based on conventional existing solar technologies until we actually have these turn into compellingly cost effective technologies.

This is where many in the field call for a break through. They call for a need for something that will take us off the just the extrapolative improvement in solar cell efficiency and that will take us into a new regime. Here people talk about generations of solar cell, a first generation such as the silicon solar cells that we will talk about together during this lecture that have offered improvements in efficiency over time in reductions and cost, but not a disruptive change, not a step change. A second generation of solar cells that have been these flexible solar cells that have led to the emergence of the much lower cost approach, but where the efficiencies have not represented improvement over what silicon can get us.

In the vision, and this is much of the vision for the present work ongoing today is for a third generation of solar cells, which doesn't have a compromise anymore, but which instead achieves lower cost and higher efficiency. It's quite easy to see why this point about efficiency is so important. You might until you think about these so-called balance of systems considerations; you might say surely if I can just make my solar cells cheap enough, it's not particularly important that I harvest every photon from the Sun efficiently. The photons from the Sun are free, but when you then think about the fact that the cost of installing and maintaining solar cells, I feel like the cost of ownership and the cost of installation these scale with the area of space that you are filling them into, then ultimately you need very much to think about efficiency because if you don't achieve reasonably high efficiencies from solar cells you may be able to overcome the cost of the cells themselves, but you're not able to overcome these fixed costs associated with the installation and maintenance of the solar cells.

This is the reason why this third generation of solar cells is envisioned to be an area of very big opportunity for the energy sector. To be specific about the challenge that we're posing for the solar energy field, it's the following. It's that using existing technologies which we'll dive into now, we've achieved certain efficiency and improvements, but there are fundamental upper bounds, physical boundaries that we'll describe on how efficient you can ever get a solar cell based on a single semiconductor junction to be. We're starting to get reasonably close to those bounds and so with the incumbent technologies there are limits to our capacity for further improvement.

The opportunity for the third generation solar cells is to take us beyond those limits, is to make such better use of the Sun's broad spectrum that we overcome the traditional limitations on solar cells based on a single semiconductor junction. Let's now dive in and let's talk about the basics of solar cells, how they work, how they relate to some of the materials that we've spoken about in the course together, and then ultimately how we're going to make them better using nanotechnology. Let's now talk about the semiconductors themselves.

We've referred to semiconductors throughout the course. We've spoken of their different spectral absorption characteristics. We've spoken about how they're photon energies that are too small to be absorbed within a semiconductor and others that are sufficiently energetic, but they do get absorbed. Let's put a little bit more formalism or vocabulary around these ideas of absorption inside a semiconductor. I'd actually like to start back at where we began. I'd like to start with atoms, the atoms that make up the semiconductor.

When the elements, let's take a silicon element, silicon atoms for example exist in isolation; they're not part of a semiconductor, but when an atom exists in isolation it has these shells that we talked about, these shells that correspond to the energetic levels that electrons fill up; that account for silicon's particular membership in a particular column of the periodic table. These are what we call discrete energy levels. They're very well defined. They're distinct, only certain transitions, energetic transitions are available say through a silicon atom. In fact, those discrete transitions are much of the basis for how we're able to detect certain chemical elements. It's based on these very specific transitions, optical energetic transitions that are available inside atoms.

In a semiconductor material what matters is not just the behavior of the constituent atoms, what matters is what happens when they come together. When these atoms come together, electrons which as we know are delocalized, have some extent. They start to merge and they start to participate and existing over many atoms. Now that inside a semiconductor is very advantageous. It accounts for the good electronic transport in semiconductors, the fact that as we discussed earlier in the electronics context these electrons can set up waves that have extent, that can propagate along a semiconductor; this is a basis for very good electronic transport inside semiconductors.

What it also leads to is the establishment of what are called energy bands. Instead of having these discrete defined steps now there are ranges, entire ranges of energy where electrons are allowed to exist. They're allowed to propagate freely. Instead of having these original big chasms of energy in which no energetic states existed, now we have in between these bands what's called a band gap. This too is a chasm, but it's not a chasm between just a pair of discrete states, it's a chasm between a band and another band. Now, there is a range of energies, less than this energy gap or this band gap for which photons are not able to excite an electron from a lower band to an upper band. In this case, there's no optical absorption. The material is transparent.

In fact, even this concept exists in things we don't think of traditionally as semiconductors. Diamond, for example, also has a band gap. It just happens to have a very large band gap, which is why it's transparent to our eyes whereas if you were to look at a piece of silicon, to our eyes it looks opaque, that's because it's absorbing all of the light across the visible wavelength spectrum. Its band gap lies out in the infrared. You can see through silicon when you look in the infrared, but you can't if you look inside the visible.

How does this idea of band gap then relate to how we build a solar cell? We need to match the band gap of our semiconductor to the spectral properties of the Sun reaching the Earth to the Sun spectrum. Certain semiconductors, such as silicon, have a band gap that's actually very well matched to the emission properties of the Sun or in particular the Sun spectrum that reaches the Earth. In the case of silicon, it's actually just about the perfect choice. It was not something that we made a conscious choice to make silicon's band gap this way. This is a property of silicon atoms themselves, but it's a reason why we use silicon as a very appropriate semiconductor for making a device, for making a junction that's able to absorb the Sun's light and turn it into electrical power.

In fact on that, it's worth pausing for just a moment and thinking about the relationship between the sensors, the light sensors that we spoke about earlier, and solar cells. They have quite a bit in common. Each is responsible for absorbing light, each typically—in the case of silicon covers—in the visible and a little bit into the near infrared wavelengths. But in the case of the Sun there's a preordained spectrum that we have to work with and there's a preordained intensity. In fact, researchers working in the field don't even speak, usually when they speak of the Sun they don't even speak in terms of the absolute formal units, they talk about one Sun. One Sun is the unit of intensity to describe how bright the Sun is. It's such a universal phenomenon that everybody having to deal with solar energy is conversant in.

In the case of light sensors, typically the intensities that are being dealt with are much, much lower and so they're both doing this optical through electronic conversion, but typically in different ranges of light intensity, many factors of 10 different light intensity. The other thing that is the case of sensors, we are converting information about the physical world into an electronic representation and that means that if we need to apply a little bit of a voltage bias, we need to put a little bit of potential across our photodetector, that's perfectly fine, because we don't mind expending a little bit of power to run our sensor integrated circuit, but the name of the game in solar energy is in harvesting energy. When our goal is to harvest energy we're looking for this device to take the Sun's power, its photons, and to deliver to them to us in the form of an electrical current which can be driven across a load so there's some voltage as well. The mode of operation of photovoltaic devices and solar cells is different as a result of that need to transfer power from the Sun into some either system where we want to charge our car or to some means of storage, such as the case of a battery or a fuel cell, topics that I'll talk about a little bit later when we get to the field of storage.

Let's dive in now and look at the heart of a solar cell a little bit. This is called a p-n junction solar cell. Some of details in the nomenclature aren't important, but what's key is to understand that when we build really any solar cell, we bring together two materials typically having the same semiconductor properties, the same semiconductor band gap that are dissimilar in their affinity for electrons. One of these materials will be rich in electrons. We will achieve that richness of electrons by introducing selectively a certain number of impurities that add electrons to the lattice, that donate electrons to participate in conduction.

On the other side of this junction, we will utilize a material that is depleted of electrons and so now we have a structure which is electron rich on one side, electron poor of the other, and we've created the potential for a cascade. When we excite a charge on one side of this junction we now have a propensity for the electrons to want to go from one side to the other as a result of this built in cascade; this built in potential as it's called. That asymmetry is one of the crucial conceptual building blocks of any solar cell. The reason is that we're not going to be plying an external electrical bias. We don't get to have an applied potential on this device because we're trying to harvest energy. Instead we've built a device that likes to absorb light and then funnel the energy that's extracted from that light in a specific direction towards a circuit.

The other point that we need to think about when we think about solar cells and their use of the spectrum and the limits on their efficiency is that as we've discussed because of this concept of a semiconductor band gap there will be certain photon energies below which there's no absorption so these colors of light simply pass through our solar cell and there will be others that just barely cross the band gap, they just barely cross this chasm. These will lead to absorption and, in fact, this is a very efficient region of the spectrum for these solar cells because all of the energy in the photon that impinged upon the semiconductor is utilized, is extracted from this.

However, a Sun spectrum is broad and there are photons at much shorter wavelengths corresponding to much higher energies where there's an overabundance of energy in each photon. Now, if we could take that entire photon energy and harvest it, we'd be in great shape, but the way semiconductors work is that if you excite an electron well into a band then extremely rapidly it trickles down right to the band edge. We say that these states that arise from silicon atoms coming together and forming these bands, we say that these states within a given band are very well coupled to each other and so very rapidly at room temperature we get a loss of energy and it's just converted into thermal energy, not something that we harvest inside a photovoltaic device.

Now this idea of loss within a band, loss of energy from a given photon, is very important in understanding the limits on solar cell efficiency because you might say from this loss consideration well okay let's go find a semiconductor having a larger band gap. They're available, and then we won't throwaway as much energy, we'll be able to deliver more voltage to our device. Ultimately we'll be able to extract more power. However, if we were to do that we would also absorb fewer photons because we would've made a larger band gap and there would be more photons in the Sun's spectrum that were not able to breach that band gap.

This lead essentially to a tradeoff. It leads to our choosing a semiconductor band gap that is small enough that we harvest many of the Sun's, a good fraction of the Sun's photons, but large enough that we don't do too much throwing away of energy from the juiciest, from the most energetic of these photons that come in. But, it is a tradeoff. As a result when one works with a semiconductor device, a photovoltaic device that is based on a single band gap, a single type of semiconductor, one is limited not to 100 or 97 or 95% overall power conversion efficiency, but instead the upper bound on the efficiency with which one can extract energy from one Sun intensity from the amount of intensity reaching the Earth's surface is closer to 30%. It turns out for the right price that's not a bad efficiency either, but it's important to think about the limitations of solar cells based on a single choice of semiconductor and how they arise from making this choice to work with a material that has a fixed band gap and that leads to some loss of energy through this thermalization process within the bands.

The final introductory concept that I'd like to spend a moment on with respect to solar cells is how we think about this efficiency in terms of a current delivered and in terms of a voltage. It turns out that the power, the electrical power that can be delivered say to your car for charging or to a fuel cell or to a battery, the power of this is given by the product, multiplied together, the product of the current and the voltage and so it's very important in solar cells to get as much current as possible and to get as much voltage as possible. It's really managing this trade between those two through the choice of band gap that leads to the optimal band gap device and leads to the best management of this tradeoff.

I'd now like to start in and talk about some nano concepts that allow us to make solar cells more efficient. The first one of these I'd like to talk about relates to the management of light, to the management of photons. In fact, these concepts are already being utilized in solar cells that can be purchased today that are available. One of these concepts it's actually quite simple to think about in terms of fabrication. It involves trying to make a rough surface, taking to make a textured solar cell. The reason for doing this is the following. Within silicon—we talked about this in the context of photodetectors—silicon is a reasonably good absorber. It's actually a very good absorber of blue photons of the more energetic visible photons, but it gets much weaker in its absorption of light as we go to longer wavelengths, even those above its band gap. The name for this phenomenon is that silicon's an indirect band gap semiconductor.

When we try to make an efficient solar cell clearly we're trying to absorb all of the light across the Sun's spectral region that we are absorbing at all, anything that's above the band gap. It turns out to be necessary in silicon in particular to make a very thick wafer of semiconductor in order to absorb all of the light in the infrared because of this weak optical absorption that occurs in the infrared wavelengths. That is one of the things that's driven up the cost of silicon solar cells historically, is the need for a very thick quantity of very,

very pure, very, very high temperature fabricated material. What happens when we roughen the surface of a silicon solar cell is that instead of light simply passing into the cell and then if it see a mirror bouncing back out.

We instead create the opportunity for multiple passes through this device. Light is able to pass in and then it sees this roughened surface, it's like it sees a rough mirror, and instead of turning right back around and bouncing back out of our solar cell and losing its chance for absorption, it's typically reflected or scattered off in a different direction. Instead of just leveraging the thickness of the device for absorption if we can couple in and then couple sideways we're able to increase the interaction life. We're able to overcome this weakness in the rate of absorption that occurs within silicon by using a textured substrate. It turns out that the exact shape that you want to do this with is actually very important. You want to think about the angles and even the sharpness of the angles that are used for scattering of light.

In fact, this phenomenon where we get light into one of these semiconductor materials and then we get it trapped in there and we give it multiple opportunities to bounce around. It's called exactly that. It's called light traffic. Many interesting techniques have been devised in order to achieve this. Of course, if you had to make these spiky structures every one exactly perfectly the same as all the others; that would be a challenging and probably a costly semiconductor patterning and etching process that would start to look like what we do in microelectronics and nanoelectronics, but for solar cells we're trying to make things that are big. We're trying to make things that can be spread across a roof and do so in low cost. Fortunately a number of techniques have been discovered to make structured silicon surfaces without having to go in and actively pattern every little spike, every little valley in order to make one of these light trapping structures.

The techniques actually uses a chemical etching where silicon has these particular directions, like all crystals, silicon has these particular directions known as facets; these are like the facets of a diamond that you can see. When you introduce a chemical etchant, they can chemically etch in a particular direction. They could etch along a particular facet and so they're naturally prone to taking a planar surface and starting to carve it into these triangles, into these hills and valleys or spiky mountaintops and valleys.

As a result, there are now very low cost and convenient methods to make nanostructured silicon surfaces that are very prone to want to trap light.

We've covered the basics of solar cells. We've covered the huge opportunity that solar energy harvesting represents. We've talked about the underlying principles of matching the behavior of a semiconductor used to capture light with the broad solar spectrum and we've just started to touch in on how nanotechnology can be our friend in enabling the efficient capture of energy from the Sun. In our next lecture, we're going to dive in further and really spend time on how we're able to take advantage of the nanoworld, control over the coupling of photons to electrons inside semiconductors to make solar cells that break the historic compromise between cost and performance.

Photons to Electricity—Nano-Based Solar Cells
Lecture 19

This lecture continues our exploration of the fascinating ways in which nanotechnology can be used to make solar cells that are more efficient and more cost effective. Here, we'll look at plasmonics, tandem- and triple-junction solar cells, solar cells made with organic materials and with colloidal quantum dots, and dye-sensitized solar cells that use dye to achieve light absorption.

Plasmonics
- In an earlier lecture, we saw that plasmonics provided a convenient method for conveying optical information and confining light to very small regions. The basis for this was small particles of metal that act like stepping stones across a pond or a river for electromagnetic waves.

- If you're the river in this conception, those stones look like scattering centers. In photovoltaics, there's an emerging effort to use metal nanoparticles—plasmonic particles—to scatter light in various directions, similar to the function achieved with light trapping.

- Nanotechnologists know very well how to synthesize metal nanoparticles dispersed in solution into paintable materials and simply coat them onto things. This provides a ready means of making devices that have a greater capacity to enhance the absorption of light using nanoscale interactions between light and, in this case, metals.

Tandem- and Triple-Junction Solar Cells
- In the last lecture, we spoke about the limitations of solar cells that have a single junction. One obvious solution is to make a semiconductor device that has many different band gaps. In fact, before the advent of the latest solution process approaches, there was much work on tandem- and triple-junction solar cells.

- Semiconductors with different band gaps were grown on top of one another. These cells offered an advantage in terms of efficiency because they allowed a 1st cell, with a large band gap, to harvest the visible portion of the Sun's spectrum in a way that provided a good deal of voltage. Then, they stepped down to an intermediate band gap layer and a small band gap layer. These produced lower voltages, using the photons that made it through the visible band gap cell.

- The design of these devices was complicated by the need to ensure that the current generated within each layer is the same (current matching). The design of traditional triple-junction devices had an added complication: the fact that different materials have different lattice constants, the characteristic spacing among the atoms. If each material is to be a perfect crystal, then how can they be integrated with one another without slips?
  - The answer is that they can't, resulting in places where the solar cell loses efficiency or reliability.

  - In making these stacked solar cells, researchers were forced to come up with even more complex material combinations, using 3 or 4 constituent atoms in very specific ratios. This approach leads to costly solar cells.

  - Such costly cells have a place in concentrated photovoltaics, where optical methods are used to focus light from the Sun onto very small solar cells. However, the lenses for focusing inside these devices add to the cost, as does the need to ensure the cells track the Sun over the course of the day.

Organic Solar Cells
- The field of organic photovoltaics seeks to marry some of the desirable properties of organic materials with the urgent need to make cost-effective solar cells. One of the obvious advantages of using an organic approach would be in making solar cells that are physically flexible.

- The synthesis of organic molecules is well developed. Those who work in synthetic organic chemistry know how to make a broad swath of molecules designed to achieve the precise functions desired in photovoltaics.

- In organic photovoltaics, the twin goals are strong absorption and conduction of energy, but organic molecules are traditionally thought of as insulators, not conductors.
  - Researchers have found ways to use the bonds they can engineer along chains of polymers to achieve delocalization of electrons; electrons can be everywhere along these chains.

  - Essentially, this is a way to replicate the good qualities of semiconductors in an organic system and a powerful platform for thinking about how to make low-cost solar cells.

- The other component of making a good solar cell is to think about the way it utilizes the Sun's spectrum. There are some advantages to the organics on this front, as well.
  - In particular, researchers are able to design and define the optical resonances of these materials to lie somewhere in between the properties of individual atoms and the properties of semiconductors.

  - As a consequence, there is an extremely strong absorption of light in these designer molecules, which means that a very thin layer of these materials can still achieve complete absorption of light.

- The fact that this absorption is concentrated into a rather narrow band implies that we are not necessarily addressing the Sun's full spectrum. But that can be achieved through mixing semiconductors that have different properties—through the realization of tandem- and triple-junction solar cells. Each layer in these cells consists of a different organic molecule, each tailored to managing a particular portion of the Sun's spectrum.

The Donor-Acceptor Junction

- The concept at work in organic photovoltaics that was quite distinctive when it was first introduced is the donor-acceptor junction.

- As we saw, a device can be made out of a single type of semiconductor having 2 different types of impurities: an electron richness and an electron impoverished quality.

- Organic molecules tend not to be rich in free electrons, but the energy levels in 2 different molecules can be matched up such that there is an asymmetry. The electrons generated in a 1st class of molecules known as the donor can be efficiently donated to an adjacent molecule that functions as the acceptor.

- Essentially, when light comes into these solar cells, it generates an exciton—an excited particle—and that particle is split apart and pulled into the acceptor molecules, giving it a much longer lifetime for extraction.

- The reason it's important to extract these energetic charge carriers efficiently in organic solar cells is that the transport properties— the mobilities—of electrons inside these materials are much lower than in perfectly regular semiconductors. It's thus necessary to find a way station for these excited charge carriers rather than have their energy disappear before the charges can be extracted.

- Researchers have made naturally interpenetrating fingers of donor and acceptor material to enhance the absorption of light and to ensure that energetically favorable interfaces are readily available for the extraction of charge carriers. Further, work has been done to enable these cells to continually extract electrons into the acceptor without producing islands, that is, isolated regions where electrons can't be extracted.

- In donor-acceptor junctions, one of the stars of the show is the buckyball. This molecule, which looks like a soccer ball, participates in the light absorption and extraction process.

Collodial Quantum Dot Solar Cells

- As we've seen in earlier lectures, quantum dots are semiconductor particles that have a band structure we can tune or define through the quantum size effect. In the context of solar cells, that spectral tunability enables us to change whether these particles absorb visible or infrared light.

- With tandem solar cells, we had to find ways to match their lattices—the spacing of their atoms—which led to increased costs. With quantum dot solar cells, we are able to choose the band gaps through the quantum size effect.

- In working with semiconductor nanoparticles, we don't have to confine ourselves to quantum dots; we can also make elongated structures—rods—in which there is a clear preference for flow along the long axis. This is a perfect semiconductor crystal that's compatible with the delocalization of electrons along its length. These materials have attracted great interest because of their enhanced electronic transport properties.

- Coupling nanoparticles together and packing them into a superlattice shows promise for achieving the progress needed to make colloidal quantum dot solar cells highly efficient. These lattices have multiple length scales, each of which is important. The smaller length scale achieves the desired semiconductor and transport properties, while the larger one allows the propagation of electrons.

Dye-sensitized Solar Cells

- Dye-sensitized solar cells achieve light absorption using a dye, such as what you'd find in food coloring. These molecules are very good at absorbing light, but on their own, they are not conductors. The dyes must be put on essentially a sponge of semiconductor that is good at transporting electrons.

- The surface area of the sponge ensures that every pigment is in immediate proximity to an electron acceptor that can extract the electrons. This concept is similar to the interpenetration of materials we saw in the organic solar cells. Both ideas take advantage of our capacity to maximize surface areas for beneficial effects in engineering nanomaterials.

- Some of these exciting new technologies are being commercialized, and some of their commercial applications are taking advantage of the attractive properties of physically flexible materials. We can go beyond just thinking about installing these materials on rooftops or integrating them into building materials to imagining solar backpacks or tents or mobile phones in which we're able to achieve energy harvesting.

Suggested Reading

Green, Emery, Hishikawa, and Warta, "Solar Cell Efficiency Tables."

Nelson, *The Physics of Solar Cells.*

Sargent, "Infrared Photovoltaics Made by Solution Processing."

Questions to Consider

1. Nanoparticles are small, yet solar cells must be large. What advantages do nanomaterials offer in solar energy harvesting, and what new challenges do they present?

2. What are the advantages and disadvantages of a solar cell that, like dye-sensitized cells, requires the use of a liquid electrolyte to make one of the key electrical connections inside the solar cell?

Photons to Electricity—Nano-Based Solar Cells
Lecture 19—Transcript

Ted Sargent: We've spoken about some of the fascinating ways in which nanotechnology can be used to try to make solar cells that are more efficient, more cost effective, ideally both. We touched on one concept, the photon trapping concept, in which it's possible to capture light inside a solar cell, give it multiple opportunities for absorption. It turns out that there's another way in which we can use nanoparticles for a similar purpose and it's a very convenient one from the point of view of fabrication.

Let's think back to when we talked about plasmons or plasmonics. At the time, we were talking about ways of communicating information across a chip using light. Plasmonics provided a particularly convenient means of conveying information, optical information, and confining light to very small regions. The basis for this was particles of metal that are very small (10–100 nanometers), and we talked about how it was a bit like stepping on stones across a pond or across a river. Well now think of being perpendicular to those stones and think of being the river. Those stones now look like scattering centers if you're the river. Well in photovoltaics there's an emerging effort where people are trying to use metal nanoparticles, these plasmonic particles, in order to scatter light in various directions. This is analogous in its function to what we do with light trapping. Now instead of using the spiky silicon interface in order to give light multiple chances to bounce around inside our device, instead we send light in from the Sun and it scatters off in multiple directions off of these scattering points that are the metal nanoparticles.

What's so convenient is that nanotechnologists know very well now how to synthesize metal nanoparticles, colloidal particles, dispersed in the solution into solvent paintable materials and simply coat them onto things. It provides a very ready means of making devices that have a greater capacity to enhance the absorption of light using nanoscale interactions between light, and in this case, metals. We spoke quite a bit about the limitations of making a solar cell having a single junction, having one semiconductor type and so the obvious solution there is to make a semiconductor device that has many different band gaps.

In fact, before the advent of the latest solution process nanotechnology based approaches there had been much work on what are called tandem and triple-junction solar cells and they were very effective in making very efficient devices. The concept looked like this. Semiconductors of different types having different band gaps were grown on top of each other. For example, we were able to use compound semiconductors like the gallium arsenide that we heard about in our lecture on optical communications and grow semiconductors with different compositions. One layer could be made with gallium arsenide, another with indium arsenide. These different compositions led to different band gaps.

These cells offered a real advantage in terms of the efficiency of the device because they allowed us to make a first cell—the one closest to the light—that produced the absorption of visible light primarily. The visible light, as we discussed, had very energetic photons in it and we used a large band gap in this material. We were able to harvest this portion of the Sun's spectrum in a way that gave us a lot of voltage corresponding to the abundant energy in those photons. Only then did we step down to an intermediate band gap layer and then to a small band gap layer. These produce lower voltages, but they mocked up the photons that made it through the visible band gap cell.

Now the design of these tandem and triple-junction solar cells is not trivial at all. They're passing a single current throughout this entire structure, but their voltages are adding up. They need to be designed in such a way that the current generated within each layer is the same. This challenge is known as current matching. It's a well-known are, but it complicates the design of the devices. In the traditional triple-junction devices there's an added complication. It's the following, we're trying to grow a perfect crystal having a single lattice with a defined spacing amongst the atoms, but we're doing it with different materials. Every different material has its own lattice constant; it has its own characteristic spacing amongst the atoms.

If each one of these will be a perfect crystal than how can they be integrated with one another without having slips, without say the gallium arsenide having a slip in its lattice periodicity relative to the different periodic indium arsenide material? Well the answer is that actually we can't and that these slips are a problem. They create interfaces dangling bond, unpassivated states, they're places where we can lose efficiency or lose reliability in our solar cell. As a result, in making these stacked solar cells researchers were forced to come up with even more complex materials combinations using three or four constituent atoms in very specific ratios such that the atoms got spaced out and could be matched. This is referred to as lattice matching. It's effective, but you can imagine that the approach leads to costly solar cells.

It turns out that there is a venue in which these multi-junction solar cells, even the very costly ones, can be used very effectively. The reason cost ends up being a problem, of course, in solar cells is if we need to have a very large area solar cell, which is normally how we do things. If we cover an entire roof or a building with these kinds of materials it will be very sensitive to very large high costs per surface area. However, there's a field within solar photovoltaics known as concentrating photovoltaics in which we use optical methods in order to focus light down from the Sun onto a very small solar cell. In fact, we're able to achieve very high concentrations in this manner so instead of operating at one Sun, we can operate at 100 or 400 or 500 suns. Now because we've focused the light down onto an individual solar cell that's much, much smaller than the area from which we're catching our photons we can get away with making a solar cell that has higher cost.

These very efficient, very good and the spectra utilization solar cells do have a place and it's in concentrated photovoltaics. Here though the challenge now on the cost front becomes twofold. The first is that these concentrated photovoltaics have these optical systems that need to focus all the light down onto these solar cells so there's an additional element. Now we're starting to use some optics and lenses for focusing inside these devices and that adds some cost.

The other component is that now we're looking up at the Sun and we're focusing it down to a spot where if we were to tilt our solar cell a bit relative to the Sun or more likely if the Sun is passing overhead as a function of time of day and therefore it's a different angle relative to our device, unless we orient our concentrating optical solar cell, just right relative to the Sun's rays, we won't end up focusing onto our solar cell, we'll be off focus. As a result, these concentrated solar cells also require tracking so that they end up having to follow the Sun over the course of the day and follow its angle. This can be done.

It also creates additional complications in terms of cost and reliability and maintenance of these installations. What we would love to do is to be able to achieve these triple junction solar cell efficiencies, these very, very high performance devices, but in a manner that doesn't require the cost and the complexity associated with growing compound semiconductors on top of each other in this lattice matched fashion .It is at this area where we seek high spectral utilization efficiency, full addressing of the Sun's broad spectrum, but we combine it with low cost that some of the most exciting work in nanotechnology based solar cells is ongoing today.

I'll now talk about examples of broad areas in which people are really pushing the boundaries on using the Sun's broad spectrum better through the use of nanotechnology. The first of these is called organic or polymer solar cells. In my lectures throughout this course, you've heard a lot more about what we call inorganic materials. You've heard about semiconductors like silicon and gallium arsenide, the bases for electronics and for optical electronics and optical communications, glass as well, and it's more from Shana and her discussions of biology, biomaterials, and biomolecules that you've heard about carbon containing organic molecules.

This field of organic photovoltaics seeks to marry some of the very desirable properties of the organic materials with the urgent need to make solar cells that are much more cost effective. You could immediately think of one of the obvious advantages moving through an organic approach to making solar cells which is that they're more compatible with physical flexibility. This is also the way we think about the biological world, that it's bendier than some of these rigid silicon based solar cells and that's absolutely correct. The early work on making physically flexible solar cells with their attractive properties in terms of low cost to manufacture, convenient deployment has come from this field of organic polymer solar cells.

The organic molecules themselves, this field of synthesis of organic molecules, is incredibly well-developed. It's the same field that has given us the capacity to synthesize all sorts of new drugs in the biomedical

341

applications. It's the same field that has allowed us to generate polymers that we use throughout our life that are integrated into fabrics and that are used to create synthetic rubber so this field of organic synthesis is incredibly well-developed. People who do synthetic organic chemistry know how to make a really broad swath of molecules designed to achieve the precise functions that we desire.

In organic photovoltaics, the name of the game of course is strong absorption, but also conduction of energy, conduction of electrons along the chains. Here researchers discovered a number of decades ago means of making these organic molecules, which traditionally we thought of as insulators, we hadn't thought of them as electronic materials capable of conduction. They found ways of using the bonds that they could engineer along these chains of polymers and of achieving the delocalization of electrons where electrons could be everywhere along these chains. Essentially they found ways to replicate the good qualities of semiconductors and replicate them within this organic system.

What they had done is figured out a way to molecule that could be scaled up, synthesized in a beaker, passed on to a solid substrate, printed on with an inkjet printer, but where the molecule could function as a semiconductor. This obviously is a powerful platform for thinking about how to make low cost solar cells. The other component of course of making a good solar cell is to think about the way it utilizes the Sun's spectrum. There are some advantages to the organics on this front as well. In particular, researchers are able to design and define the function, the optical resonances of these materials to lie somewhere in between the properties of individual atoms and the properties of semiconductors.

Recall that in the case of individual atoms we have these very discrete levels; in the case of semiconductors we spread those levels out into bands. Well the organic molecules are kind of in between those two length scales spatially, but typically a few nanometers in size and these very, very well-defined tight discrete energy levels characteristic of the atoms researchers are able to translate those over to the molecular scale and to keep more of the remnants of these discrete levels. As a consequence, there's an incredible strength associated with the optical transitions that occur within these organic molecules. There is an extremely strong absorption of light in these designer molecules and as a result one can put down and incredibly thin amount of these materials and still achieve very complete absorption of light.

For example, if for silicon to achieve complete absorption across the Sun's full spectrum can require 100 micrometers of material, a large thickness of semiconductor, some of these organic molecules can achieve within their bandwidth of absorption, can achieve substantially complete absorption within a few dozen nanometers. They're incredibly strong absorbers; they're incredibly black. Now, the fact that we've concentrated this absorption into this rather narrow band of course implies that we're not necessarily addressing the Sun's full spectrum and so we need a strategy in organic photovoltaics to address the Sun's full spectrum properly.

Here it's through the mixing of semiconductors having different properties or it's through the realization of tandem and triple-junction solar cells where each one of these layers consists of a different organic molecule, each tailored to managing a particular portion of the Sun's spectrum that were able to leverage the very strong absorption of these materials and overcome this limitation of a somewhat more narrow band behavior. Now there's some very beautiful physics that people working on organic solar cells have also been able to engineer. Really solar cells operate on a somewhat different physical principle from the classical junction device, the diode, that's the basis for all electronics and that's been translated into photo diode for light sensing and the photovoltaic device for traditional inorganic semiconductor based photovoltaics.

The concept at work in organic photovoltaics that was quite distinctive when it was introduced a little while ago in the 1990s is what's called a donor acceptor junction. Here rather than making the semiconductor device out of a single type of semiconductor having two different types of impurities in electron richness and in electron impoverished quality, instead these organic molecules tend not to be rich in free electrons. They tend to be very engineerable such that the energy levels in two different molecules can be matched up such that there is an asymmetry. We've talked about the need for an asymmetry to make a good solar cell. They can be matched up such that electrons generated in a first class of molecules known as the donor are very efficiently donated to an adjacent molecule that functions as the acceptor.

Essentially when light comes in inside these solar cells it generates what's known as an exciton, so an excited particle, and that particle ends up being split apart and pulled into the acceptor molecules and therefore given a much longer lifetime for its extraction of these solar cells. The reason it's so important to extract these energetic charge carriers efficiently in organic solar cells is that the transport properties, the mobility's of electrons inside these materials is much lower than it is in these perfectly regular semiconductors such as silicon or gallium arsenide. It's important to find a way station for these excited charge carriers rather than have their energy disappear on us before the charges can be extracted. It's important to give ourselves a little bit more time to get the energy out of these devices and the donor acceptor junction gives us that.

There's also some beautiful engineering that's been done with those donor acceptor junctions now not so much in the energetic domain as I was just describing, but in the spatial domain. Researchers figured out how to ensure that the donor and the acceptor could interpenetrate. The problem if they just made a plane or interface between the donor and the acceptor was that they weren't able to make that device thick enough such that it absorbed all the light and yet also led to the efficient extraction of the energetic electrons. When they made interpenetrating fingers of donor and acceptor material, they were able to increase the amount of each material that was included which was very useful in enhancing the absorption of light, but at the same time ensure that wherever an excited electron was generated within the donor the electrons were very close to an escape hatch. They were very close to one of these energetically favorable interfaces that led to the safe extraction of the charge carrier.

What's so beautiful about these bulk heterojunctions is that to create these nanostructured materials, nanostructured on the scale of 10s, 20s, 30s of nanometers it wasn't necessary to consciously go in and manipulate matter defying formal fingers using some kind of template or an etching process, but instead the chemists designed these materials such that they liked to segregate. It's such that when they just mix them together and coated them down that material A was inclined to form a phase of its own and material B formed an interpenetrating phase so that they naturally segregated into these kinds of fingers. There's much work that's been done to get these fingers to have these defined properties that are so desired.

Clearly fingers are good, but islands are bad. If we have isolated regions of these organic materials we're not going to be able to extract the electrons out of them. Much beautiful work has gone into both building these materials such that the face segregation occurs on the right length scale and leads to a continuous junction where we're able to continually extract the electrons into our acceptor while at the same time not producing undesired islanding. Solar cells have been made using these organics that stack multiple junctions on top of each other. In fact, there's been some very nice work in the recent years in which every single layer from the electrodes, the conductors, through to the semiconductors, through to the junction that brings together the two or eventually it'll be three and more junctions inside one of these solar cells are all made by spin coating, by solution processing.

This is now compatible with the realization of organic solar cells that are very low in cost and yet through the tandem concept, through the better spectral harvesting compatible also with higher efficiencies. Another way that nano enters into the organic solar cell is through the constituent materials. In those donor acceptor junctions, one of the stars of the show is the Bucky ball. This molecule which looks just like a soccer ball is nanometers in size, is responsible for participating in the light absorption and extraction process within these organic solar cells. The Bucky balls have a very tunable electronic band structure and researchers figured out how to make them soluble in their own native state, the Bucky balls are not actually soluble in convenient solvents, but researchers were able to attach molecules to the surface of these Bucky balls to make them soluble in convenient solvents in order to render them compatible with the attractive features of making an organic solar cell this way.

Let's move on to another area that gets back more to the inorganic, to these traditional crystalline semiconductors, and that happens to be the area in which I also work. I work in the field of colloidal quantum dot solar cells; that's what my research group at the university focuses on. We've seen these quantum dots before in some different contexts throughout the course. As a refresher, they're semiconductor particles. They're a few nanometers in size and they are inorganic crystals so they're semiconductor particles that have this band structure that we get to tune or define through the quantum size effect, through the size of the particles.

That spectral tunability is one of the features that we've used in various applications throughout. For example, in our discussions of sensing the world through imaging, we've talked about how we're able to tune which colors of light these semiconductor particles absorb in order to see within spectral regimes that are previously unavailable to us using traditional semiconductor approaches. In the context of solar cells, this tunability is also extremely attractive and important. By tuning the size of these particles, by changing their band gap, we change whether they absorb visible or infrared or longer wavelengths of infrared light.

One of the things that's so appealing in working with these quantum dots as our particle is that, if you think back to the tandem solar cell that we were talking about earlier in today's lecture, there we had to find different materials of different compositions to stack on top of each other. We had to find some kind of way to match their lattices, match the spacing of their atoms; well that was what led to cost and to our discussion of concentrated photovoltaics, which is essentially trying to overcome the challenges and the cost of those devices. When we work with quantum size effect tunability we can take a single semiconductor technology based on a single composition of semiconductor. We can master the synthesis and then the processing of devices based on this single semiconductor having a single composition and then through the quantum sized effect, through how we change the recipe at the time of the synthesis of these particles. Through that method alone, we are able to choose the band gaps.

With these semiconductor nanoparticles, we have an avenue towards making tandem and triple-junction solar cells based on colloidal quantum dots. Just recently, we reported the ability to make a solar cell where the band gaps of the constituent junctions were chosen purely through the quantum size effect to be optimal for the two junctions of a tandem cell. This proved the concept that we can really working with a single material, we can utilize quantum effects to gain dexterity in our control over the band gap without actually having to change the material itself, just with a little tweak to our recipe.

One of the beautiful things about these semiconductor nanoparticles is we don't have to limit ourselves to a single shape. We don't have to confine ourselves just to these quantum dots, the semiconductor nanoparticles, but we're also able to make elongated structures which we refer to as rods. In these rods, there's clearly a preference for flow along one axis, the long axis. Here we just have a perfect semiconductor crystal that's very compatible with the delocalization of electrons along its length. These materials have shown, have attracted great interest, because of their enhanced electronic transport properties.

Of course, when you think about what will happen when you take some of these rods out of solution and you coat them onto a substrate the most likely thing is the rods will lie down in the substrate and that is exactly what happens. Now their transport is in the plane, but in all the solar cells that I've been describing, the vertical direction is the one in which we need to extract out the electrons. We need some kind of technique to allow these light absorbing materials to stand up. There is some beautiful work in which rather than just making rods researchers were able to make tetrapods. One had little pointy up rods with little legs that sat on the ground like little stools and that became oriented as a result of this geometry. It combined the fact now that electrons were able to flow along these longitudinal directions through the rods sticking up and then through the legs of the stool, it combined that with this orientation such that now the direction in which the transport of electrons was the best, was also the direction in which transport of electrons was most urgently needed.

Another area in which quantum solids have seen great promise and great progress recently is in making solar devices and making materials for solar cells. We take these quantum particles, we take advantage of their size effect tunability, and we pack them the way eggs are packed into a carton into what we call a superlattice. We've seen some of these images actually before when we were speaking of nanomotifs. They're beautiful and they're also a fascinating exploration in engineering on multiple length scale because the things that we're building these superlattices from are themselves crystals.

We have ordered oriented atoms on the scale of a half nanometer repeating themselves again like eggs in a carton to make up a nanoparticle say 3 nanometers in diameter, but here in this transmission electron micrograph we see many of these identical particles ordering, self-organizing into a perfect lattice themselves.

We have multiple length scales of order and each of those length scales is important. The first one, the smaller length scale, the arraying of the atoms ends up achieving the semiconductor properties and the transport properties that we desire. Then the second, the larger length scale of a few nanometers, well that's the characteristic wavelength of electrons. That's the length scale over which we need electrons to propagate. Whereas in the initial work on colloidal quantum dot solar cells, the electron transport has been rather poor and has limited the performance of these solar cells. There's a great sense of optimism the transport associated with coupling these nanoparticles together and packing them into a superlattice can achieve the rest of the progress needed to make these colloidal quantum dot solar cells highly efficient as well as very convenient to manufacture and correspondingly low in cost.

Finally, I'd like to talk about a third class of so-called third generation solar cells. These are called dye-sensitized solar cells. Dye-sensitized solar cells are really a fascinating convergence of some traditional fields of chemistry like the electrochemistry that's the basis for batteries with solar energy harvesting. The way in which they work is they achieve light absorption using a dye, using a pigment, such as what you'd find in food coloring or to dye clothing with. These, of course, are very good, these molecules are very good at the absorption of light, but on their own they're not conductors. The insights from the field of dye-sensitized solar cells is the dyes have been put on essentially a sponge in the inner surfaces of a sponge of a semiconductor material that's very good at transport of electrons.

In fact, the way in which these are built is that this sponge is infiltrated so the huge surface area of this sponge, a transparent sponge, is used in order to make sure that every pigment, every dye is directly coupled immediately and in immediate proximity to an electron acceptor that can extract the electrons out. The concept actually has a relationship to the bulk heterojunction that we were talking about in the case of the organic solar cells in which we had there this interpenetration of materials. In both cases, what we're really taking advantage of is our capacity when engineering with nanomaterials to maximize surface areas for beneficial effects in this case. In this case, it's to achieve very strong absorption and yet to ensure that every one of our dyes, every one of our pigment molecules is coupled to an electron acceptor.

In fact, there's another way in these devices to take advantage of the nanoworld, which is instead of making a sponge with the kind of packing of spheres together and then tacking the dyes onto that, there's been recent work in which one makes a bunch of fingers, an array of fingers, instead of nanowires, and the dye is placed onto that, is coupled to that. Instead of going through a tortuous path of transport through this set of spheres that are loosely coupled at their junctures, at their points of contact. On has a straight line, one has a direct avenue towards the extraction of photogenerated electrons that are produced inside the pigments, but then are transferred to these elevator shafts that directly transmit the electrons out of the device, the intent being to achieve a maximum of efficiency in the extraction of those electrons.

Some of these exciting new technologies are being commercialized and some of their commercial applications are taking advantage of the attractive properties of physically flexible materials. We can go beyond just thinking about installing these materials on rooftops or integrating them into building materials. Those concepts are exciting in themselves, but things like solar backpacks or mobile phones or tablet devices that are self-charging or tents in which we're able to achieve energy harvesting. These are all on the near horizon for taking advantage of new breakthroughs in the conversion of energy from the Sun into practical electricity.

Nanotechnology for Storing Energy
Lecture 20

W e've spoken about harvesting energy from the Sun, but another essential part of managing energy, especially renewable energy, is storing it. In this lecture, we'll talk about how nanotechnology is enabling us to advance and enhance the storage of energy. We'll discuss the use of nanomaterials to improve the density of energy storage, and we'll look at some novel concepts for energy storage, such as ways of using viruses to assemble new styles of batteries.

Harvesting versus Storing Energy
- In the future, we anticipate that a much larger fraction of our energy budget will come from renewable energies, such as solar or wind energy. But of course, one of the challenges these renewable energy forms present is that we can't turn them on and off. Further, the time-of-day variations in the Sun require a buffer to map to our energy needs.

- A new concept has emerged recently in the management of energy known as the smart grid.
  - This idea recognizes that the traditional power distribution network is based on a unidirectional flow of energy: a small number of large, centralized power-generating stations that spread energy out toward the consumer.

  - With renewable energy, however, consumers are also producing energy and may sometimes produce more than they need. Consumers may wish to sell their excess energy, which means that the grid becomes 2-dimensional.

  - One of the key elements in building a smart grid that's 2-dimensional and allows the flow of energy in a managed fashion is energy storage.

- Our challenges on the energy storage front may occur on many different scales, from the battery packs inside our laptops to the storage of energy needed to run a community.
  - In addition to batteries, fuel cells represent another strategy for storing energy. In a battery, the means of energy storage and replay are integrated with one another, but in a fuel cell, they are decoupled. The fuel, such as hydrogen or ethanol, is separate from the cell, which takes in energy and replays it.

  - Depending on the scale we're interested in and other requirements, such as cost and portability, we may be interested in different systems.

Batteries
- In a battery, there are 2 electrodes; of course, any electrical circuit needs 2 electrodes to complete the circuit. Chemical energy in a battery is typically stored in the form of some kind of anion, such as lithium, in 1 electrode.

- Playing back that energy and turning it into a current involves the ionic flow through an electrolyte of these ions toward the opposite electrode.

The building blocks of batteries go back a couple of centuries, but today, nanomaterials are enabling increased energy densities inside batteries.

  - In the case of nonrechargeable batteries, that's it; the available energy is expended. The anions flow downhill to release their energy and provide a voltage to a circuit.

  - With rechargeable batteries, we're able to reverse that reaction and drive the anions back to be stored at their original electrode.

But even rechargeable batteries have finite lifetimes; thus, it's important to look at new electrode technologies that enable batteries to have longer usable lifetimes.

- Lithium is a particularly logical metal to use for batteries because it is the most electropositive metal available in the periodic table. That means it gives us the opportunity to develop the largest potential— the largest voltage—which translates directly into energy. It's also the lightest metal, the least massive per anion. As a consequence of those two properties combined, the density of lithium in terms of energy per kilogram can be very high.

- In traditional lithium-ion batteries, the lithium is stored in a graphite electrode, but silicon can also store a large density of lithium ions. Further, exploiting the full energy capacity for storage of lithium within silicon—which is about 10 times the capacity per unit mass that can be stored within graphite—would enable expansion of the volume of the silicon electrode by about 400%.

- Silicon offers this incredible energy density, but it will collapse after a couple of cycles of expansion and contraction. This challenge can be overcome by using nanowires, which can accommodate a good deal of strain without fracture. The silicon nanowires also electrically connect directly to the metallic connector of current. As a result, they don't have isolated regions where their electrons aren't efficiently collected.

Genetic Engineering and Energy Storage

- Some very exciting and creative work has been done at MIT, in which viruses have been used to assemble new classes of batteries. Angela Belcher, whom we discussed in a previous lecture, collaborates in this work with Yet-Ming Chiang.

- One of the ideas behind this work is that a virus can have various genetic options injected into it. Various families or classes of viruses can then grow, and we can use selection approaches to preserve and amplify only the ones that are desired.

- This concept has been used in genetics for some time, but using it in the context of building up inorganic materials—selecting viruses that could, say, build a battery—is a novel approach. Belcher and Chiang were particularly interested in building cobalt oxide, an interesting electrode for new battery technologies.

- There were two stages to building a virus that was coated with cobalt oxide nanoparticles and could then be useful in conduction: (1) put cobalt oxide particles on a surface and (2) make the material more conductive.
  - The researchers first searched for and selected viruses that were particularly prone to attract cobalt and to grow cobalt oxide on their surfaces. Using transmission electron microscopy, they verified that the viruses had a rich coating of cobalt oxide nanoparticles on their surfaces and that these particles were consistent in size.

  - To make these viruses more conductive, the researchers put an additional protein on the surfaces to enable the growth of gold nanoparticles, leading to a dramatic improvement in conductivity.

- Belcher and Chiang also determined the conditions under which they could coat their viruses onto a flexible piece of plastic. By managing the charge on the viral particles, they ensured that the viruses assembled into smooth lamellar structures. Building batteries in this way consumes very small amounts of energy.

Supercapacitors
- Supercapacitors are another paradigm in energy storage, allowing for rapid acceptance, charging, and playback of energy.

- Capacitors are one of the building-block circuit elements that allow us to store a charge. In electrical engineering, we usually think of having 2 plates separated by an insulator; by putting a positive charge on 1 plate, a negative charge is induced on the opposite plate. With the presentation of a voltage to drive the device, we can release the resulting electrical field in the form of a current.

- With supercapacitors, the goals are to achieve the greatest possible energy density and a long lifetime. Because they are primarily moving electrons around—instead of moving ions around and imparting true chemical changes—supercapacitors can accommodate many more cycles than batteries.

- Researchers at Stanford have been working on making a wearable supercapacitor. In fact, the field of wearable electronics has attracted a great deal of attention and excitement.
    o The idea here is you could collect energy through, perhaps, a flexible solar cell, and you could store that energy for later use.

    o The Stanford group figured out how to incorporate single-walled nanotubes into traditional cotton in such a way that the fabrics themselves were able to store a great deal of charge. Playback was also achieved through tens of thousands of cycles.

Suggested Reading

Aricò, et al., "Nanostructured Materials for Advanced Energy Conversion and Storage Devices."

Ryhänen, Uusitalo, Ikkala, and Kärkkäinen, *Nanotechnologies for Future Mobile Devices*.

Voelcker, "Lithium Batteries Take to the Road."

Questions to Consider

1. What are the most important qualities in a battery used in a mobile device and in a home? Where would you expect nanotechnology to have a greater impact?

2. What are the fundamental physical properties that limit the energy density of a medium—the amount of energy that could ever be stored per unit volume of matter?

Nanotechnology for Storing Energy
Lecture 20—Transcript

Ted Sargent: We've spoken about capturing energy from the Sun and capturing is the right word for this. Sometimes we talk of energy production, but really we're just harvesting what's been given to us from the Sun. There's another key part of managing energy, especially renewable energy and that's storing it. In this lecture, we'll talk about how nanotechnology is enabling us to advance and enhance the storage or energy. We'll speak about using nanomaterials to improve the density measured either by weight or volume or both by which we can store energy and we'll also talk about novel concepts, ways of using viruses, for example, to assemble new styles of batteries for us.

First, I'd like to speak just a bit about the balance between harvesting energy and storing it. We anticipate in the future a much larger fraction of our energy budget coming from renewable energies. Solar energy is an example; wind is another good one. There are so many attractive things about these: abundant, clean, pollution free. One of the challenges that renewable energy forms present is that we don't turn them on and off. They're not what we call dispatchable sources, the way say a coal generating station would be where we can turn up and turn down the amount of energy production at our will. In the case of renewable, solar for example, a cloud comes by and the amount of solar energy available to us at that moment changes.

That doesn't necessarily map perfectly on to our energy needs. In fact, if you look at the time of day cycles, if you look at the way solar the Sun rises in the morning and then right at midday we got a great deal of energy and towards the end of the day less so and overnight none, this also mandates the need to buffer, kind of hedge these temporal variations in the amounts of energy. That's kind of a time of day variation perspective. We have some cycles throughout the day where our energy needs vary, kind of along the lines with the Sun. For example, an air conditioner is typically needed more at the peak of the day when the Sun is up and so that's a good alignment, but there are many other reasons why it would be attractive to be able to play back energy at a different time from when it's made available.

In fact, a new concept has emerged recently in the management of energy known as the smart grid. The smart grid recognizes that the traditional power distribution network is based kind of on unidirectional flow of energy. It's based on the idea that we have a small number of large centralized power-generating stations that spread energy out towards the customer, but with renewables, now the customer for energy, you or I, is also producing energy, say, on our own rooftop. In fact, we may produce sometimes more energy than we need. We may wish to sell our energy to our neighbor or to somebody in another state, another part of the continent, and so now the grid needs to become 2-dimensional. We need to be able to buy and sell energy from many, many local points.

One of the key elements in building a better smart grid that's 2-dimensional, 2-directional, and that allows the flow of energy in a managed fashion without losing control, without leading to blackouts or brownouts. One of the key elements is energy storage. What that means is that our challenges on the energy storage front occur on many different scales. There's a familiar one, say the battery inside your mobile device or inside your laptop. These are obviously crucially important for a variety of reasons, they enable us to go anywhere, go everywhere with energy computation and communications. We've marveled in our discussions of nanoelectronics at the rapidity with which mobile computing has become available. We've marveled at how nanostructured materials, nanoscale transistors have allowed us to communicate at remarkable rates anywhere.

Until now, we haven't marveled at the fact that we're able to take the power with us that we need anywhere. In fact, people often remark at how the computing power that you have in your laptop is vastly, vastly greater than the power in some of the computers that used to fill a room. The same could be said from the power standpoint: We're able to take this power with us anywhere we go, have our battery packs last for ten hours, enable continued use and enjoyment. The mobility that batteries and related devices enable is tremendous.

This can also be scaled up. Imagine in the context of the overall energy system, our desire to take large quantities of renewable, say solar energy for a community or on a solar farm and store that. That's where batteries can play a role, but fuel cells which we'll speak about a little bit today provide another strategy for storing energy. What they do is they decouple the playback of the energy from the storage of the energy. In a battery, which we'll talk about in a second, the means of energy storage and replay are kind of integrated with one another. In the fuel cell, we have the fuel such as hydrogen or ethanol and separate from that we have the cell which takes in that cell and which spits our energy. Depending on the scale we're interested in, depending on the cost, depending on whether portability is a requirement, or whether just looking for a stationary and very cost effective method of energy storage and playback we're interested in different systems.

In fact, there's another exciting technology that we'll also speak about today and that's benefitting from nanotechnology called supercapacitors. What supercapacitors do is they function kind of like batteries; they're closed systems, they're also self-contained, but they allow us to charge them up much more rapidly and then also play back their energy in much bigger spikes and more rapid spikes. One of the example areas in which supercapacitors are expected to have a use is in automobiles where when we start it up we need a real burst of energy; typically that's challenging for a battery to supply and when we use the breaks and when we want to store the energy in some kind of electrical device, storage device, inside our electric vehicle supercapacitors are able to receive that energy very rapidly and very efficiently.

Let's dive into batteries now and these of course are familiar and they've been around for awhile. The building blocks of batteries go back a couple of centuries and so these have not always been consciously devices in which we're using nanomaterials. We'll talk today about how nanomaterials are enabling better energy densities inside batteries. To do that, to talk about how nanomaterials are helping us, we should talk just a little bit about the basic principles of a battery. In a battery, there are two electrodes, such as in any electrical device or any electrical circuit needs two electrodes to complete the circuit. In a charged up battery, we have chemical energy stored typically in the form of some kind of anion, lithium is a famous example, and of course we're very familiar with lithium ion batteries. We have energy stored in the form of lithium all being kind of piled up. We use the word intercalated to mean this anion, this ion is interpenetrated into this electrode.

Graphite is an example of a typical electrode that's traditionally been used to store this energy.

The form of playing back that energy and turning it into current involves the ionic flow through what's called an electrolyte of these ions towards the opposite electrode. In the case of non-rechargeable batteries, that's it. We've expended the available energy, you can think of it as kind of having been uphill and the energy, the anions flow downhill to release their energy, provide a voltage to a circuit, to a device. In the case of rechargeable batteries, we're able to reverse that reaction and drive them back to be stored at their original electrode and we can do this back and forth and back and forth many times.

As you know, even rechargeable batteries have finite lifetimes. The various electrodes that we use to build batteries can be degraded over time after we discharge and recharge them many times and so it's very important to look at new electrode technologies especially that can enable batteries that have longer usable lifetimes, more charges and discharges. Just thinking back to our periodic table, why is lithium a particularly logical metal, a particularly logical element to be using?

Well lithium is what we call the most electropositive metal available to us in the periodic table. That means that it gives us the opportunity to develop the largest potential, the largest voltage, which is going to translate directly into energy. It's also the lightest metal, the least massive per anion and as a consequence of that those two things combined, this large amount of potential that every ion can store combined with the low mass of each of the ions means that the density in terms of energy per gram or energy per kilogram can be very high with lithium. It's an extremely good choice from this point of view.

Where do the nanomaterials come in? Well I mentioned that the graphite electrode is where we store the lithium in the traditional lithium ion batteries. Graphite has a reasonable capacity for storing these ions. It turns out though that silicon, so familiar from our discussions of nanoelectronics and also of light guiding, that silicon has another remarkable property on top of all of its attractive electrical properties, and that's that it is extremely good at storing lithium ions. By good, I mean that it can store a huge density of these ions. In fact, if you look at a picture of the silicon lattice it's got kind of a crucible right inside the lattice where the silicon crystal is ready to receive a very high density of lithium ions.

This is very appealing, but if you look at this lattice you'll also realize that this lithium ion doesn't just penetrate into the lattice without disrupting that lattice, without changing it. In fact, if you were to exploit the full energy capacity for storage of lithium within silicon, which is about 10 times the capacity per unit mass that you can store within graphite, if you were to exploit that full capacity you'd also expand the volume of the silicon electrode by about 400%. As a result, if you just do this straightforwardly, if you take a bulk piece of silicon or a non-crystalline piece of silicon, like a amorphous silicon what you'll find is you can stuff it full of lithium atoms you can get an incredible energy density in there and then after a couple of cycles it will crumble, it will collapse because of all this expansion and contraction and expansion and contraction. It's like the thermal wear on parts of your house where it gets cold and hot and cold and hot and the joints start to wear out. The joints also start to wear out within silicon if we change its volume back and forth too many times.

Well this is where the opportunity for nano comes in. There's been some really exciting work going on at Stanford that takes advantage of nanomaterials to overcome these limitations to allow us to exploit the incredible energy density of silicon for the storage of lithium, but without suffering these challenges related to the volume expansion. The way this works is that the researchers have built these long, very, very skinny nanowires and so their surfaces are not accessible for lithium ion intercalation, for the penetration of lithium ions into the silicon. Now the nanowires can expand and contract and expand and contract rather than a single bulk solid which would suffer these catastrophic fractures. The small nanowires diameters enable these silicon based materials to accommodate these significant changes in volume.

Another great thing about the silicon nanowires is they're functioning now as wires, as electrical wires, and so they're able to directly electrically connect to the metallic connector of current. As a result, they don't have isolated materials which can't be collected electrically or where their electrons aren't efficiently collected. In contrast, we're able to make very good use of every one of the nanowires. All of the silicon is active. There are no islanding effects. Finally, it's a direct path; it's a straight line path. We get a direct connection between the silicon nanowire and the electrodes that we seek to connect it to.

Looking a little bit further out into the distance, into some conceptually disruptive or transformative techniques to try to build batteries, there's been some very exciting, very creative work that's gone on at MIT in which viruses have been utilized to try to assemble new classes of batteries. One of the stars of this show, it's been actually an amazing example of teamwork, part of the team is Angela Belcher who's distinguished herself over the last decades as somebody who's able to work with viruses and use genetic engineering to create families of viruses that have particular properties that dovetail with material science that allow us to use bioentities such as viruses to build materials for us. She's been collaborating with a researcher Yet-Ming Chiang, who's distinguished himself for a long period in the field of energy storage, in the field of batteries, and they've brought their work together to form a very creative collaboration that's completely breaking all the rules of traditional disciplinary boundaries.

You don't traditionally see genetic engineering in viruses combined with the kind of electrical, mechanical, chemical engineering of energy storage. Angela Belcher herself has this fascinating story. She really distinguished herself a little over a decade ago in understanding how living beings build hard inorganic materials. The abalone shell is a great example of this. Of course, we've been familiar with the fact that you can get these organic entities, animals and vegetables that as well as forming softer malleable materials, which is more what we're familiar with in the biological world, but they can also form hard shells like the shells on seashells. Dr. Belcher looked at understanding exactly at a molecular, at a nano level, how this occurred.

What she discovered was the mechanisms by which proteins were being expressed by these organisms that we're able to capture out of the sea particular elements such as metals that were used to build up say calcium carbonate, so capture the calcium component to build these shells up, and then another class of proteins were able to promote the formation of the complementary, let's say the oxide of the carbonate, and so they were able to build up layer by layer by layer by layer these very hard shells. Essentially they were utilizing organic materials, biomaterials, proteins, to build hard inorganic materials. She saw this as a real inspiration for her own work. After she kind of did the science of it, she understood how these biological entities were building these hard, very structured inorganic materials using their proteins. She thought well maybe we can exploit this, maybe we can engineer with this.

In order to try to engineer with these things, she needed to have some kind of capability to select. She needed to be able to tailor viruses in a direction that she desired. The approach that she took here, which was taken from the world of phage display and the idea is that a virus can have various genetic options injected into it. These various families or classes of viruses can grow up and then we can use selection approaches to only preserve the ones and then amplify the ones that we desire. What would be a selection algorithm, say you wanted to build a material that was based on say cobalt, well you could coat some kind of sieve effectively with cobalt, introduce your various viruses into it, and only those viruses that happen to have a gene that led a protein to be expressed that would strongly bind cobalt would stick to the walls of your sieve and everything else would fall through. In fact, people refer to this panning, or biopanning, an analogy with panning for gold where what you're looking for, the viruses that you desire to select in favor of, remain inside your container and everything else goes out. You then have these viruses stuck to the wall of your container, you elute them, which means you bring them back out into the solution, and then you can amplify them. You can have them reproduce and have families and as a consequence you can get more and more of the ones that you desire.

You run this essentially biological selection and rapid evolution within the laboratory where you prefer the evolution of certain viruses that have certain functions. People have been using this concept in genetics for a long time, but using it in the context of building up inorganic materials, selecting viruses that could do the work of building say a battery for you, this is a very novel concept. Dr. Belcher and Dr. Chiang working together were particularly interested in building cobalt oxide. Cobalt oxide is a very interesting electrode for new battery technologies. It's been found to have particular promise also enabling the dense and reliable storage of a great deal of energy.

There were really two stages to building a virus that was coated with cobalt oxide nanoparticles and it could then be useful in conduction. The first was to put these cobalt oxide particles on the surface and the second was to make the material more conductive. For the first one, the researchers searched for, used their selection techniques, to find viruses that were particularly prone to attract cobalt and to grow cobalt oxide on their surfaces. They were able to show using transmission electron microscopy that they could generate viruses that had a very rich coating of cobalt oxide nanoparticles on their surface and these particles were very similar to one another. They were quite consistent in their size.

In fact, some of the power of transmission electron microscopy is that it goes beyond just our ability to look in what we call real space, to actually look at the image itself. We can also focus the electron beam onto individual particles and see how the crystals that the electron beams impinge upon spread the energy out cause it to defract. The way in which these defract gives us a clue as to the composition to the structure of our crystals and these researchers were able to show that they had indeed built viruses that were able specifically to grow cobalt oxide single crystals on the surface of their viruses.

This was one of the building blocks that they needed; the other building block that they needed was something to make these more conductive. The researchers found a way to put an additional peptide—so an additional protein—on the surfaces of their viruses to make a kind of, they called it a bifunctional virus, something that could enable them both to grow the cobalt oxide nanoparticles which were crucial to the battery function, but also be able to grow gold nanoparticles that led to a dramatic improvement in the conductivity of these devices and so the viruses as a result had these coats that consisted of two classes of particles, one the cobalt oxide, another the gold, and the researchers were able to show that they were able to generate these hybrid or bifunctional viruses that allowed them to achieve their purposes in making a battery in this manner.

Of course making a battery is more than just making one wire which these viruses effectively have become. They needed to put them down onto a substrate. They needed to make a practical device out of them and they found the conditions under which they were able to coat onto just a flexible piece of plastic effectively their viruses. By managing the charge on the viral particles they were able to ensure that the viruses assembled into nice smooth, what are called lamellar structures. There were these kind of stripy patterns of viruses with their coatings of nanoparticles of cobalt oxide and of gold on top of them.

That's a discussion of one very important storage technology and how nanotechnology is enabling us to make better batteries that allow for greater capacity or in the case of this very intriguing work on viruses allow us to do the synthesis under very environmentally benign conditions. We consume very small amounts of energy in building the batteries this way. It's a very friendly approach to building storage devices. Another area where there's a real need to build devices with greater performance and also with the kind of flexibility that you can sometimes get by using nanomaterials to make devices is in the area of supercapacitors.

I was mentioning earlier as I introduced energy storage generally that supercapacitors are another paradigm in storing energy, their advantages is that they allow you to store, accept energy very quickly, charge up very quickly, and playback very quickly as well. It was worth it to find just the ideal of capacitor. Capacitors are actually traditionally the domain of electrical engineers; capacitors are one of the building blocks circuit elements that allow us to store a charge. We usually think in electrical engineering of having two plates separated by an insulator and on one of the plates we can put a positive charge and by putting that positive charge there, a negative charge is induced on the opposite plate.

As a result, there's an electric field and we have the potential to then release this charge in the form of a current with the presentation of a voltage in order to then drive the device. They're storage devices, but not typically in the electrochemical sense that's used in batteries where we're actually moving lithium anions uphill for storage and subsequent replay. Instead, these are typically based simply on the storage of electrical charges themselves of electrons. Now in supercapacitors the name of the game is to try to achieve the greatest possible energy density while also achieving a very good lifetime.

This is one of the great things about supercapacitors is that a result of not moving more massive ions around and imparting true chemical changes, but instead of principally moving electrons around we're able to achieve devices that can go through many more cycles. If you think of something say an electric vehicle that needs to happen many, many times, how many times do you apply the breaks for example in your car, if it needs to go through 100,000 or more cycles then often supercapacitors can supply the solution. Some of the exciting work that happened also at Stanford was figuring out how to make a wearable supercapacitor. In fact, the field of wearable electronics has attracted a lot of people's attention and excitement.

The idea would be that as well as perhaps making a flexible solar cell that you can go around wearing, you could also store that energy. You could later use it to charge up a mobile device. In fact, people even think of the devices themselves as being wearable. Of course, there's the emerging wearable electronic glasses that can have cameras and processors embedded in them, any number of things that you can imagine doing, but what we'll need to do this is to have flexible fabrics that are also electronic materials. The Stanford group under Yi Cui figured out how to build fabrics really right on top of traditional cotton in such a way that they were able to store a great deal of charge in them.

The way they did this is they started with a millimeter or two thickness of just a fluffy cotton sheet and then they dipped it into single-walled nanotube ink, so basically a solution containing many nanotubes and the nanotubes instead of being of the multi-walled sort, which contain rings and rings, kind of a coaxial set of nanotubes; instead they focused on single-walled nanotubes which have a better defined and more straightforward and controllable properties. They dipped their sheet of cotton in a couple of times, dried it at 120 degrees C to remove the water from it, and this actually had a foldable textile that was now a conductor. As well as being a conductor they were able to synthesize and modify the properties of their single-walled carbon nanotubes where there's a lot of control over the surface properties to build two properties into it.

First of all, they were able to make it what we call hydrophilic. Hydrophilic means that it's friendly to water and water likes it. Water was able to adsorb on these electrodes. That was important because the electrolyte that they were using to make their supercapacitor was water-based. They wanted to keep everything simple and environmentally friendly, not use solvents that people might wonder about whether they should be wearing on their clothes and so they used a water-based electrolyte, but that meant they needed to convert carbon nanotubes over to being hydrophilic. The succeeded in doing that and they also used the structure, the nanostructure, the area of these carbon nanotubes as their means to enhance the capacity of their devices to store a charge. They proved the idea that they were able to enhance both the density of storage, but also the lifetime of their devices, their ability to playback charge, playback their devices many, many tens of thousands of cycles even though they were making an electronic device that was on a piece of cotton, that was on a piece of textile fabric.

We've talked in today's lecture about a few strategies for energy storage and how nanotechnology through the large area of nanostructures, through the ability to process nanostructures from the solution phase and through the ability to use biological organisms like viruses now to build inorganic materials, how nanotechnology is giving us new ways to make storage elements that are denser, lighter in weight, or cheaper in cost, or integrated with flexible fabrics. We're going to continue this discussion in the next lecture. We'll talk about additional energy storage strategies and then more broadly about how we can use nanomaterials to control the flow and the playback of energy and also how we can use nanotechnology to implement desirable chemical reactions with high efficiency through a process known as catalysis.

Nanotechnology for Releasing Energy
Lecture 21

Our usage of the word "catalyst" in everyday conversation represents a good analogy with how the term is used in science. Just a little injection of something—a surface on which a reaction can occur, a particular shape, a particular angle, a particular availability of electrons—can lead to a rush of chemical activity. In this lecture, we'll see how nanotechnology helps us engineer these reactions toward higher yield and, thus, better use of the input materials, better use of energy, and generation of purer substances as the output.

Catalysis

- A catalyst is something that fosters a reaction without being consumed in the reaction. In a hydrogen fuel cell, stored hydrogen is the fuel. Simply using oxygen from the air, we're able to produce H_2O, a lower-energy molecule. The energy that is extracted in the production is harvested and turned into electrical power. This reaction requires a catalyst.

- Platinum is an extremely effective catalyst, and it has been widely used to make fuel cells operate. Of course, cost is a concern in using platinum, as is the phenomenon known as catalyst poisoning, in which the catalysis can no longer be effected after large numbers of uses.

- The idea of a crucible is also important in discussing catalysis. We cannot let reactions that require specific interactions proceed without some kind of surface or tether; otherwise, the interactions between the molecules in the reaction may not take place or they may not take place with the required alignment.
  - With a crucible, we create a surface that attracts one of the molecules that will participate in the reaction and orients those molecules at the right angle such that the second molecule will be exposed to a reactive site.

o   In other words, the crucible presents the optimal angle and orientation for causing the reaction to occur.

Zeolites

- Some reactions can be catalyzed simply by planar metal surfaces, but in the nanoworld, templates called zeolites are helping to achieve innovations in catalysis. Instead of being planar, zeolites present a 3-dimensional structure—a kind of complex, like a crystal, but built out of things that look more like molecules.

© Dorling Kindersley RF/Thinkstock.

Zeolites are catalysts used in the process of hydrocarbon cracking—breaking down heavy hydrocarbons, such as diesel fuel, into lighter ones for use in powering our cars.

- Zeolites are used in the process of converting crude oil to the kinds of fuels we wish to consume. In this process of hydrocarbon cracking, the goal is to break down heavy hydrocarbons into the lighter hydrocarbons that are used as gas in our cars. Here, zeolite is designed to achieve the size and shape that will allow the reactions to proceed that break these longer molecules into shorter, lighter molecules.

- In addition to providing the surfaces for these reactions, zeolites also produce what is called steric hindrance. "Steric" refers to the effects of size. Here, the term is used to refer to the fact that certain molecules will preferentially adsorb inside the tubes that make up the zeolites, or they'll be blocked, or they'll move through them very rapidly or slowly.

- Some specific examples of the zeolites that are used in crude oil–cracking include the aluminosilicates, which combine various aluminum, silicon, and oxygen atoms in order to make rings with defined sizes.

- In the hydrocarbon-cracking process, the heavy hydrocarbons are first brought into contact with the catalyst and combined with elevated temperatures to inject the energy that's needed for the reactions to occur.

- We can think of the zeolites as sort of a molecular sieve. They enable us to achieve size selection and, to some degree, chemical selection based on the structure of the materials that are produced.
  - Chemical interactions on the inner surfaces of these tubules can be managed such that those materials that are smaller or less interactive with the surface are prone to move through quickly, whereas others move more slowly.

  - In this case, the purification provided by the sieve isn't necessarily based just on what does or does not go through. Here, we can drive a solution through the molecular sieve and collect the products on the other side, but what comes out first will be the least interactive or the smallest molecules and what comes out last will be the larger molecules.

  - This sequential purification is attractive because we may have different uses for the different constituents of an impure substance. A similar process is also used in experimental laboratories when we want to remove, say, water from an organic solvent to control the interactions of water and metal. In addition, zeolites can be used to separate molecules into different size categories.

- We can define the chemistry that takes place in all these reactions using the regularity of the zeolites, the symmetry of their pores, their shape, and our knowledge of the chemical reactions required to form these rings. We can think of these pores as forming traps that molecules get stuck in.

- We are also able to gain greater selectivity with zeolites through the way in which we impart energy into the reactions. Rather than imparting energy into the matrix of zeolite, which means that every molecule participating in the reaction gets some energy, we're able to use laser light to selectively excite only certain classes of molecules inside the reaction.

o This allows us to achieve control of the reaction via position, size of molecules, shape of molecules, and the amount of energy we put in.

o This control, in turn, allows us to create new molecules that we weren't able to build before and to enhance yields, that is, to produce the desired molecule with a higher probability.

o In the process, we consume less source material and less energy, and we generate less waste.

Fuel Storage

- Consider for a moment the properties that would be desirable for hydrogen storage. For an automotive application, we would like to store this fuel in the smallest possible volume. We'd also like to maximize the density of fuel per volume and the ratio of the amount of fuel stored to mass. For applications that involve a stationary storage region, we would focus on minimizing the cost of storage, but the energy density per unit mass might not be as important.

- Metal organic frameworks are particularly attractive in these application areas. Here, metal atoms are bound together using organic molecules; we refer to organic molecules that are particularly prone to bind metal atoms as ligand.

o A network or framework is created in which metal atoms occur at various apices or vertices, and connectivity is achieved through organic molecules that are inclined to bind selectively to the metals.

o This structure enables us to achieve an exceptionally high inner surface area where we can control chemical reactivity. In other words, we've engineered structures in which the combination of metal, organics, and architecture enables us to achieve chemical tunability.

- This chemical tunability is a powerful capability in storing hydrogen molecules on the inner surfaces. In contrast to a canister used for storing hydrogen gas—where much of the volume would be occupied by nothingness—these metal organic frameworks are free of dead volume.

- Given that we're using chemical effects to bind the hydrogen molecules onto the inner surfaces of these metal organic frameworks, you might think that the molecules would be irreversibly stuck there. But in fact, we distinguish in this field between the ideas of chemisorption and physisorption.
  - In chemisorption, there is a binding event that forms a strong tether between a molecule and a surface or between 2 molecules.

  - In physisorption, there is a sort of light relaxing of a molecule onto a surface, and the amount of energy associated with this activity is quite small. We do not need an enormous amount of energy to break the bond to, in this case, extract hydrogen fuel from a region of storage.

- How much hydrogen can we store in metal organic frameworks? Can we pack a hydrogen molecule on atoms that are spaced 0.5 nanometer from one another? The metal organic framework is compelling, but it can't overcome the basic personality of hydrogen. There is a particular transition for this gas into the liquid phase, and we can't get beyond that density limit. But we can approach that limit as closely as possible by using the structure, the selectivity, and the chemical reactivity of these interfaces.

Nanotechnology Applied to Energy Challenges
- Having dexterity at the nanoscale gives us many options in energy storage and playback. We're able to control and maximize the surface area of a material in order to maximize the density of energy we can store on it. We're able to ensure optimal angles and orientations for causing reactions to occur, and we can engineer the structure of nanomaterials to leverage steric effects.

- One of the exciting opportunities in these kinds of catalytic efforts is in taking further advantage of optical control—bringing energy into these reactions using light.
  - This represents an exploration of many of the most attractive building blocks of the nanoworld: our ability to poise electrons, atoms, and molecules; take advantage of their interactions with photons; and selectively bring in laser light, like a knife, in order to sever bonds.

  - This kind of control translates into better use of materials and better use of energy toward our purposes.

Suggested Reading

Gates, "Catalysis: Individual Nanoparticles in Action."

Larminie and Dicks, *Fuel Cell Systems Explained.*

Withers, "Fuel Cells: Catalysis on the Cheap."

Questions to Consider

1. In everyday English, the term "catalyze" is commonly used in a manner analogous with its use in energy playback. Where does the analogy fit, and where does it fall apart?

2. What factors limit the rate at which energy can be played back from a stored state?

Nanotechnology for Releasing Energy
Lecture 21—Transcript

Ted Sargent: In the last lecture, we ended on another way to think about storing and replaying energy, which is fuel cells. In this lecture, we'll begin with fuel cells. We'll also use them as a way to enter into the fascinating world of catalysis. Catalyst is a word that's very familiar. We use it in the English language all the time outside of the context of science. What do we mean by it? Well somebody catalyzes a good dinner party conversation, a brief little toss off remark; a little comment leads to an hour's worth of vigorous debate. That represents a good analogy with how we use the term in science. Just a little injection of something, a surface on which a reaction can occur, a particular shape, a particular angle, a particular availability of electrons can lead to a rush of chemical activity.

The idea in science is that a catalyst is something that fosters a reaction without being consumed in the reaction. It can have huge leverage; it can have huge impact. In fuel cells, the rule of catalysis is as follows. We have a fuel, let's take hydrogen as an example, this is a very attractive way to operate a fuel cell with stored hydrogen and simply using oxygen from the air, we're able to produce H_2O, water, lower energy molecule and the energy that's extracted in going from the higher energy hydrogen down to producing with the reaction with oxygen, the emission of clean water, we take that energy, we harvest it, we turn it into electrical power. We can use it to run a car or to heat a home. That reaction requires a catalyst.

Platinum is an example of a metal that's an extremely effective catalyst and it's been widely used to make these fuel cells operate. However, you can imagine that cost is first and foremost on the list of concerns about platinum. There's also a phenomenon known as catalyst poisoning where the platinum can no longer be affected after large numbers of uses. Researchers and nanotechnology are very motivated to find ways either to make better use of the platinum and so to make it more available and here the large surfaces of nanomaterials are very helpful and attractive to us. There are also efforts to find new catalysts that are not based on precious metals like platinum, but they can dramatically lower the cost of these materials.

Another theme that we'll spend time on today is the idea of using nanomaterials for the efficient storage of things such as hydrogen, hydrogen fuel. You can, of course, store hydrogen fuel inside a tank. It will be under pressure and there are some concerns about the dangers associated with that, but many people think they can be managed. Nevertheless, you can condense even more hydrogen into a finite space if you can get rid of all the free space, if you can have a large surface area material, such as those we'll talk about in this lecture called Zeolites and metal-organic frameworks that are specifically tailored to adsorb these hydrogen molecules producing large surface areas through which these molecules are attached and available for subsequent replay.

The excitement over fuel cells comes from the fact that it does provide a means to playback energy and so when we use wind energy or solar energy to generate power, we can store it in a chemical format and then efficiently play it back. When you think of the hydrogen based fuel cells, what's so appealing is that you can simply use clean and available molecules in the air and your emissions are water. The other advantage over battery technologies and of course these are complementary technologies; it's not a question of one or the other, it's a question of where the fuel cells can play the most effective role. One of the advantages in large-scale storage applications, especially to the fuel cells, comes from the fact that we separate out the fuel from its playback so the batteries are integrated, but in the case of the fuel cells we have a separate tank or region or material in which we store the fuel and then we have a separate device for its playback and so we can optimize those two components separately from each other.

I tossed around the word catalysis. I described its analogy with the way we use it in common everyday language. What do we have in mind and why are surfaces so important in the process of catalysis? By this word catalysis we mean fostering a chemical reaction. Sometimes what we mean is that it can increase the probability or the efficiency or the yield of a reaction. Other times catalysts make reactions possible that simply wouldn't otherwise occur. One of the key pieces of vocabulary that we use in catalysis is the idea of a crucible. The concept is that certain molecules, say in a gas phase can interact with each other. They can collide with each other occasionally, but there are two problems.

If we let a reaction that needs some very specific interactions, if we let it proceed kind of open loop like that, if we let it proceed without some kind of surface or a tether, one is that the frequency of collisions or of interactions between the first molecule and the second class of molecules making up the reaction, that may be infrequent, it may not occur very often. The other challenge is even when these two molecules bash into each other they may not do so at the right angle. If for the reaction to occur, we need a particular alignment of sites, if we need a kind of very careful lock and key interaction and you need to put the key into the lock at just the right angle and just the right way; that's difficult to do and unlikely to do with two molecules that are just bouncing around and fluctuating at room temperature like little billiard balls bouncing off of each other.

The idea of the crucible in catalysis is that we create a surface, which attracts one of the molecules that will participate in a reaction. Further that it will orient those molecules at just the right angle such that the second molecule that needs to participate in a reaction with it will see a set of bonds, an exposed available bond, a reactive site, maybe an electron that wants to jump ship and participate in the reaction, it will see those very readily. It will present in just the optimal angle and orientation the right conditions for creating this reaction causing it to occur. The crucible just is when we think of a crucible bubbling up with a little reaction within it, this is a crucible now at the molecular length scale, with the nanometer length scale.

What specifically does nanotechnology have to do with this because after all some of these reactions can be catalyzed simply by planar metal surfaces. They can be unexposed facets say of platinum, can have just the right orientation and spacing of the atoms and just the right reactivity to present an opportunity for molecules to come together, interact, and bounce off. One of the areas in which nanotechnology has a role to play in, which there have been some very exciting recent advances, is in what are called Zeolites which instead of being planar, they prevent a 3-dimensional structure. They present a complex kind of, it's like a crystal, like our silicon crystals, but it's also essentially built out of things that look more like molecules. These templates, these structures, they're on a larger length scale. There can be pores that are 1/2 or 1 or 1-1/2 nanometers in size. These pores can penetrate long distances in these materials.

Often there are rings that make up these pores and the ring diameter can be controlled by the choice of elements that make up the Zeolite, the bonding between these various elements in how prone they are to form these kinds of tubules. Often because this is a question of various elements coming together and forming a preferred structure, the synthesis of the Zeolites themselves is very clever and very tricky and involves a deep understanding of the affinities that various atoms have for each other. Often getting the temperature just right during the growth of these materials is crucial as well because one needs to give these materials enough energy to react with one another and form these stable and very structured materials.

Where can we take advantage of these 3-dimensional nanostructured materials in order to achieve innovations, make new products, make new materials? One of them rather than being in the area of renewable that we spend quite a bit of time on in this course is actually in the area of the cracking of hydrocarbons, taking crude oil and producing the kinds of fuels that we actually wish to consume. You might look at this and say well it's not as maybe environmentally appealing as talking about renewable energy technologies. In fact, first of all this is actually just an illustration of a chemical reaction that can be controlled and enhanced in its yield through the use of nanostructured materials. In addition these kinds of fossil fuels have been used for a long time and we haven't solved all the problems related to providing renewable energy sources. So, it continues to be important, to be cost effective, and also to be energy efficient in how we utilize the hydrocarbons that continue to be used in industry and in society.

The role here of the Zeolites comes in a couple of forms. What we're trying to do in the case of hydrocarbon cracking is to take what are typically the very long hydrocarbons, think of diesel fuel for example, but even longer, even heavier, and we're trying to break it down to the lighter hydrocarbons that we're more accustomed to using, for example, as petrol in our cars. We want to design our Zeolite to give it the size and shape such that the reactions proceed to break these longer molecules down into lighter molecules, maybe 5 or 10 repeat units long, these shorter hydrocarbons, these more volatile hydrocarbons. The way in which the Zeolites work is first they provide the surfaces for these reactions, but they also produce what we call steric hindrance.

Whenever we use the word steric effects or steric bulk in nanomaterials or in chemistry, we're referring to the effects of size. We're referring to the fact that certain molecules will preferentially be able to adsorb inside these tubes that make up the Zeolites or they'll be blocked or they'll move through them very rapidly because they have a good mobility through the tubes or through the pipes or they'll be slow in their motion because they see these surfaces and they interact with them a great deal. Some specific examples of the Zeolites that are utilized in crude oil cracking include the aluminosilicates and these combine various aluminum, silicon, and oxygen atoms in order to make those structures, those rings with these very defined sizes.

The heavy hydrocarbons are introduced. They're brought into contact with the catalyst and elevated temperatures are combined to inject the energy that's needed in order for these reactions to occur and then the catalytic cracking, as it's called, proceed. In fact, the word catalysis is the word in catalytic converter. Here in each of our cars the emissions that come out of the primary exhaust from our internal combustion energy are further processed so we're able to further breakdown some of the emissions into more environmentally manageable materials. This idea of purification or selection of molecules, it can also be implemented using these Zeolites.

We use, I think a very appealing term here which is the idea of a molecular sieve, the analogy of course being with the sieve, typically we think of a sieve used in the kitchen as being something with pretty defined openings in it, let's say a millimeter or two little squares and so the water is able to pass through, but the pasta or the peas stay inside the sieve, and so what we achieve in that case is size selection on the millimeter scale. Zeolites and their friends are able to achieve size selection and also to some degree chemical selection based on the structure of these materials that are produced.

It's really the size and also the shape of the pores that control access from molecules into the Zeolite and so that's the most direct form of the sieve. Another one that's a little more subtle is about speed. It's about selection based on when things come out the other side of our sieve. For example, we're able to manage size, but also chemical interactions on the inner surfaces of these tubules such that those materials that are smaller or less interactive with the surface are prone to move quickly through whereas others move more slowly, they're stuck behind. In this case, the purification isn't necessarily based just on does it go through or does it not, is it retained on one side or is it transferred. Instead, we can start a process of purification, drive a solution through one of these molecular sieves, collect the products on the other side, but the stuff that comes out first will be the least interactive or the smallest molecules and the stuff that comes out at the end will be the larger ones. That's actually very attractive.

We may have different applications or different uses for the different constituents of an impure substance. Say we have a large-scale chemical reaction where we make a large amount of something, well we may be interested in all of what's produced, but there may be different people, different customers who may be interested in the small and the medium and the large molecules and so these kinds of sequential purification where speed translates into time translates into composition can be very effective. These molecular sieve ideas are also used in the experimental laboratory all the time. As you well know, water is something that is widely utilized in our world, including in chemistry, including in biology, sometimes we want to do our reactions purely within water. Sometimes we want to do chemical reactions where there's no water there at all.

Water and metals, for example, have lots of interactions with each other. Sometimes we want to control those interactions and just use say an organic solvent that doesn't include any water in order to control our reactions with great control and purity. What we can do because of that strong interaction with metals, also cations, which refers to positively charged ions, is that we can make Zeolites that have an abundance of cations inside them of metal ions and when we pass the solution through all of the water molecules will stick to this abundant surface area, highly metal rich, highly reactive, highly water attractive surface, and what will pass through will be just the organic solvents that we want. It's actually quite a simple thing to do in the chemical lab. If you want to dry out a solvent that's supposed to be dry, but you want to make it even drier, it only consists of the organic molecules, you can just toss in some of these Zeolites and let them sit there for a little while or agitate a little bit, give them the chance to interact and this sponge will suck the water out of your reaction.

One can do the converse, one can work with these organic solvents, organic solvents often have impurities of organic molecules of slightly bigger or smaller sizes or they consist of molecules of different shapes or different polarities. By polarity, I mean a propensity to be polarized so for a charge to point towards a complementary charge or not, whereas many organic molecules we're interested in are very nonpolar. They don't have this inclination to turn around in the presence of an electric field. They don't really see the effects of other charges. We can use very hydrophobic Zeolites, which means these materials that are specifically designed to be anti-water; water is very afraid of them, but they're very interactive with organic molecules. We can use these to separate organic molecules into their different sizes. Essentially we can do molecular sorting. It's a bit like taking a deck of cards that have been randomly shuffled and being able to put them into their categories, being able to put them into their bins, and then potentially every one of the sets of cards is useful. We can use all of them.

It's really the regularity of these structures, it's the symmetry of their pores, it's the shape, it's the circularity, it's the fact that we're able to use these known chemical reactions between the aluminum and the silicon and the oxygen in order to form rings of a defined size that allows us to define the chemistry that goes on. We can think of these pores as forming traps, little cages, or caves that the molecules can get stuck in. the precision and it's the specificity that we leverage in these molecular sieves. In fact, we're not limited to using sieves on liquids alone, like probably how one would think of it, or separating a liquid in a solid is the kind of thing that you do inside a sieve. Really because it's not just about size, we can even work with extremely small molecules, we can work with say water, carbon dioxide, say sulfur dioxide, we can work with these kinds of gases as well. Based on their reactivity's, we're able to take input natural gas from a low grade natural gas stream and retain only what we want and so remove, extract from it, some of the components that we don't want in the ultimate natural gas that will sell to people.

In fact, in recent years there's been great progress on this and one of the attractive things about being able to develop these Zeolites and engineer their properties so well is that we're able to desulfurize transportation fuels. We're able to take the sulfur out, which is often responsible for some of the smell in some of these fuels, and we're able to remove that and do so now at room temperature. That's one of the impressive things about catalysts is that by making reactions more efficient, often a chemical reaction requires a bit of energy to be introduced in order to proceed, but we can introduce the minimum required amount of energy to enable a reaction to proceed. We're able to be more efficient in the ways in which we process molecules, process fuels.

One of the really exciting things about what we can now do with these Zeolites, with these materials, is that we're able to gain greater selectivity as well through the way in which we impart energy into the reactions. If you think about adding a little bit of heat to a reaction vessel, you're putting energy into everything contained there, so say it was inside one of these Zeolites. You'd be putting into the matrix, into the Zeolite itself, and then every molecule that was participating in the reaction would also get some energy. It's possible to use molecules that participate in our reactions that are light absorbing and that absorb very specific colors of light. If we think back to our discussions of monochromatic light of a single color consisting with single photon energy, we're able to use laser light to selectively excite only a certain class of molecules inside this reaction.

This allows us to drive forward the reactions that we desire by putting the energy, putting the excited electrons onto one of the classes of molecules that's going to participate in the reaction and then by embedding it in the Zeolite, we have the catalyst, we have the crucible sitting right there for us and we now start to be able to design both where we put the energy and where we put the molecules. We start to achieve control via position, size of molecules, shape of molecules, and also the amount of energy that we put in. This is both leading us to being able to create new molecules that we weren't able to build before, but also even when we were able to do some syntheses before we're able to enhance yields, we're able to produce the desired molecule with a higher probability. That has all sorts of advantages. It means we consume less material in the first place. We consume less energy in the realization of these molecules. There's less waste as a result so it's a much more efficient process. Even the purification steps at the end become simplified as a result of increasing these synthetic yields.

I touched earlier on in the context of fuel cells, there's the playback, there's the fuel cell which often till these days has used platinum catalysts that help translate the stored fuel into electrical energy. There's also the matter of storing the fuel. Let's take a moment to think about what properties we would desire of a means of let's say hydrogen storage. We obviously would like, let's say for an automotive application, we'd love to be able to put this fuel into the smallest volume. We'd like to maximize the density of fuel per volume, but if you're thinking especially for a portable application we'd also like to be able to maximize the ratio of the amount of fuel stored to the mass of this because if it's in a portable application we'll be carrying this mass around with us. Any extra mass associated with the storage mechanism will be kind of a penalty that we pay in the efficiency of our car. On the other hand, there are applications in which we'll just have a stationary storage region. There we may be very focused on keeping the cost of storage down, but especially the energy density per unit mass may not be particularly important because we have a stationary storage site.

It's in these kinds of application areas that the so-called metal organic frameworks are particularly attractive. In the metal organic frameworks, metal atoms are bound together using organic molecules. We refer to organic molecules that are particularly prone to bind metal atoms as ligand. We say that they ligate the metal atoms and so we create this network, or this framework, in which metal atoms occur at various apices or vertices and connectivity is achieved, the network affect is achieved through these organic molecules that are particularly inclined to want to bind selectively to the metals. As a consequence of this, we're able to achieve an exceptionally high inner surface area and the surface area is one where again we control the chemical reactivity very nicely.

If you like, we've engineered chemically tunable structures where through the combinations of the metal selected, the organics selected, and then the architecture, the spacing, the periodicity in all directions, we're able to achieve a degree of chemical tunability and this chemical tunability ends up being very powerful in storing hydrogen molecules on the inner surfaces here. We say that they're free of dead volumes so whereas if you were to have a canister in which you were trying to store a gas such as hydrogen, much of the volume would be occupied by nothingness that within these metal organic frameworks we're able to move the dead volume. We're able to condense these materials as much as possible.

You might think if we're using chemical effects to bind the hydrogen molecules onto the inner surfaces of these metal organic frameworks that they'd be kind of sucked there. They'd be irreversibly stuck. In fact, we distinguish in this field between the idea of chemisorption and the physisorption. In general, across physical chemistry and physics we use chemisorption to mean that there's actually a binding event that there is a very strong tether between a molecule and a surface or two molecules with one another. Physisorption, often referred to on a surface, we use to refer to the idea of just sort of a light relaxing of a molecule onto a surface. The amount of energy associated with that is quite small. The surface is present, it provides a little place of repose for the molecule, but it's not a bond that has a huge amount of energy that we need to break in order, in this case, to extract a hydrogen fuel from our region of storage. Another way to say that is there's no large activation barrier, no large energy barrier that we need to overcome in order to liberate this hydrogen.

You might ask, what are the limits of this? How far can we go? How much hydrogen can we store in here? Can we pack a hydrogen molecule on atoms that are spaced half a nanometer from each other? Well the metal organic framework is very compelling, but it can't overcome the basic personality of hydrogen. There's a particular transition for this gas into the liquid phase and we can't get beyond that density limit. We're not getting beyond the intrinsic limits on the densification of this class of molecules. Instead, we're trying to approach those as closely as possible by utilizing the structuring, the selectivity, the chemical reactivity of these interfaces.

What we've discussed broadly in this pair of lectures on energy storage and playback is that by having dexterity of the nanoscale we have a lot of options. We have a lot of degrees of freedom. We're able to do things like control and maximize the surface area of a material, of a structure, in order to maximize the density of energy that we can store on it. That concept is very related to catalysis by orienting certain molecules relative to others. We're able to ensure that when a collision does occur that it occurs at just the right angle to have the greatest impact or to have a chemical reaction that will yield what we desire. We're able to achieve a selectivity. We're able to engineer the structure of these materials to leverage what we call steric effects, effects that relate to the size of molecules. As a consequence, when we're able to control the size of pores, we're able to engineer the inputs of the chemical reaction and also the output, so ultimately we're able to engineer the reaction itself towards high yield. High yield means better use of the input materials, better use of energy, and generation of a more pure substance at the output.

One of the exciting opportunities in these kinds of catalytic efforts and that has been partially explored, but where there's much more to be done, is in taking advantage further of optical control, bringing energy into these reactions using light, often a very pure color of light such as that which we can obtain from a laser. What this really is is an exploration of many of the most attractive building blocks of the nanoworld. Our ability to poise electrons, atoms, molecules, take advantage of their interactions with photons, selectively bring in laser light, like a knife, in order to sever two bonds. This is the kind of control that engineering of the nanometer scale gives us and what it translates into is better use of materials and better use of energy towards our purposes.

Energy's Holy Grail—Artificial Photosynthesis
Lecture 22

W e've talked so far about capturing the Sun's abundant energy and turning it into electricity. We've also talked about storing that energy. Do we have to think of these things as separate? As we know, plants take energy from the Sun and convert that energy into stored fuel. The dream of artificial photosynthesis, which has made vast progress in recent years, is that we could mimic nature by using sunlight to directly generate fuel.

Photosynthesis

- Photosynthesis is the conversion of carbon dioxide into organic carbons. This process occurs in plants, algae, and many species of bacteria. Organisms that are capable of harvesting energy and creating their own food are called photoautotrophs.

- To make the solar cells that we discussed earlier, we have to invest energy. Photoautotrophs use the energy from the Sun to build themselves. It's wonderful to dream about a photosynthetic apparatus that would build itself without our having to consciously engineer it.

- In photoautotrophs, the chlorophylls that are used in the absorption of light turn photons into energetic electrons, which are then available to participate in reactions. The chlorophylls are part of a membrane, tightly folded into cylindrical

Nanomaterials and nanotechnology may allow us to realize the dream of artificial photosynthesis— converting energy from the Sun directly into fuel, as plants do.

sheets. These structures are used to fill up the interior of a cell, ultimately giving the membrane a large surface area.

- Chlorophyll is also what gives leaves their green color. Recall from our discussion of solar energy that the Sun finds its peak in the visible spectrum, and green is in the center of that wavelength spectrum.
    o That aligns nicely with the fact that the energy required to drive forward photosynthetic reactions is less than what we can get out of the energies available in the photons coming from the Sun.

    o We have sufficient energy within each photon—within each of these quantum particles—to perform the chemical synthesis that is needed to turn carbon dioxide into organic compounds.

Energy Transfer
- Green pigments are embedded in plants and algae in antenna proteins. The process that occurs inside these reaction centers is known as energy transfer.

- When we think of energy transfer occurring using light, we might think of light being emitted and then absorbed somewhere else.
    o For example, we could convey energy across a room using a laser; that would be energy transfer within the optical domain. Inside the antenna proteins in plants, a virtual photon emission event takes place.

    o Energy has the capability to funnel itself downhill without changing from being an excited electron to a photon to another excited electron. With this downward cascade, the flow of energy can be directed.

    o Earlier, we spoke about nanomaterials that were being engineered to have different sizes and, thus, different energy levels. Wherever we are able to concentrate all the energy from an outer ring of nanoparticles onto a central receptor, we're doing something similar to what takes place in the photosynthetic reaction apparatus of plants.

Energy Conversion

- The efficiencies plants have in their energy conversion are in the range of 3 to 6%, which is considerably worse than the 40% efficiency range in the best solar cells. Yet the photosynthetic approach is the one that has caught on and dominates our global use of energy because there are no system costs associated with photosynthesis.

- There is so much more solar energy available than we need that we don't need to be perfectionists in efficiency in building a device that will mimic photosynthesis. Such a device would have a large area to receive sunlight. The input into the reaction would be water, and the output would be a splitting of that water into 2 innocuous products: oxygen and hydrogen (the fuel).

- What's nice about these reactions is that they evolve gases; thus, we'll simply be responsible for collecting the hydrogen gas out of this cell and storing it or playing it back directly.

Nanowires and Nanocubes

- Nanowires have been extremely important in making progress toward the vision of artificial photosynthesis because they're capable of conveying electricity in a directional fashion and they have an abundance of surface area. We can even put catalysts on the surface of these materials to ensure that the reactions move forward in the desired direction and with high efficiency.

- Peidong Yang and his group at Lawrence Berkeley National Laboratory have recently done some exciting work involving the use of nanocrystals and part of the catalytic process to pave the way toward artificial photosynthesis.
  - By controlling the facets that are presented in nanocubes, researchers have been able to achieve shape-controlled and

size-controlled metal oxides that have particular promise for artificial photosynthesis applications.

o Yang's group realized that they could put together a stack of materials in which different layers carried out sequentially different reactions, somewhat analogous to the cascade that occurs in the photosynthetic reaction.

- Among the techniques used in building up multi-material stacks is the formation of what's called the Langmuir-Blodgett assembly.
  o Here, we have a bath—a solution filled with molecules. Often, the molecules have a propensity to stick in one direction on a particular surface. Thus, we can dip a substrate into this bath and gradually produce layers of molecules that are consistently oriented at an appropriate angle.

  o The result is a bit like a 2-dimensional array of crystals based not on the traditional organic picture of crystals but on organic molecules that pack themselves into certain regions.

  o Yang's group has used this technique to deposit layers of nanocubes of platinum and cerium oxide on top of a silicon dioxide substrate. The result is two distinct interfaces that enable sequentially catalyzed reactions.

- Yang's bilayer structure is somewhat similar to the tandem solar cells we spoke about in the context of solar energy harvesting.
  o Earlier, we were thinking about how to harvest visible photons and infrared photons in sequence and achieve a total energy output from the solar cell that was the sum of the energies of these inputs.

  o The Berkeley group was able to stack these two reaction systems on top of each other and achieve a similar sequential process for catalysis.

Carbon Nanotubes

- Carbon nanotubes have also played an important role in some of the progress that's been made in artificial photosynthesis. One of the key components of making these devices work is to achieve an oxygen-evolving anode.

- Researchers in Italy, collaborating with an Austrian group, have used multi-walled carbon nanotubes to make a particular style of oxygen-evolving anode. In this case, the device was also a multilayered stack, but it was not just a planar device. The researchers were able to functionalize the surface of the carbon nanotubes, wrapping a variety of organic molecules around them. These molecules had "fingers" that were able to grab the constituents needed to participate in the reaction.

- Instead of building a planar sandwich vertically, these researchers built an analog of that sandwich, but they built it out radially. This approach provides more surface area and more opportunity for interaction.

- It's possible now, using the best transmission electron microscopy techniques, to see the composition of elements in these reactions. We can see spectral signatures through the loss of electrons.

- The nanotubes themselves played a couple of different roles in this work on making oxygen-producing anodes. First, they provided a basis for control over the material morphology. The researchers were able to control the surface, control the binding to that surface, and thus, build the structure they desired. This strategy successfully increased the surface area and provided more opportunities per unit volume to achieve particular reactions.

- Second, through the conductive properties of the nanotubes, the researchers were able to funnel the sequential electron transport to the electrode. Here, they used the fact that the tube was engineered to convey energy in a particular direction and to drive reactions in the perpendicular directions and the radial directions.

Genetic Engineering and Artificial Photosynthesis

- The Belcher group at MIT has also worked on the challenge of making self-assembled materials or devices for water-splitting.

- This group has engineered a virus scaffold allowing the assembly of a virus with two key components: (1) the photosensitizer, the material responsible for absorbing light and converting energy from the optical domain into the form of an excited electron ready to participate in a reaction, and (2) attraction to an iridium oxide cluster that serves as the reaction catalyst.

The Role of Nanotechnology in Energy Harvesting and Storage

- In discussing the role of nanotechnology in energy harvesting and storage, we've integrated a number of concepts embodied in the field.

- One of the broadest of those concepts is simply that nanotechnology is an intrinsically interdisciplinary science. In order to build an artificial photosynthesis system, we need researchers who understand biology, physics, and chemistry, as well as material scientists and engineers.

- Large teams of these experts are working to create devices that mimic what trees and plants have evolved to do over the course of millions of years, but we don't have the luxury of that much time. Our energy challenges require solutions in only the next couple of decades.

Suggested Reading

Lewis and Nocera, "Powering the Planet."

Regalado, "Reinventing the Leaf."

U.S. Department of Energy, *Basic Research Needs for Solar Energy Utilization.*

1. How is a system that integrates energy capture and storage preferable to one that separates these functions, for example, a solar cell connected to a battery or a fuel cell?

2. How does an integrated capture/storage system compare with the process of leaves capturing the Sun's rays and turning them into stored chemical energy and our then burning these leaves as wood? Consider both efficiency and net environmental impact.

Energy's Holy Grail—Artificial Photosynthesis
Lecture 22—Transcript

Ted Sargent: We've talked so far about capturing the Sun's abundant energy, turning it into electricity. We've also talked separately about storing that energy that's been turned into electricity. Well do we have to think of these things as separate, as disjoined? Is there some precedent perhaps in nature for this? Of course, there's a very familiar precedent. What do trees do? What do plants do? They take energy from the Sun and they convert that energy into a stored form. They convert it into a fuel. You may not necessarily think of the food that you eat as being fuel, but that's exactly what it is.

There's a dream, and a dream that's made vast progress in recent years, a lot of relying on nanomaterials and nanotechnology that involves mimicking all of the good qualities of photosynthesis. It's called artificial photosynthesis and the idea is that we could use sunlight to directly generate fuel, such as direct production of hydrogen. Let's start off by taking a bit of a look at photosynthesis and to how that works. We'll find that nature is, as we already know from this course, very much a nanotechnologist in the way it engineers materials to a particular purpose.

Photosynthesis is the conversion of carbon dioxide; take it out of the air, into organic carbons. It's from the carbon dioxide that the photosynthetic reaction takes the carbon as a source and with this it produces sugars, which as I said are fuels. We know that it occurs in plants. It also occurs in algae and lots of different species of bacteria. There's a nice word to describe these organisms that are capable of harvesting energy and creating their own food. We call them photoautotrophs and this references the fact that they're self-sufficient. They're really capable of building their own nutrition rather than relying on others as we humans do to be our sources of food; if you like, they eat photons.

Attractively they consume carbon dioxide in water and they release oxygen as their waste product. It sounds very clean as waste products go. We talked earlier when we were talking about solar energy of how we could readily in terms of the amount of solar energy that's available reaching the Earth, we could readily meet the world's energy needs 10,000 over using solar energy, using solar electricity. Of course, plants and algae and bacteria that perform photosynthesis are already harvesting a huge amount of solar energy. In fact, if you look across the globe, around the globe at all of the energy harvesting activity that's happening right now, there's about 100 terawatts. This translates into about six times more power than human civilization is consuming.

It just reinforces the idea that there is this vast source of power and the key is to find cost-effective ways of harvesting it. What's a cost-effective way? The brilliance of plants is unlike the solar cells that we've been talking about earlier in the course (where we have to go engineer them, we have to invest energy, we have to purify materials to make them), the plants, of course, are ultimately using the energy from the Sun to build themselves and so they're self-sustaining, they're self-constructed, they're self-assembled. It's wonderful to dream in the context of this notion of artificial photosynthesis ultimately of the photosynthetic apparatus that we engineer to build our fuels, having it build itself rather than having consciously to engineer it ourselves. We'll finish this lecture with some progress in that direction as well.

Back into what happens at the heart of the organism during the photosynthetic process. In fact, the chlorophylls that are used in the absorption of light and that capture that energy from photons turn them into energetic electrons which are then available to participate in reactions; they're actually part of a membrane tightly folded into these cylindrical sheets called PhyloCodes. They're bunched up together and these structures are used to fill up the interior of a cell ultimately giving the membrane a very large surface area. I want to emphasize this because it's so resonant with any of the themes of the course so far where we are trying to maximize surface area by folding, by creating richly textured surfaces on the nanoscale. We may think we're smart, but bacteria had already thought of this. This kind of strategy is already widely used throughout nature.

When light absorption occurs in these proteins, they're called photosynthetic reaction centers and here the photosynthesis is really at work. Light is coming in and then reactions are occurring relating to chemical synthesis or actually building fuels within leaves. It's right at the chlorophyll; that is the heart of this and it's the chlorophyll that gives leaves their green color. I mentioned when we were talking earlier about solar energy that the Sun finds its peak right in the visible spectrum. The green is right in the center of the visible wavelength spectrum. This is a very abundant source of energy coming from the Sun. That aligns nicely with the fact that the energy required to drive forward these photosynthetic reactions is less than what we can get out of the energies available in the photons coming from the Sun.

We have sufficient energy within each photon, within each of these quantum particles to perform the chemical synthesis that we need to do to turn carbon dioxide into organic compounds. It this chlorophyll that's giving these plants their green tinge that's this pigment really. It's like a dye, something that's used to dye clothes. It's very persistent, hence grass stains in pants, and these pigments are embedded in plants and algae in what we call antenna proteins. This is where some fascinating physics occurs. The process that's occurring inside these reaction centers is known as energy transfer.

When we think of energy transfer occurring using light, what we would often think of is light being emitted and then absorbed somewhere else. For example, if I wanted to convey some energy from here across the room I could construct a laser here and I could drive it with electrical energy, convert that into a beam, try to focus that beam onto say a photovoltaic cell across the room. That would be energy transfer within the optical domain. Inside the antenna proteins within the reaction centers that make up plants we have what we call a virtual photon emission event.

We have the capability for energy to funnel itself downhill, to roll downhill through a series of centers, without actually ever going from being an excited electron to being a photon, to being another excited electron. With this downward cascade, we're able to direct the flow of energy. When we spoke in the lecture about nanomotifs, about nanomaterials that were being engineered to have different sizes and that therefore had different energy levels and wherever we are able to concentrate all of the energy from an outer ring of nanoparticles onto a central receptor, what we're really doing there is we're being inspired by the photosynthetic reaction center that occurs inside plants within the photosynthetic reaction apparatus as it's called.

What kinds of efficiencies do plants have in their energy conversion? Well this too raises an interesting point. It turns out that the range is typically 3 to 6%. How does that compare to the best solar cells that we can make? That's actually considerably worse than the best solar cells. The best solar cells, the records are in the 40% solar conversion efficiency range and there are commercial solar cells that are a little bit under 20%. This incredibly successful predominant source of energy harvesting, which is the photosynthetic approach rather than our artificial solar electric approach, the one that's less efficient, the one that's 3 to 5%, the photosynthetic one, the one that really has caught on and dominates our global use of energy.

Why is that? Well think back to the solar lecture where we were thinking about both the costs of making the solar cells and panels, but we were also thinking about what we called the balance of systems cost. We were thinking about installing solar panels, the maintenance of those solar panels. The brilliance of the way in which life and biology manage photosynthesis is in part this self-assembling process that we described. There's no balance of system cost, in fact, we enjoy having plants and trees around. It's not a cost it's a benefit to have photosynthesis at work, the production of oxygen is a benefit for us.

This aspect to where in the self-assembly of these devices as an engineer might think of them, these trees and plants, is one of their many very attractive features and it's a reason why perfection in terms of energy conversion isn't required after all. There's so much more solar energy than we need. We don't need to be absolute perfectionists in the efficiency in which we concert a certain photon having a certain energy into a stored chemical, such as a sugar inside a plant. Our analogy in building a device that will mimic photosynthesis looks kind of like this. We also will have photons coming in. Here we imagine having a large area device available to receive a lot of Sun. There will be an input into the reaction and in this case it will be water. The output of the reaction will be to split that water into two essentially innocuous things: one of them oxygen, a byproduct of the reaction just as the byproduct of the photosynthetic reaction is oxygen; the other, our stored fuel in much of this work, will be hydrogen.

Here again, we will think about fuel cells as a very attractive means of replaying that stored energy. What's nice about these reactions of course is that they evolve gasses and so we'll be simply responsible for collecting the hydrogen gas out of this cell and storing it or playing it back directly. Storing it for future use is one of the ways we can insure that we have the desirable buffering characteristics that we're very interested in, in our energy storage lecture when we were discussing things previously. Another way to picture one of these artificial photosynthesis devices is that it's kind of a fuel cell turned around into a fuel cell. We input hydrogen, we evolve water, and there we generate electricity and in of these artificial photosynthesis devices we've taken our solar fuel, we've taken photons coming from the Sun, and we also input water and then we split it and generate our storable fuel in the form of hydrogen.

Now, the idea that we discussed in the context of photosynthesis of having an abundance of surface area is a theme, of course, that we've used throughout this course and it will definitely come up here in the context of artificial photosynthesis. Here the field of nanowires has been extremely important in making progress towards this vision of artificial photosynthesis for again they have these properties that we've now seen a number of times. They're capable of conveying in a directional fashion electricity, so their electrical connectivity is very good, and they have an abundance of surface area. We can even put catalysts on the surface of these materials in order to ensure that our reactions move forward in the desired direction and with the high efficiency.

One of the leaders in this field is a really remarkable person. His name is Peidong Yang. He's at Lawrence Berkeley Labs and actually Peidong also manifests some of the qualities that make him such a successful nanotechnologist. One of those is that people going through those graduate training these days or doing their postdoctoral fellowships, becoming profs, they can go around to a number of different labs and collect knowledge, depth, methods of research from these different labs. Peidong was in a group that was one of the leaders in the development of nanowires and he personally is a graduate student, led a lot of the most exciting work in the nanowires field for its own sake even before they were being thought of for artificial photosynthesis.

395

Then he joined a group that was leading in the area of making these nanostructured materials for energy, storage, and catalysis, and conversion. He then went on his own and started his own Berkeley group as an assistant professor. He had this set of skills in engineering nanomaterials and thinking about their use in catalysis and energy and electrochemistry that very few other individuals around the world did. It's this confluence of skills, how people are able to go accumulating a number of different sets of capabilities from different traditional disciplines that allows a lot of the innovations to occur within nanotechnology. Often it's not even so much a single brilliant ideal although that happens too. There are certainly breakthrough insights, but sometimes bringing up an individual who has a set of competencies or capabilities that no other individual in the world has, and that's certainly the case in some of this work.

Some of the most exciting stuff that's happened recently coming out of this group, the Berkeley group, has involved the use of nanocrystals as well as part of the catalytic process in order to pave the way towards artificial photosynthesis. One of the great things about nanoparticles is that they're not always just spherical like some of the ones that we've seen, these quantum dots. Instead researchers are able to synthesize things like nanocubes, and here the facets that are available are different. Maybe when you picture a little cube of salt, you can picture the fact that potentially if you were to instead of having it be a cube, if you were to slice off one of the corners you'd see a different atomic arrangement of sodium and chlorine atoms.

It's the same with these nanocubes that are used in the synthesis of artificial fuels, the artificial photosynthesis that by controlling which facets are presented we're able to achieve shape-controlled and also size-controlled metal oxides that have particular promise in achieving some of these interesting devices. In fact, one of the exciting recent discoveries that came out of Dr. Yang's group was the realization that one could put together a stack of materials where different layers within the stack carried out sequentially different reactions so it's a bit analogous to in the photosynthetic reaction case where there's a cascade; there's a number of steps that each need to occur in sequence. They were able to first make a cerium oxide to platinum interface, so a first metal oxide to metal interface to catalyze the first reaction, which is to catalyze methanol to produce carbon monoxide in hydrogen.

A second reaction was catalyzed to the second interface, but very near by a platinum to silicon interface where the first product of that first reaction was then used as an input to the second reaction. It's this kind of cascade or sequence of reactions that we can engineer when we make multi-material stacks. There are some techniques that are now extensively used in building up multi-material stacks. One of these techniques is called Langmuir-Blodgett assembly. In this technique, people talk of using a Langmuir-Blodgett trough and essentially one has a bath, a solution filled with molecules.

Often the molecules have a propensity to stick one way down on a particular surface and stick their tail up in the air so they have a head and a tail and the head has an affinity for a substrate or a surface that one will work on and one can dip the substrate into this trough and gradually withdraw at the appropriate angle and the appropriate rate and produce layers of molecules that are very, very consistent. In fact, one can even come along using an atomic force microscope or other kinds of scanning tunneling microscopes and one can even see these dense forests of individual molecules that pack themselves. It's a bit like crystals, the 2-dimensional crystals and not based on the traditional inorganic picture of crystals, but based on organic molecules that pack themselves into certain regions.

Peidong's group used this same technique, but now to deposit layers of nanocubes of platinum and cerium oxide on top of a silicon dioxide substrate. You need these nanocubes, each on the scale of about 10 nanometers, and then made these two distinct interfaces that I spoke about and these sequentially catalyzed the reactions and so in the vertical dimension he was able to build up a more complex stack, not just a single monolayer or a set of layers of the same thing, but a complex stack of materials. He called this a bilayer structure.

Here the analogy is a bit with those tandem solar cells that we spoke about in the context of solar energy harvesting. Then we were thinking of how to first harvest the visible photons, the energetic photons as efficiently as possible and subsequently harvest the infrared photons and achieve a total energy output from the solar cell that was the sum of the energies of these two inputs. Here the Berkeley group was able to stack these two reaction systems on top of each other and achieve this series process at tandem cell for catalysis as distinct from the tandem photon cells that we were talking about earlier.

Carbon nanotubes have also played an important role in some of the progress that's been made in artificial photosynthesis. One of the key components of making these devices work is to achieve an oxygen evolving anode as it's called. With oxygen being the product here, there's a lot of focus on making the electrodes that will lead to the production of oxygen, one of the outputs of these. In fact, this is really part of the broader dream. It's to make the device where the catalytic splitting of water ultimately gives rise to this production of oxygen and to the production of the hydrogen fuel. Oxygen is the byproduct from the splitting of water. Hydrogen is the desired fuel that we're trying to generate.

Researchers in Italy collaborating with an Austrian group were able to demonstrate that with the aid of multi-walled carbon nanotubes, really a conductive bed of these nanotubes, that they were able to make a particular style of oxygen evolving anode. It was also a multilayered stack, but in this case it wasn't just a planar device, but instead they were able to functionalize the surface of their carbon nanotubes, wrap a variety of organic molecules around them and these organic molecules kind of had fingers that reached out from being along the tubes. They reached out into solution and were able to grab the constituents that were needed to participate in the reaction.

Instead of building sort of a sandwich shop, a planar sandwich vertically, they built an analog of that sandwich, but they built it out radially. You can see that through this approach there's obviously more surface area and more opportunity for interaction as well. Some of the images of the materials that they produce this way are really spectacular and they showcase how much we can see now at the nanoscale. We've seen lots of transmissional electron micrographs throughout this course in which we looked at structure, where we looked at how even where the individual atoms were placed in quantum dots we could see the crystallinity.

We haven't looked at too many so far in which people were actually looking at the elemental composition so not just asking and answering the question, is there an atom present, but which atom is it. Using the best TM techniques that we have available to ourselves now, we can do spectroscopy on the constituents, what we're looking at. We can actually see this is based on the electron orbitals that we discussed—the basis of the periodic table. We can see spectral signatures in the loss of electrons as they propagate within these transmission electron micrograph systems. We can see spectral signatures through their energy loss of what is present. We can look for the atoms that should be abundant, but we can also look for those that are present at a low concentration.

In the context of our semiconductor discussions, we called these dopants. They were available at very low concentrations, but they were used to influence the electronic properties of our semiconductors. They would donate an electron to the lattice or they would create a semiconductor that was depleted in its density of electrons. With these remarkable advances in microscopy we're able to actually see the elemental constituents that build up in this case on the surface of these multi-walled carbon nanotubes.

The nanotubes themselves played a couple of different roles in this work on making these oxygen producing anodes. One of them was they provided a basis for control over the material morphology. The researchers were able to control the surface, control the binding to that surface, and therefore build the structure that they desired. As we've seen many times now, it was a strategy that successfully increased the surface area, which gave them more opportunities per unit volume to achieve a particular reaction that was desired.

Finally through these tubes, through their conductive properties, they were able to funnel this sequential electron transport to the electrode. Again, they were using kind of the orientation, the fact that they hadn't just made a nanoparticle that was essentially the same in all three dimensions, but instead a tube that was engineered to convey energy in a particular direction and to drive reactions in the perpendicular directions and the radial directions in that manner. As you might have guessed with the analogy with biology the inspiration from the photosynthetic reactions, from our desire to see whether we could make self-assembled materials or devices for water-splitting, it's of course tempting to ask what Angela Belcher's been up to because her work on engineering viruses that we discussed in the previous lecture for batteries.

It seems logical that especially if you're trying to build a system or a system inspired by living organisms that can achieve these photosynthetic reactions, but produce a different fuel, one such as hydrogen that might be preferable for many purposes that the engineering of viruses towards this function might be attractive.

Indeed, the Belcher group at MIT has worked on exactly that. Again, it's using this concept of biological templating because that research group is so capable in engineering a library of viruses and then identifying the few within that library that are inclined to stick to a particular surface, say one that's particularly prone to achieving a desirable synthesis reaction such as in order to achieve artificial photosynthesis. They were able to use the same set of techniques to engineer a virus scaffold that could allow them to assemble a virus that had two key components on them. One of these was the photosensitizer, was the material that was responsible for absorbing the light, and producing the excited electrons so converting the energy from the photonic domain, from the optical domain from the Sun into the form of an excited electron ready to participate in a reaction.

They were also able to engineer their viruses such that they attracted a particular metal oxide, an iridium oxide cluster that served as the catalyst. They were able to build these kind of integrated devices, and here again, the analogy is with the antennas that are so important in the photosynthetic reaction center, here the group was able to make these elongated viruses, but from a shape in overall structural standpoint they had something in common with the carbon nanotubes that had this 1-dimensional linear character. Here they were able to use the actual peptides or proteins that were displayed on the surfaces of these viruses to grow their nanoparticles to put in place the porphyrin so essentially the light absorbing dyes that were required for initial energy harvesting from the Sun and then also to put in place the catalyst that they required.

This discussion wraps up our conversation about the opportunities to use nanotechnology for efficient energy harvesting and also for storage of that energy and then also for its integrated harvesting and storage. We touched on quite a number of themes, in fact in a way we've had the opportunity to integrate a whole bunch of the concepts that nanotechnology embodies.

In fact, one of the broadest ones of those is simply that it's an intrinsically interdisciplinary science and technology. In order to, especially for this last lecture, in order to build an artificial photosynthesis system one needs researchers, professors, graduate students who understand how photosynthesis works in the first place so they have some biology, who understand the inner physics and chemistry of the reactions that occur then, who understand it so well that they can come up with new materials and new strategies that can implement these same broad concepts, but implement them in the case of hydrogen production.

One needs materials, scientists, materials, engineers, who have the capability to put together new material sets in very reproducible and reliable ways. When these people who are capable in the analysis of these materials, these transmission electron micrographs, they're now available, everybody can do it, I mean every university has the capacity to take these images, but it takes a special person with the finesse and the delicacy to take these kinds of images. Often you'll find that the efforts that go on in these fields now, they involve people who have the breadth to be able to think across disciplines, but they also involve quite big teams.

These efforts are so ambitious, I mean think of trying to create devices that mimic what trees and plants took millions and millions of years to figure out how to do. They're trying to do something much more rapidly than that or our energy challenges are urgent. We don't have millions of years. We maybe have a decade or two to come up with some new solutions on the energy front. These teams of very brilliant people are working together very collaboratively, very much across disciplines and as the approaches taken get more interdisciplinary, these teams grow into quite large groups of people working very, very closely together. I think that energy represents one of the most important societal challenges that we have in front of us, but it also represents one of the most exciting opportunities to integrate some of the many, many concepts from across the science and across the technology of the nanoworld.

Nanorobots and Nature's Nanomachines
Lecture 23

Throughout this course, we've looked at many kinds of manmade nanomaterials, which might lead you to think of nanotechnology as something humans invented. But the fact is that nature is even better at making nanomaterials than we are! In this lecture, we'll look at a series of natural nanomaterials and nanomachines that are far more advanced than those that have been generated artificially.

Manmade Nanomachines

- Typically, a machine converts electrical or chemical energy into another type of energy or force. Movement is one way this conversion is manifested, as we see in cars or sewing machines.

- One simple example of a nanomachine is a nanoscale motor made from a collection of fancy organic molecules. It has different domains that link 2 ends with a chain in between, and then there's a ring threaded onto the structure. When an electron is removed from the complex, this changes the charge on part of the chain, and in response, the ring moves from one site to another.

- Another example of a nanomachine is the nanodragster. This was built at Rice University and uses carbon fullerenes as wheels. The researchers who built this were able to get it to zoom around on a flat substrate, but in order to get the dragster to move, they had to heat it up to about 200° C. There haven't yet been any breakthroughs that allow the nanodragster to power itself like a real car with chemical fuel.

- A nanomachine that can use chemical energy consists of a nanorod that is half platinum and half silver. In a solution of peroxide, this nanorod zooms around like a rocket. What happens here is that the gold portion reacts with the peroxide to generate oxygen, which then helps the rod to move. A magnetic field can be used to orient the rod and control the direction of travel. This same system can also carry a small cargo around and drop it off at a defined location.

The size scale of nanomachines means that billions or trillions of them will be needed to perform functions that may be manifested in the macroscopic world.

- Another application of the nanorods involves using them for sensing. Because they speed up in the presence of certain chemicals, tracking their velocity can tell us how much of a certain substance is present. This idea was recently used to detect cancer cells by a group at the University of California in San Diego.

Natural Nanomaterials
- In building nanomachines, one of the concerns is determining what levels of nanomaterials might be harmful to humans or the environment. Such concerns are reasonable, and there are many studies that show we need to be cautious when we scale up the manufacturing of nanomaterials. But it's also true that natural nanomaterials are everywhere in our environment and are not inherently dangerous.

- Among the most abundant natural nanomaterials are diatoms, a type of unicellular algae that are basically everywhere. They handle almost half of the recycling of carbon dioxide into organic molecules and are also an important part of the food chain.
  - o There are more than 16,000 species of diatoms, and they come in all shapes and sizes. They also have a fascinating structural feature—an intricately detailed shell made of silicon.

o Diatoms take in silicon from the environment in a soluble form. Once it's inside their cells, the diatoms put the silicon into tiny vesicles with various shapes. The presence of other molecules then causes the silicon to form a nanoparticle, which is transported to the surface of the diatom to build its shell.

o Diatoms are just single cells, so they divide in order to reproduce. What happens here is that 2 cells are made inside of the silicon capsules, and as they grow, they push the halves of the shell apart. Eventually, the parts of the shell separate, and each diatom grows the part that is missing.

o Nanotechnology researchers are dreaming up ways to use diatoms for different applications. For example, a group of researchers in Oregon figured out how to substitute titanium for the silicon in diatoms, which may be useful for hydrogen production or solar energy conversion.

• Certain types of bacteria produce magnetic nanoparticles and keep them within their cells. It's not completely clear what the bacteria use the magnets for, but the presence of the particles means that the bacteria are always aligned with the magnetic fields that surround the Earth. Birds have a more obvious use for magnetic particles; they use internal magnets to help them navigate when they're migrating.

o The magnetic particles found in birds and bacteria are made of magnetite, a common material composed of iron and oxygen. In nature, the magnetite particles probably get made in the same way as the silicon nanoparticles in diatoms: The iron is processed inside a vesicle and a particle is formed.

o Homing pigeons have a set of 3 neurons that have magnetite particles within them. We don't know how birds transduce the information coming from these particles, but we do know that the magnetic particles help them figure out whether they're pointing north or south. Birds may also use this information to know where they should stop for food.

- Nanostructuring determines the shape of the patterns and the colors on butterfly wings, which are important for recognition and mating.
  - Coloration comes from a variety of different effects, such as interference, diffraction, and scattering.

  - The colors on most butterfly wings come from thin-film interference, where the coloration is due to alternating layers of high– and low–refractive index materials. The patterns that are used to generate the interference and produce the colors we see originate at the nanoscale.

Natural Nanomachines

- All the energy produced in our bodies is made by a nanoscale machine called ATP synthase. This machine uses hydrogen atoms as fuel and produces a molecule called ATP, which is essential for almost all of the functions of our bodies.
  - The most important component of ATP synthase is a rotating stalk that sits in the membranes of our cells.

  - When a hydrogen atom is taken into the ATP synthase, this causes the stalk to twirl. The protein then uses the energy created by the movement of the stalk to make a molecule of ATP.

- There are also nanomachines in the body that produce all of the proteins needed by cells. This machinery is called the ribosome, and it's a complex of 3 very long RNA molecules and about 75 different proteins. It measures about 30 nanometers, and there are many copies of the ribosome throughout our cells.
  - The ribosome carries out a complex set of steps. It first binds a messenger RNA—a transient copy of a sequence found in the DNA genome. The ribosome then recruits transfer RNAs, which match up with the sequence of the messenger RNA. Each transfer RNA has an amino acid attached.

  - In response to the sequence of the messenger RNA, the transfer RNAs line up, and the ribosome zips together all the amino acids to form a protein, rarely making a mistake.

- Another impressive natural nanomachine is made possible by a substance called actin, a protein that polymerizes and can form extended structures. Actin forms a nanomachine with another protein, myosin, that gives our muscles the ability to move us around.
  - Myosin harvests energy from ATP to propel itself along actin filaments; this is how we get movement at the nanoscale.
  - This movement is translated to movement at the macroscale through the action of billions of myosin molecules consuming billions of ATP molecules in our muscles.

Functionality in Manmade Nanomachines
- Have we been able to reproduce artificially the functions of these kinds of natural nanomachines? We haven't even come close. As you saw at the beginning of the lecture, we've really only been able to make machines that can move around in simplistic ways. We have not yet created a machine that could actually make a product like the ones made by natural nanomachines.

- On the other hand, our ability to understand and use the astonishing nanomachines provided by nature is getting better and better. It may be that our best bet when it comes to making nanomachines is to take what nature has come up with and figure out how to control it using the tools of nanotechnology.

Suggested Reading

Jones, *Soft Machines*.

Mallouk and Sen, "How to Build Nanotech Motors."

Williams and Adams, *Nanotechnology Demystified*.

1. What would motivate living organisms to manufacture and use nanomaterials?

2. Are nanomaterials and nanotechnology-enabled products inherently high in cost? If not, what drives some to be low and others to be high?

Nanorobots and Nature's Nanomachines
Lecture 23—Transcript

Shana Kelley: Throughout this course, we've looked at many different kinds of nanomaterials. All of the materials we looked at were man-made materials. This could lead you to think of nanotechnology as something that humans invented. That's not the case and nature is even better at making nanomaterials than we are! What we'll find out is that nature can make nanomachines that are far more advanced than those that have been generated artificially. In this lecture, we'll look at a series of natural nanomaterials and nanomachines and I think this will really give you an appreciation for the role of nanotechnology in nature.

But so you are calibrated, let's start by looking at a few examples of nanomachines that humans have created. We've not yet talked about nanomachines and this may have been something that you thought would actually take up much of the course. If you are familiar with Michael Crichton's book *Prey*, you may be especially curious to hear about nanoscale robots, a type of nanomachine he describes in that book. The nanobots in that book are pretty nasty and they're intent on taking over the world. You haven't seen anything remotely similar to this and that's because no one has ever made a nanorobot—this is a long way off and perhaps even impossible. Let's begin with a look at some nanoscale machines that humans have created and consider their abilities and limitations.

Before we do let's stop and think for a minute about what machines in general actually do. They typically convert one kind of energy into another. For example, many machines convert electrical or chemical energy into another type of energy or force. Movement is one way that this conversion is manifested, and then we have to be clever about what to do with the movement. For a car, it's pretty straightforward; we can convert chemical energy, a force that propels the car forward by causing an axle to turn with the two wheels attached. In a sewing machine, a needle moves up and down in response to consuming electrical energy. So in order to call something a machine, there really needs to be some kind of movement.

Let's look at a pretty simple example of a nanomachine. This is a nanoscale motor that is made from a collection of fancy organic molecules. It has different domains that link two ends and there's a chain in between, and then there's actually a ring threaded onto the structure. When an electron is removed from the complex, this changes the charge on part of the chain, and in response, the ring moves from one site to another. This is the idea behind making a simple nanomachine. We can use an external stimulus to create motion that could hopefully be harnessed to do some kind of useful work.

Another very neat example of a nanomachine is the nanodragster. This was built at Rice University, and uses carbon fullerenes as wheels. If we zoom in on the molecular structure, we can see that it has two large fullerenes at the back, and then two smaller ones at the front. The overall structure is actually like a nanodragster. The researchers who built this were able to get it to zoom around on a flat substrate, but in order to get the dragster to move, they had to heat it up to about 200 degrees. This nanomachine is functional, but it uses lots of energy (kind of like a real dragster), and using thermal energy as fuel is not very practical. There haven't yet been any breakthroughs that allow the nanodragster to power itself like a real car with chemical fuel, but there's lots of effort that is being invested in reaching this goal.

Here's an example of a nanomachine that can use chemical energy. It's a nanorod that is half platinum and half silver. If you give this nanorod a solution of peroxide, it zooms around like a rocket. What's happening is that the gold portion is reacting with the peroxide to generate oxygen. The presence of the oxygen then helps the rod to zoom around. They're pretty fast, so the first nanorods that were engineered to do this could travel a distance 10 times their length in under a minute. A next generation version that contains other more efficient catalysts travels 100 lengths in a second.

The first model of this type that was generated had completely random movement, but eventually ways to control its movement were developed. A magnetic field could be used to orient the rods and get them going in one direction. Using a concentration gradient of fuel was also an effective way to control the movement of these nanorods. The gradient was produced by making a solution with different levels of fuel in different spots in a tank. The nanorods would then orient themselves to travel up a concentration gradient of fuel, and eventually they would congregate at the source of the fuel. Eventually this same system was shown to be able to carry small cargos around—a switching mechanism was even built in so that they could drop off the cargo at a defined location.

Another application of the nanorods involves using them for sensing. Because they speed up in the presence of certain chemicals, tracking their velocity can tell you how much of a certain substance is around. This idea was recently used to detect cancer cells. A group at the University of California in San Diego attached an antibody to the surface of the nanorod, and then they showed that the nanorod could pick up a cancer cell selectively, and then carry it through solution. By watching how quickly the rod moved, they could determine whether or not cancer cells were present in a sample.

Now I could give you many more examples of early-stage nanomachines with limited functionality, but I think by now you get the picture. We are a long way off from Michael Crichton's nanorobots. What he described were nanoscale creatures that could self-replicate by injecting themselves into bacteria. Not only is this is a work of fiction that shouldn't be taken too literally, there are specific reasons why what Crichton envisioned could never come to pass.

Many things, including friction, scale up when you miniaturize things. This means that a tiny robot would experience much more viscous drag, and flying through the air would be more like swimming through molasses, so these nanorobots could not even keep up with a human in a chase and they would be lucky to move even a tenth of an inch per second—making it difficult for them to even keep up with a snail! There are obviously technical challenges with making a robot move as Crichton envisioned. Other properties that he gave his fictional nanomachines, like self-replication, are also extremely remote or perhaps impossible. At present, I think most people in the nanotechnology field believe that this is not necessarily where we should invest our efforts given that we have so many important problems to solve in medicine, energy, and computing.

A more realistic concern than dangerous, self-replicating nanorobots are questions about which nanomaterials, at what levels, might become harmful to humans, or to other features of the environment. For example, silver nanoparticles that kill harmful bacteria might possibly get released into the environment and kill beneficial bacteria, such as those that are used in waste water treatment plants. Some of metals used in nanoparticles like cadmium are known to be toxic, and the unfamiliar properties of some materials at the nanoscale may possibly include new forms of nano-based toxicity.

Concerns like this are reasonable, and there are many studies that show that we need to be cautious when we scale up the manufacturing of nanomaterials, and we need to think about downstream consequences. We also need to ensure that people who work with large quantities of nanomaterials take appropriate measures to avoid inhalation or ingestion. But it is also easy to get carried away with these concerns, and contemplate throwing out the baby out with the bathwater. But given what I hope you've learned about the promise of the materials we've described in this course makes that seem like something that should really be avoided. Moreover, natural nanomaterials are actually everywhere in our environment so they're not inherently dangerous and I think this is an important point to consider when confronting claims about the danger of nanomaterials.

Let's take a look at one of the most abundant natural nanomaterials. Diatoms are a type of tiny unicellular algae that are basically everywhere. They're in fresh water, they're in sea water, they're in our soil, and even ice. They are an important part of the environment and they handle almost half of the recycling of carbon dioxide into organic molecules. Diatoms are also an important part of the food chain and many fish rely on them as their main food source. They've been around for a long time, so the first fossils of diatoms date from the Jurassic period 180 million years ago.

Diatoms have a fascinating structural feature and this is why we're talking about them. They have a coat made of silica with really intricate detail. Diatoms are really the ultimate nanoengineers—they put all kinds of nanoscale features onto their shells and these are really amazing to look at. These things come in all shapes and sizes—there are over 16,000 different species. Some of the diatoms are circular, while others are square. Here you're looking at a diatom that's actually shaped like a peanut. Diatoms very often have shells that actually have multiple layers or parts and this one has an extra covering around its middle.

These structures can be as small as 1000 nanometers across, but what is really amazing is the detail in the diatom's shell—these organisms are somehow able to make nanoscale patterns in their shells. Now how do they do it? Well, they take in silicon from the environment in a soluble form, and then once it's inside their cells, the diatoms put silicon into tiny vesicles. Vesicles are like really small soap bubbles and some diatoms know how to make them shaped like rods or even donuts with holes in the middle. They put silicon into the vesicle, and then the presence of some other molecules that are around causes the silicon to form a nanoparticle, or nanorod, or nanodonut—depending on the shape of the vesicle.

The diatom then transports the nanoshape onto its surface, and particle by particle, it grows a shell. Very intricate patterns get built on the surface of the diatom. We're not exactly sure how they template the pattern, but now that the genomes of several diatoms are sequenced, we have an idea of what proteins they have in their cells, and we'll probably be able to figure this all out. We also don't know what the function of the patterns is, but it's really amazing that nature can do this kind of nanoengineering, and there's undoubtedly more to learn.

Another very interesting aspect of these organisms is how diatoms reproduce. They have to have some way of getting out of their shell if they're going to have any chance of reproducing, and we know that given their abundance that they must be really good at replicating. It turns out that their shell actually has two parts that fit together, kind of like a Petri dish. Sometimes there is a strip wound around the middle—we saw an example of one of these a few minutes ago and this strip can help hold the two pieces together. Now keep in mind that diatoms are just single cells, so they divide in order to reproduce. The two cells end up getting made inside of the silicon capsules, and then as they grow, they push the two parts of the shell apart. Eventually the parts of the shell separate, and then each diatom grows the part of the shell that it's missing and I think it's very neat that they can reproduce this over and over again.

Nanotechnology researchers are inspired by how good diatoms are at making nanomaterials, and they're also dreaming up new ways to use diatoms for different applications. For example, a group of researchers in Oregon figured out how to substitute titanium for the silicon in diatoms. They grew diatoms in the lab in reactors that contained a soluble form of titanium, and when they were done they were able to determine that the diatoms were about 2% titanium. This may not seem like much, but it should be enough to give these diatoms special properties. Titanium dioxide—unlike silicon dioxide—can be used for hydrogen production or solar energy conversion. By manipulating the composition of the diatom's shells, we may be able to use them to produce energy in new ways.

There are also organisms in nature that are very good at producing a different type of nanomaterial—magnetic nanoparticles. There are certain types of bacteria that make these particles and keep them within their cells. It's not completely clear what the bacteria use the magnets for, but it does mean that they always stay aligned with the magnetic fields that surround the Earth. You're looking at a picture of a bacterium called magnetospirillum and you can see that it has a chain of tiny particles running along its side.

The presence of these magnetic particles was discovered relatively recently. It was 1975 when the bacterium and its particles were discovered in shallow pond water. The scientists that were studying them observed that when they took a solution of bacteria out of the pond and they put on a microscope slide, the bacteria would all line up on one side of the slide. They originally thought that the bacteria were navigating towards light—bacteria sometime do this to stay close to the surface of water because the oxygen concentrations are usually higher there. But the scientists eventually realized that they were actually responding to a magnetic field—a really interesting property, an unprecedented property, for a bacterium to have.

Birds have a more obvious use for magnetic particles—you may have heard about this. Birds can use internal magnets to help them navigate when they're migrating. The Earth has a defined magnetic field that varies in strength according to where on Earth a bird is, so then the magnetic particles that they carry can give them navigational information. Let's take a closer look at these particles and how they get made.

The magnetic particles that are found in birds and also the bacteria we just talked about are made of a material composed of iron and oxygen. It's called magnetite and it's very common. Magnetite has a metallic black color and it's found in a crystalline form. We think that in nature, the magnetite particles get made in the same way as the silicon nanoparticles we just talked about—the iron is processed inside a vesicle and then a particle is formed. The locations of these particles have been studied in great depth in homing pigeons, who are obviously really good at finding specific locations. These pigeons have a set of three neurons that have magnetite particles within them. Now we actually don't know how birds transduce the information coming from these particles, but we do know that the magnetic particles help them figure out whether they're pointing north or south. We think that birds use this information not only to make sure that they're pointed in the right direction, but also to know where to stop for food.

A study done a few years ago showed that nightingales that were exposed to the same magnetic field as they would experience in Northern Egypt would eat more and really try to bulk up a bit. Northern Egypt, it turns out, is an important stopping point for these birds, and it's one of the last places that they can stop before they have to cross the Sahara desert. Birds are really smart about not loading themselves down with too much body fat, but to make it across this desert; they usually need to gain about 3 grams of fat. This is the same amount they gained when they were exposed to this magnetic field, so there seems to be a strong link here. Some kind of signal is being transmitted to the neurons that are in contact with these nanoparticles. It's really amazing that these nightingales and other birds have evolved to use nanomaterials as a homing system.

Now let's look at one last example of a natural nanomaterial. We've all marveled at the beautiful colors in butterfly wings and the intricacy of the patterns that different butterflies have. Beyond being nice to look at, these patterns are actually really important for the mating of butterflies and the ways that they recognize one another. It turns out that what determines the shape of the pattern and the actual colors that show up on butterfly wings is the nanostructuring of their wing scales.

If we zoom in on the wing of this butterfly and this is a butterfly called a juniper hairstreak, we see a very complex pattern. There are structures there if we really zoom in with fine resolution we can see structures that are about 2000 nanometers, but you can see that there are even finer nanostructures underneath them that are about 100 nanometers. This is what actually produces the light green color on this butterfly's wings. Small changes in the spacing or the shape of the pattern would cause the wing to reflect a different color. This type of nanopatterning, which can be controlled very finely, is used to create very intricate designs on butterfly wings.

You've probably also seen iridescent beetles and other brightly colored bugs. What's behind the actual colors that we see? Colors can come from a variety of different affects. They can be the result of interference—like when we see colors on the surface of a soap bubble that's coming from interference, or color can come from diffraction—this is something that happens when a beam of light interacts with features that are really the same size as the light waves. Color can also be the result of scattering; the very blue color that we see on a blue jay results from scattering rather than the presence of actual pigments. Similarly, the color that we see on most butterfly wings comes from thin-film interference where the coloration is due to alternating layers of high and low refractive index materials. In short, the patterns that are used to generate the interference and produce colors that we can see, all of these colors really originate at the nanoscale.

These are few examples of nanomaterials made by living organisms that seem to be very safe and compatible with sustaining life. Now let's turn back to the idea of machines at the nano scale and let's look at what kinds of machines nature has developed. Scientists are really just endlessly impressed and inspired by the intricate variety of molecular machines that nature has created.

Also, nature is really good at making very efficient machines. All of the energy produced in our bodies is produced by a nanoscale machine called ATP synthase. This machine uses hydrogen atoms as fuel and it produces a molecule called ATP which is essential for almost all of our bodies' functions. ATP synthase has many different components; it's quite a complex nanomachine. The most important component is a rotating stalk that sits in the membranes of our cells. When a hydrogen atom comes along and is taken into the ATP synthase, this causes the stalk to twirl and the protein then uses the energy created by the movement of the stalk to make a molecule of ATP. This is an incredibly efficient machine; every hydrogen produces one molecule of ATP and the synthase never misses.

There are also nanomachines within our body that produce all of the proteins our cells need. This machinery is called the ribosome and it's a complex of three very long RNA molecules and about 75 different proteins. It measures about 30 nanometers and there are many, many copies of the ribosome throughout our cells. This image shows ribosomes lined up on a long strand of RNA and what they're doing is they're reading a sequence of RNA and they're converting it into a protein sequence. This is a really amazing machine—it does all this by consuming chemical energy. A very complex set of steps is carried out by the ribosome. It first binds what is called a messenger RNA—this is a piece of RNA that is, you can think of it as a transient copy of a sequence found in the DNA genome. It's just converted into RNA. Then the ribosome recruits what are called transfer RNAs. The transfer RNAs are what match up with the sequence of the messenger RNA, and each transfer RNA has an amino acid attached. In response to the sequence of the messenger RNA, the transfer RNAs line up, and then the ribosome zips together all the amino acids to form a protein. The function of the ribosome, a tiny nanomachine, is highly programmed and really specific. The ribosome very rarely makes a mistake—it can't afford to, given how important our proteins are to the functions of our cells.

Another very impressive natural nanomachine is made possible by a substance called actin. Actin is a protein that polymerizes and can form extended structures. This image shows the actin filaments in a cell lit up with a dye—you can see that it forms a really complex network across the cell. Actin forms a nanomachine with another protein, myosin, and this complex between actin and myosin gives our muscles the ability to move us around. Myosin harvests energy from ATP to propel itself along actin filaments—this is how we get movement at the nanoscale.

This movement is translated to movement in the real world, at the macroscale, because our muscles have fibers in them that have lots of actin and myosin.

So billions of myosin molecules consuming billions of ATP molecules is the basis for how we get around. It's all because of the nanomachines that can get the work done. This is a really good example of the collective impact of lots of nanomachines. We have to keep in mind that the size scale of nanomachines makes it such that for their work to be manifested in the macroscopic world, we'll probably need to put billions or trillions of them to work at once.

Have we been able to reproduce artificially the functions of the kinds of natural nanomachine we've just spoken about? Not even close unfortunately. As you saw, we've really only been able to make machines that can move around in pretty simplistic ways. We've not yet come very close to making a machine that could actually make a product—chemical or otherwise—like the ones that natural nanomachines make all the time.

On the other hand, our ability to understand and use the astonishing nanomachines provided by nature is getting better and better. The development of all the tools that nanotechnology researchers have at their disposal allows us to take a look at biology at a very detailed level and learn from it. It may be that our best bet when it comes to making nanomachines is to take what nature has come up with and figure out how to control it using the tools of nanotechnology. This is an approach that is currently being pursued to generate what are called biohybrid devices. These devices might be able to harness, for example, the contractile movement that actin and myosin can produce and control individual muscle fibers to get more controlled movement at the nanoscale than we've seen so far. I think this is a hugely promising approach that has a lot to contribute, and it may well move ahead faster than our trying to replicate or replace what nature does from scratch.

This lecture is the last that we'll discuss the biological aspects of nanotechnology. In the concluding lecture, Ted Sargent will describe another set of very exciting discoveries and developments on the horizon. I hope you now have a better appreciation for what a good nanoengineer nature is; a perspective that really ties together nicely with the previous material we covered on nanomedicine. Here, we've seen that biology is really good at nanoscale engineering because all of its building blocks are nanoscale. This is the very same reason that nanotechnology is so important for medicine. In medicine, it's essential to be able to get down to the nanoscale in order to make drugs more effective, surgery more precise, and disease diagnosis more sensitive. We also know that if we want to convince cells to form tissues, we need to give them the same nanoscale cues that they get within the body.

I hope this material has given you a clear picture of the promise of nanotechnology for important medical advances, the central role of nanomachines in nature, and how the nanoscience of nature and medicine are related and will become even more interrelated in the future. Most of all, I hope you've found these areas of nanotechnology as fascinating as I do.

On the Horizon and in the Far Future
Lecture 24

In this, our final lecture on nanotechnology, we look at some exciting topics that are a little less explored than those we've covered throughout the course. To conclude our course, we'll look at Richard Feynman's predictions about what we might find at "the bottom" and think about what the future might bring.

Smart Dust

- The term "smart dust" is used to describe the idea of having sensors everywhere that could measure properties in our environment. This would be useful for military applications, in which we would like to be able to send tetherless sensors into an environment for monitoring purposes.

- We have all the building blocks already to create such small, ubiquitous sensing devices, but there's an integration problem: putting together the storage of energy. For such a system, we would want to harvest energy from the environment. We might do so photovoltaically or by scavenging energy.

- A further challenge is presented by networking. When we launch these sensors into a region, how can we ensure that they all communicate back to some kind of base station? It might be possible to form ad hoc networks; these would allow the smart dust motes to talk with one another and gradually relay the information back to a central point. There are also small smart networks that can figure out how to form and propagate information in an energy-efficient manner.

- As mentioned, smart dust would be useful for military applications and environmental sensing. Another application might be found in the smart grid. One of the key components of a smart electrical grid would be effective sensing of the electrical properties of the power that is conveyed or delivered to the grid, combined with management of energy across the grid.

The Cloak of Invisibility

- The idea of a cloak of invisibility is to wrap an object in a material that essentially ensures that electromagnetic waves, such as light or microwaves, will pass around it and recombine as if the object was not present.

- Normally, an object alters light impinging on it or microwave-frequency radiation impinging on it both at the source and in transmission on the far side of the object. The object alters what happens to the wave fronts. Instead of being planar and flat, they become rippled. When they're interfered with in this fashion, the waves render the object causing the interference detectable.

- To make something truly invisible, we would need the optical wavelengths to manifest a property of not being disrupted by the object. We would also need to ensure that there's no absorption. Metamaterials have made progress in this direction.

- Metamaterials are artificial materials, in which pure phases of one crystal, metal, semiconductor, or other material are combined in a periodic or partially periodic structure such that they influence the dispersion of electromagnetic waves.

- These metamaterials were initially implemented at microwave frequencies, but there has been recent progress in building and using them at optical length scales. There are, however, two challenges that remain unresolved.

  o First, the way these dispersion properties are engineered means that we can mostly achieve cloaking only in a single frequency. Cloaking something across the full visible spectrum will be much more challenging.

o   Second, there is still some absorption of light that occurs within these metamaterials, which means that they remain detectable, for the moment.

Conformable and Deformable Nanomaterials

- We've talked in this course about numerous subjects: the capabilities of semiconductors, such as silicon, in electronics; the fact that gallium arsenide is a good material for light emission and for making solar cells; single-walled and multi-walled carbon nanotubes that can be coated onto substrates; and quantum dots.

- We've also noted that in working with these materials, we're often interested in integrating multiple functions. We might like to put down an electronic device on silicon, combine it with an energy-harvesting device based on gallium arsenide, and perhaps add a photodetector made out of a third material.

- Traditionally, semiconductor processing and growth have worked based on a process known as epitaxy, the growth of perfectly lattice-matched crystals on top of one another. But some of the materials we've discussed don't even necessarily have lattices; they could be amorphous, or crystalline, or have non-planar shapes. Thus, it's not obvious how we can use our traditional stack of crystals to build stacked heterostructures.

- John Rogers, a professor at the University of Illinois at Urbana-Champaign, has made incredible strides in this area. He has developed ways to put down a diverse array of materials on a template and then use a transfer printing process to transfer this layer onto another substrate. The ability to combine rigid and flexible materials Rogers has achieved in this way is quite powerful.
  o   This innovation has allowed us to combine devices that look in different frequency regimes. We can, for example, take the building blocks of radio-frequency electronics—the basis for our cell phones—and combine them with materials that are suited to imaging in the optical domain.

o   Rogers's work is also enabling devices that allow cardiac mapping by integrating electronics and biological materials. This could lead to implantable electronic materials that could be used in medical applications.

o   The integration of rigid and flexible substrates also shows promise for reducing the cost of devices used for solar energy harvesting.

o   Another interesting application for conformable materials that have a shape memory is in the introduction of cardiovascular stents. These could be engineered to have a condensed phase to enable insertion and an expanded phase for function once they are in place.

Environmental Risks

- Many researchers are exploring the consequences of either deliberate or accidental introduction of nanoparticles into the environment. Certain nanomaterials are broken down in the environment in the same way as organic molecules. Others are retained for longer periods of time and have the potential to be taken up as part of an ecosystem and do damage.

- From a regulatory and environmental standpoint, the issues that are presented through nanotechnology are not qualitatively different from the issues that exist across processed chemistry. Like all fields involved in the synthesis of new materials or structures, it's important for nanotechnology to be part of the regulatory process and to be aware of the health implications of new materials.

Richard Feynman's Predictions

- In 1959, Richard Feynman issued an invitation to enter a new field of physics with his speech "There's Plenty of Room at the Bottom." Feynman did not believe that the regime of the very small would further illuminate fundamental physics but that it would provoke great interest in what happens when phenomena are combined in complex fashion.

- At the time that Feynman was speaking, the transmission electron microscope was available, and researchers were imaging natural materials on the length scales that we have discussed. Feynman wondered how we could turn this capability around and start to engineer on these length scales ourselves. He pointed out that it was not beyond our capabilities to imagine writing the 24 volumes of the *Encyclopedia Britannica* on the head of a pin.

- Feynman asked: Why not transform our electron microscopes from readers to writers? Let's orient our atomic beams and carve matter, change the properties of materials. Interestingly, electron beam lithography is one of the major ways of crafting matter at the nanoscale.

- Feynman also pointed out that DNA already showcased the ability to write the *Encyclopedia Britannica* on the head of a pin. In that sense, he anticipated that nanotechnology would get inspiration from biology.

- Although Feynman said that there's plenty of room at the bottom, he was taking a top-down view. Further, he didn't anticipate the crucial role the field of electronics would play in the exploration of the bottom, and he didn't touch on the ways in which the rules of physics are altered at smaller length scales.

- Feynman noted that the capability to work on smaller length scales would have significant technological implications, but he didn't speculate about what they would be. Such applications are hard to anticipate because they are often driven by the needs of people and society.

- Just as Feynman wasn't able to anticipate all the areas of application, we, too, have just scratched the surface of the implications and applications of working with materials at the nanoscale. We invite you to stay tuned to this field as it evolves and we witness remarkable developments in the future.

Suggested Reading

Allhoff, Lin, Moor, and Weckert, *Nanoethics*.

Alvarez, Colvin, Lead, and Stone, "Research Priorities to Advance Eco-Responsible Nanotechnology."

Berube, *Nano-Hype*.

Poslad, *Ubiquitous Computing*.

Wikipedia, "Metamaterial."

———, "Smartdust."

Questions to Consider

1. How could smart dust be deployed for (1) peaceful environmental and/or water quality monitoring purposes and (2) military purposes?

2. If a company or a country wanted to gain a distinctive place as a leader in nanotechnology, what would it have to do to secure such a competitive advantage?

3. Which of the ethical and societal issues that nanotechnology raises are nano-specific? Which are shared with any new technology? In light of the potential rewards and risks—foreseeable and unforeseeable—of nanotechnology, should it be pursued and, if so, how?

On the Horizon and in the Far Future
Lecture 24—Transcript

Ted Sargent: In this our final lecture on nanotechnology, I'd like to begin with a discussion of some exciting topics some of which are a little less explored as those that we've covered throughout the course. Then I'd like to see how we can pull it all together. We can look at the history of nanotechnology till today and think about the future going forward.

We started on the first of one of a number of exciting topics that we haven't gotten to spend too much time on. In a way what I'm going to describe is kind of an integration problem. The idea is sometimes called Smartdust and the idea is one where sensors could be everywhere, sensors that we desire to measure properties of our environment to monitor a vulnerable environmental enclave. There are military applications in which we would like to be able to send tetherless sensors into an environment to monitor what's going on there.

The reason I call this an integration problem is because we have all of the building blocks in place already for this. We've talked in this course about methods of sensing, like optical detection, our ability to make cameras that are incredibly small, lightweight, low in cost, low in their power consumption. We've also talked in Shana's discussions about biosensors. We're able to detect biomolecules or chemicals in the environment. This is very relevant to industrial sensing or to learning information about our biological environment. We know that we're able to communicate information at vast information rates using the transceivers that are inside our cell phones and we're able to do so in a very manageable way.

Building these sensor networks based on ubiquitous small sensing devices that are so low in cost, you can imagine just kind of letting a powder puff of them into the air and having them land in the environment. It's something that in principle we should be able to do. There's that integration problem of putting together the storage of energy. In fact, we're going to want to harvest energy from our environment. We may do so photovoltaically. There's also ways to scavenge mechanical energy, vibrations, or thermal energy, changes in temperature from one region to another and to use these to scavenge a little bit of energy from our environment, store it up and use it in powering our remote sensors, sometimes called a mote.

The communications as I said is something we can take care of, but how about the networking side of it. When we launch a bunch of these little sensors into a region that we're interested in monitoring, how are we going to ensure that they can all communicate back to us to some kind of base station? One of the ideas is the formation of what are called ad hoc networks, spontaneous networks, where wherever these little bits of smart dots land they're able to talk with one another. Because they're close to each other the amount of power that they need to communicate with each other is very small and then they can gradually relay the information back to a central point.

These are also smart networks or intelligent networks that can figure out how to form and propagate information in the most energy efficient manner. Here're a couple of pictures of some of the early prototypes. They're kind of millimeters in size and they're very compact as a result and there are a whole lot of functions that can now be integrated into them. The applications I mentioned already were some military applications prospectively, espionage, you can easily imagine environmental sensing. But, there's another application area that's a very interesting one for these sensors and we touched on it just a little bit when we were talking about power and energy, we were talking about the smart grid.

There we were talking about how when we bring renewable, such as solar energy, wind energy, on line that we can be pushing energy in either direction from the direction of production to consumption or now vice versa that each of us can become an energy producer. One of the key components of a smart electrical grid, one which is robust which can accommodate renewable, which doesn't have to throwaway some sources of energy simply because they can't be accommodated, which negotiates across the grid. One of the components of this will be effective sensing of the electrical properties of power that's conveyed or delivered to that grid and then kind of a synchronization, a management, across that grid of the waves of energy that are being conveyed.

Here again, these sensors that are very low in cost, ubiquitous, robust, very good communicating and where we introduce somebody new onto the grid they can rapidly become part of that network, kind of an ad hoc version of network formation, all of these concepts apply as well there in the realization of one of these intelligent energy grids. Another topic that's seen great attention really captures people's imagination, it's referred to as cloaks of invisibility. In fact, cloaks of invisibility are just an example of one of the exciting application areas for new materials that are referred to as metamaterials and when we shrink them down they become nanomaterials. They're interesting, not just at the nanoscale, but also at larger length scales.

Let's talk a bit about these metamaterials and how they relate to cloaks of invisibility. Here's the idea that we can wrap an object that we wish to cloak in a material that essentially ensures that electromagnetic waves such as light or also microwaves will pass around it and then recombine as if the object was not there. Normally if you were to have an object and it would see a light impinging upon it or say a microwave frequency radiation impinging upon it, then that object would alter both at the source, so in the reflections, and also in transmission on the far side of the object. That object would alter what happened to those wave fronts. Instead of being planar and flat, they would become rippled, it would be like how in an ocean with waves lapping up on shore.

If you were to stick a buoy there, the buoy would alter how the waves formed in the longitudinal direction. And so waves, therefore, when they're interfered with in this fashion render the objects that interfere with them detectable. This is of course how we experience a light and how it's transmitted or not transmitted through objects and how we see objects in our way. The idea with these metamaterials is that instead we're able to surround an object with a cloak that ensures that the waves pass around it and then recombine as if the object was not there.

To make something truly invisible what are you actually going to want to do? Well first of all if you're thinking in the optical wavelengths that we see with our own eyes, clearly all the colors of the spectrum, you're going to want them all to manifest this property of being not disrupted by the object. Another is that you're going to want to ensure that not only does the shape of the waves, the optical waves that make it around this object, combine and keep its structure, not be perturbed. We're also going to want to ensure there's no absorption.

Metamaterials have made progress in this direction. By metamaterials what we mean is artificial materials, entities where instead of just using a pure phase of one crystal or one metal or one semiconductor or one dielectric of transparent material, we combine these together often in a periodic structure or a partially periodic structure and the ways in which electromagnetic waves propagate around them have their dispersion influenced. By dispersion, a concept we talked about when we were discussing fiber optic communications, we mean how the behavior of this light depends on its frequency.

These metamaterials had initially been implemented at microwave frequencies. There's now been recent progress in building them and implementing them and utilizing them at optical length scales, but there are two challenges that remain not fully resolved. The first of these is that the way these dispersion properties are engineered, the way the frequency dependence of these behaviors are engineered, ensures that we can mostly do this essentially in a single frequency. For example, if you're interested in flying a plane through some airspace and you know what people may be looking at, what frequencies they may be using to look at you, if you can predict that they'll use a particular frequency of the electromagnetic spectrum then you may be able to cloak relative to that frequency.

If as when you think of visible wavelength applications in using our own eyes, if you're interested in being able to cloak something across the full visible spectrum that's going to be much more challenging because these metamaterials are actually using dispersive properties, which are inherently narrow band in order to guide light around their edges and have it recombine as if it were not disturbed. The other component that makes this metamaterials field in cloaking still challenging is the fact that there still is some loss, some absorption of light that occurs within these materials and for the moment then these remain detectable, that perhaps the shapes of the waves are kept as they were on the front side of the object, but the amplitude of the waves is not perfectly retained. There still is a means of detection; it's subtle, but there's a means of detection. These challenges of bandwidth and loss will need to be addressed and these are exactly the kinds of questions that researchers are continuing to work on.

I wanted to talk about another very exciting area for the world of nanomaterials that has made great progress, but has yet to be fully drawn to a complete conclusion with commercial products generated and things like that. I'll call these conformable and deformable nanomaterials. Let me describe a bit what I'm talking about. We've talked in this course about how semiconductors such as silicon are so capable in electronics. We've talked about how gallium arsenide is such a good material for light emission, in fact, it happens also to be an extremely good material for making a solar cell out of.

We've discussed single-walled and multi-walled carbon nanotubes, which can be coated onto things. We talked about quantum dots, but often we're interested in integrating multiple functions. We're interested in putting down an electronic device on silicon, combining it with an energy harvesting device, such as one based on gallium arsenide, perhaps making a photodetector out of a third material, putting them all on the same substrate. Traditionally semiconductor processing and growth have worked based on a process known as epitaxy which we described in the solar lecture where we were talking about triple junction devices about growing perfectly lattice matched crystals on top of one another.

Now this panoply of materials I just described don't even necessarily all have lattices, some of them could be amorphous, some of them could be crystalline, some of them are shapes that are even non-planar and so it's not obvious at all how to use our traditional stacking of crystals on top of each other to build stacked heterostructures or hetero-materials. This is where a professor at the University of Illinois at Urbana-Champaign, John Rogers, has made incredible strides and has really captured the world's imagination. Professor Rogers has come up with a number of ways to take really a diverse array of materials and first put them down onto a first template and use a transfer printing process in order to transfer this layer onto another substrate.

He's able to do this many, many times. He's able to use repeated application of this additive process that used these soft stamps and these donor substrates that donate their materials that we've coated onto them and integrate them onto a set, to make a 3-dimensionally structured heterogeneously integrated material. He's able to combine in this way both rigid and flexible materials and devices. That combination is very powerful. In fact, it's caused a lot of people to question whether the need for nanomaterials for their flexibility alone is required because what John Rogers has managed to do is integrate rigid materials onto flexible substrates, singulate them appropriately, and have them flex. He's shown that there's more than one way to build a flexible material if one uses some flexible thinking in assembling the entire stack of materials.

This has a whole diversity of potential application. One of the things it allows us to do is to combine together devices that look in incredibly different frequency regimes, are able to take the building blocks of radio frequency electronics, the basis for our cell phones, also the basis for some gigahertz imaging or microwave imaging and we're able to combine it now with materials that are much better suited to imaging in the optical domain or perhaps in the terahertz domain. It allows us to combine things like carbon nanotubes and carbon nanotube arrays, which have had diverse applications ranging from catalysis as we discussed together energy harvesting, but also biological sensing.

It's enabling some interesting devices that allow cardiac mapping by integrating electronics and biological materials together. It's potentially leading to some implantable materials and implantable electronic materials that can also be used in medical applications. It really is changing the way we think about a world divided into the rigid and the flexible, but instead this strategy finds ways to integrate those things that are traditionally made on rigid substrates and puts them onto flexible substrates. In fact, the concept is potentially also very useful in solar energy harvesting because some of the most promising materials from an efficiency standpoint in solar energy harvesting are based on these more exotic compound semiconductors grown on a costly compound semiconductor substrate.

There's recent indications that we can slough off the upper layer of that compound semiconductor substrate that we've grown towards our photovoltaic purpose and transfer it to a much less expensive substrate and then reuse the costly substrate to grow the next layer, to grow the next device. These conformable or flexible materials, in a way, they're just one example of materials that have shape that's changeable and one of the more interesting concepts is to have materials having these shapes that are alterable, but where the materials also have a memory. In fact, these shape memory materials, such as shape memory polymers are able to retain two or three shapes in their memory. Then we can switch them, we can tune them using temperature or an electric or magnetic field or even light in order to alter their shape.

There's a very practical example of where one would want to do this such as in the introduction of cardiovascular stents. Here the stent needs to be small, kind of in its condensed phase as we insert it along a vein or an artery, but then we want to expand it to prop it open and to leave it in place at the appropriate location inside the patient. In this case, the concept of using shape memory materials is very attractive for it allows us to alter from the shape suitable to insertion to the shape which we will want it installed within the patient.

We've spent a lot of time in this course talking about technology, talking about its potential, talking about applications or anticipated applications of nanotechnology, but it's very important including in a field like this that's filled with excitement and optimism to think about the risks, to thinks about the downside. There certainly are researchers looking at the environmental implications of nanomaterials. They ask things like, what if there were an unintentional release of certain nanomaterials into the environment? What would their fate be? There's also people who look at questions in ethics of nanotechnology and nanomaterials, questions such as how far will our power extend to work at the nanoscale, what new properties might we be able to endow nature with? How do we ensure that we don't cross the boundaries of what's societally appropriate to work with nanotechnology?

On the nanomaterials questions, there's been a lot of work looking at the fate of nanoparticles in the environment. Again, what if, either deliberately or accidentally, certain nanomaterials were introduced into the environment? The answer is that there are many answers; it depends on the nanomaterials. There are certain nanomaterials that essentially get broken down into the environment the way any number of organic molecules would. There's others that are retained for longer or longer within the environment and those, of course, are the ones that have the potential to be taken up as part of an ecosystem and do damage, so there have been studies for example on how carbon nanotubes at very elevated concentrations can be dangerous to the health of certain fish and small mammals that have been studied in the context of this research.

My own opinion on this work is twofold. First, it is extremely important for all of us in the field to be participants in these investigations, into the fate of nanomaterials in the environment. For those of us who work more on advancing the technology for its own sake towards a particular application, it's tempting to put all our energy just into those question, but in fact we will be part, we need to be part of shaping how the community, the regulatory agencies respond to the emergency of new classes of materials with new properties.

I think my other thought is that fundamentally the issues that are presented from a regulatory and environmental standpoint through nanotechnology, through nanomaterials, the issues are not qualitatively different from the issues that exist across processed chemistry, from the creation of new molecules and materials. Like all fields involved in the synthesis of new materials, new molecules, new structures, it's important for nanotechnology to be part of the regulatory process, to be aware of the health implications of the materials that it's generating, and it needs to participate in that dialogue, but that the fundamental nature of the questions that emerge in from nanomaterials, from a regulatory standpoint, the fundamental nature is not different, but the details are likely to be different and so we need to be part of that conversation and we need to look at it early. We can't wait until something is just ready to go onto the market in mass production, now is the time to be participating in that conversation.

I'd like to close our course with a couple of reflections back onto the history of the field of nanotechnology, including the early history, and then also think a bit about the directions in which this field can go in the future. To do this, I'd like to recall a speech that Richard Feynman, a professor from Caltech gave in 1959. The speech was called "There's Plenty of Room at the Bottom: An Invitation to Enter a New Field of Physics." In this speech, Dr. Feynman who wasn't explicitly working in this field—he was a more fundamental, theoretical physicist—he went into some very intriguing speculations about the possibility of working in the scale of the very small.

Let me just touch on a couple of things that he mentioned. One was that he felt that going into the regime of the very, very small, where he talks about the bottom, where there's an abundance of room, it's not going to illuminate fundamental physics. In fact, this fundamental physics, even by that time was becoming extremely well-known, Feynman himself was diving deeper and deeper into the strange particles that make up matter that constitute the protons and neutrons that constitute matter so it was in the subatomic world. He did say that perhaps there was an analogy with solid state physics and solid state physics then was relatively young in that it wasn't' so much that it would be illuminating the fundamental new concepts of how matter is constituted, but instead it would provoke great interest into what happens when you combine phenomena in complex fashions.

I think that insight is very real and in a way one could consider nanotechnology simply to be the quantitative improvement in our dexterity in manipulating matter and turning it into more and more complex structures. Dr. Feynman also remarked that even though he didn't give too many details of this, which is itself interesting, but he said that he felt that gaining dexterity on the scale of the very small would have a huge number of technological applications. That I think is hard to argue with and I think one of the areas in which Dr. Feynman was broadly right, what there would be huge numbers of applications, but one of the areas that was so hard to foresee is what those applications would be.

He spoke specifically about manipulating and controlling things on a very small scale and he called out, he predicted that in the year 2000, again this was 41 years before the year 2000, he said that in the year 2000 when they looked back at this age, people will wonder why it was not until about 1960 that anybody began seriously to move in this direction. That itself is an interesting point that they were as Dr. Feynman noted at the time, there were a number of capabilities that were just emerging that allowed people to start exploring, manipulating matter at the nanoscale. The transmission electron microscope was already well in place and people were able to image down to the length scales that we've been looking at together.

Primarily they were imaging natural materials, things that had already been made and one of Dr. Feynman's insights was to say, how can we turn this around and start to engineer on these length scales ourselves? Specifically to that point, he said why can we not write the entire 24 volumes of the Encyclopedia Britannica on the head of a pin? It sounds like a crazy thing to do, but he did the math and worked out that essentially it would be necessary to reduce the font size by a factor of 25,000. Those little dots that made up the fine half tone reproductions of images in the Encyclopedia Britannica that were about 1/150 of an inch across, by the time you scaled them down 25,000 fold, they would become about 8 nanometers in diameter. The word nanometer was available then, he used 80 angstroms, which was a more conventional unit for people to use, especially then before people explicitly talking of nanotechnology.

He pointed out that this would be 32 atoms across in a typical material or a metal and so the dot, if you took a square of that area, would be of the order of about 1000 atoms. Then he said well this is not beyond our capabilities to imagine doing. It hadn't been done yet, people hadn't started writing on this kind of length scale at the time, but he imagined how it could be done, and he essentially said let's take our electron microscopes and let's turn them into writers rather than just readers. Let's orient our atomic beams and let's carve matter, let's change the properties of a material using these electron beams, let's modify it that way, and as a result we can focus down using the much smaller wavelength of electrons than photons have and we're able to write. Then of course, we can essentially use the same instruments in a different mode to read.

Well what's interesting about that remark is that that's precisely how one of the major forms of crafting matter at the nanoscale did emerge. Electron beam lithography, which is one of the ways in which we get beyond the limits of photolithography, the resolution that's available there, the optical resolution, and into the electron resolution scale, that is achieved essentially by reversing the operation of an electron microscope into write mode instead of read mode. Dr. Feynman also talked about the role of DNA, the fact that when we get down to these length scales, and it seems so surprising that one could put all 24 volumes of the Encyclopedia Britannica on the head of a pin, but he then pointed out that DNA already was known to do the same thing. The amount of information communicated there is very efficient from the point of view of utilization of atoms. For one bit, one binary piece of information one only requires about 50 atoms whereas his modest proposal relied on 1000 atoms per bit of information.

In that sense, he also anticipated that nanotechnology as it evolved would be getting inspiration from what the biological had done and that many of our checks or many of our reference points us to the potential of what we were doing would come from the world around us, that there would be proof points through the biological as to what one can do, the kind of control and resolution one can have. Another interesting point that he made is that a lot of the materials that were being worked on then in solid state physics, they were based on very perfect crystals. They were based on moving towards purity and so one could achieve control and delocalization of electrons as is achieved in silicon and other semiconductors. He noted that at the time, they were making the checkerboards where you might have one material and then a second one and then the first and the second in various complex arrays. Instead, the focus was kind of on the purity rather than onto controlled impurities.

In fact, that notion of a checkerboard is really a description of the way metamaterials work. It involves combining at least two sets of materials, creating what researchers have called binary superlattices, which has now become very much something that researchers focus on in making new functional materials. It's interesting to ask what was not present, what was missing from this view? I would say that Dr. Feynman's view certainly did start if you like from the top. He said there's plenty of room at the bottom, but he was starting from the macroscopic and wondering how we could take the Encyclopedia Britannica and write it on the length scale of a nanometer. While he did certainly touch on DNA, an emergent phenomena, a material where the synthesis occurs starting at the nanometer scale rather than starting at the macroscopic scale, his focus was more on the top down.

That leads to another interesting point that he didn't explicitly anticipate because of course the field of electronics was in its early days. In 1959, we didn't have these complex integrated circuits or even precursors to them. We were still at the edge of perfecting the discrete transistors that would then be connected together to form electronic integrated circuits. He didn't explicitly anticipate the way in which the field of circuits, the field of electronics would play such a crucial role that in a way the field of photolithography would be writing the Encyclopedia Britannica with, almost the resolutions that he anticipated, today down to the sort of tens of nanometers length scale that we're now able to write at.

In fact, I think you would've been surprised that we're still using light, shorter and shorter wavelengths of light, but we're still using light to write our smaller and smaller electronic circuits. This has often been called the surprisingly long longevity of photolithography and how it's extended forward so much. Also, I think interestingly, Feynman didn't explicitly anticipate how the rules of the game would change, that he was entirely aware of quantum effects occurring at the short length scales, this was the area in which he was very much an expert. But, I think one of the most exciting things about nanotechnology today is the way in which the rules of physics that we work with, the playground, the grammar, in which we build new materials, the rules of the game are altered when we get to these shorter length scales.

Finally, I think, perhaps the broadest comment, which again he got right, which was that there would be huge technological implications. But what exactly what would they be? That is so hard to anticipate. So much of what we talked about today has been medical in nature, so much of it has been related to energy, and perhaps this comes in part because of course one hadn't explored the nanoworld and all of its details. But also, that societal needs, what people think are important, what politicians think is important, what funding agencies, what peers within the research community decide is important. These are things that influence where the focus is and so, so much investment has been made into nanotechnology focused on energy because society has such urgent needs in these regards.

With that I'd like to thank you for your interest in this field. As you can tell, it's one that I'm incredibly excited about. It's one where I think we're full of potential. I think we haven't explored that full potential and I think just as Feynman wasn't able to anticipate all the areas of application, I don't think we've even scratched the surface of all the implications and applications of working with materials at the nanoscale. I hope that with this introduction you'll stay tuned, you'll participate, you'll learn as the field evolves because it's an exciting one. I'm hoping to be along for the ride for quite a while into the future. I hope that you'll get to partake in it as well. Thank you.

Bibliography

In the fields spanned by nanotechnology, online resources, magazine articles, and academic journals are often the best available sources of information and insight, but general-interest and specialist books have been included where possible. Especially recommended readings are marked with an asterisk.

*Agrawal, Govind P. *Fiber-Optic Communication Systems*. New York: Wiley, 1997. The canonical text used by students around the world studying fiber-optic communications. Excellent sections on the device technologies that make the Internet possible.

Aldersey-Williams, Hugh, Peter Hall, Ted Sargent, and Paola Antonelli. "Design and the Elastic Mind." New York: The Museum of Modern Art, New York, 2008. Details an exhibit at the museum and includes a chapter on nanotechnology designed to appeal to the aesthetics of design and architecture.

Alivisatos, A. Paul. "Less Is More in Medicine." *Scientific American* 17 (2007): 72–79. An excellent general review of nanomedicine.

*Allen, T. R., and P. R. Cullis. "Drug Delivery Systems: Entering the Mainstream." *Science* 303 (2004): 1818. An excellent overview of the need for drug delivery systems.

*Allhoff, Fritz, Patrick Lin, James Moor, and John Weckert, with a foreword by Mihail C. Roco. *Nanoethics: The Ethical and Social Implications of Nanotechnology*. Hoboken, NJ: Wiley-Interscience, 2007. A critical view of nanotechnology's potential and challenges, with a broad overview by Mihail Roco, chair of the U.S. National Science and Technology Council subcommittee on Nanoscale Science, Engineering and Technology.

Alvarez, Pedro J. J., Vicki Colvin, Jamie Lead, and Vicki Stone. "Research Priorities to Advance Eco-Responsible Nanotechnology." *ACS Nano* 3, no.

7 (2009): 1616–1619. A superb perspective on nanotechnology and the environment. Vicki Colvin is the leading name in this important field.

*Aricò, Antonino Salvatore, Peter Bruce, Bruno Scrosati, Jean-Marie Tarascon, and Walter van Schalkwijk. "Nanostructured Materials for Advanced Energy Conversion and Storage Devices." *Nature Materials* 4 (2005): 366–377. A review of the latest advances in nano-based batteries, coauthored by J. M. Tarascon, the pioneer of the field.

*Asiyanbola, B., and W. Soboyejo. "For the Surgeon: An Introduction to Nanotechnology." *Journal of Surgical Education* 65 (2008): 155. A tutorial highlighting the promise of nanoscale tools for more precise surgery.

*Atala, A., R. Lanza, J. A. Thomson, and R. Nerem. *Principles of Regenerative Medicine.* Boston: Academic Press, 2008. A text providing a basic overview of the field and frontier areas in regenerative medicine.

Ben-Yakar, A., and F. Bourgeois. "Ultrafast Laser Nanosurgery in Microfluidics for Genome-Wide Screenings." *Current Opinion in Biotechnology* 20 (2009): 100. A review of cutting-edge techniques under development in research labs.

*Berube, David M. *Nano-Hype: The Truth behind the Nanotechnology Buzz.* Amherst, NY: Prometheus Books, 2006. A critical—even skeptical— perspective on the field of nanotechnology, assessing its revolutionary potential and its promotion by advocates.

Bohr, Mark T., Robert S. Chau, Tahir Ghani, and Kaizad Mistry. "The High-k Solution: Microprocessors Coming out This Fall Are the Result of the First Big Redesign in CMOS Transistors since the Late 1960s." *IEEE Spectrum* 44, no. 10 (October 2007): 30–35. An account of a key recent advance in transistors that was needed to keep Moore's law advancing apace; author Robert Chau of Intel is a world leader in the field.

*Brock, David C., ed. *Understanding Moore's Law: Four Decades of Innovation.* Philadelphia: Chemical Heritage Press, 2006. Shows how the rapid pace of advances in computing can be traced to the physics of semiconductors and transistors, to the planar lithographic technologies used to define integrated circuits, and to the drive toward increased speed and sophistication in computing and communications.

*Callister, William D., and David G. Rethwisch. *Materials Science and Engineering: An Introduction.* 8th ed. New York: John Wiley and Sons, 2010. A classic text that introduces how scientists and engineers think about the material world.

*Ceruzzi, Paul E. *A History of Modern Computing.* Cambridge, MA: MIT Press, 2003. An engaging historical perspective on how computing evolved—from the physics of semiconductors and transistors all the way to the design of microprocessors.

Choi, Young-Eun, Ju-Won Kwak, and Joon Won Park. "Nanotechnology for Early Cancer Detection." *Sensors* 10 (2010): 428. A thorough overview of recent development in nanosensors for early cancer detection.

*Christensen, Clayton. *The Innovator's Dilemma.* Boston: Harvard Business School, 1997. The classic text on "disruptive technologies"—the challenges that fundamental innovators have and how they can be overcome.

Cooper, J., J. Walshaw, Alan Mills, M. C. Peitsch, and N. Guex. *Principles of Protein Structure, Comparative Protein Modeling, and Visualization.* http://swissmodel.expasy.org/course/course-index.htm. An excellent resource on protein structure.

*de la Rica, R., and H. Matsui. "Applications of Peptide and Protein-Based Materials in Bionanotechnology." *Chemical Society Reviews* 39 (2010): 3499–3509. A detailed review of protein-based nanomaterials and nanomaterial conjugates.

*Dragoman, Mircea, and Daniela Dragoman. *Nanoelectronics: Principles and Devices.* Boston: Artech House Publishers, 2006. A sophisticated perspective on the physics of new generations of transistors and how these are driving forward the progress of computing.

DuPont. "Science and Technology at DuPont." http://www2.dupont.com/ Science/en_US/rd/index.html. Corporate Web site describing the research and development efforts of DuPont.

*Dvir, T., B. Timko, D. S. Kohane, and R. Langer. "Nanotechnological Strategies for Engineering Complex Tissue." *Nature Nanotechnology* 6 (2011): 13. An excellent overview of tissue engineering approaches.

Federici, John F., Dale Gary, Robert Barat, and Zoi-Heleni Michalopoulou. "T-Rays vs. Terrorists: Terahertz Radiation Lets Security Screeners Find Bombs and Weapons Wherever They're Hidden." *IEEE Spectrum* 44, no. 7 (July 2007): 47–52. An overview of how the capability to sense previously undetected colors of light—the newly sensed terahertz range—is allowing improved threat detection.

Ferrari, M. "Frontiers in Cancer Nanomedicine: Directing Mass Transport through Biological Barriers." *Trends in Biotechnology* 28 (2009): 181. A review focused on how nanocarriers can solve problems in drug delivery.

Frankel, Felice C., and George M. Whitesides. *No Small Matter: Science on the Nanoscale.* Cambridge, MA: Belknap Press of Harvard University Press, 2009. A highly visual, aesthetic view of the nanoworld by George Whitesides, a pioneer of the field.

*Gates, Bruce C. "Catalysis: Individual Nanoparticles in Action." *Nature Nanotechnology* 3 (October 2008): 583–584. DOI:10.1038/nnano.2008.295. An article reviewing some of the latest advances in using nanoparticles for more efficient chemical catalysis.

*Giljohann, D., and C. Mirkin. "Drivers of Biodiagnostic Development." *Nature* 462 (2009): 461. General information on the complexities of diagnostic test development.

*Green, Dan. *Physics: Why Matter Matters!* New York: Kingfisher, 2008. A children's cartoon-style introduction to the key physics underlying nanotechnology, including quantum mechanics, classical mechanics, and bonding principles.

Green, Martin A., Keith Emery, Yoshihiro Hishikawa, and Wilhelm Warta. "Solar Cell Efficiency Tables (Version 36)." *Progress in Photovoltaics: Research and Applications* 18, no. 5 (August 2010): 346–352. The annual update of the latest, greatest solar technologies and their performance.

*Heath, J. R., M. E. Davis, and L. Hood. "Nanomedicine Targets Cancer." *Scientific American* 300, no. 2 (February 2009): 44–51. This review provides a general overview of important challenges in the diagnosis and treatment of cancer that nanomaterials may be able to address.

*Hillery, Anya M., Andrew W. Lloyd, and James Swarbrick, eds. *Drug Delivery and Targeting.* New York: Taylor and Francis, 2001. An excellent text on the challenges and frontiers of drug delivery.

IBM. "IBM Research." http://www.research.ibm.com/. Web site describing corporate research areas.

Intel Labs. "Intel Labs Research Areas Overview." http://techresearch.intel.com/index.aspx. Web site describing corporate research areas.

InVisage. "Technology." http://www.invisageinc.com. Corporate Web site describing QuantumFilm technology.

*Jain, K. K. *The Handbook of Nanomedicine.* Totawa, NJ: Humana Press, 2008. A comprehensive text that describes the promise of nanoscale tools as surgical implements.

Jalali, Bahram. "Silicon Photonics." *Journal of Lightwave Technology* 24, no. 12 (December 2006): 4600–4615. An overview of advances in integrating light with electronics, written by a world leader in the field, Professor Bahram Jalali of UCLA.

Jones, Richard A. L. *Soft Machines: Nanotechnology and Life.* New York: Oxford University Press, 2008. A physicist's view of why the future of nanotechnology will differ from the everyday world but also from first-generation speculations about how the field would develop.

Kennedy, L. C., L. R. Bickford, N. A. Lewinski, A. J. Coughlin, Y. Hu, E. S. Day, J. L. West, and R. A. Drezek. "A New Era for Cancer Treatment: Gold-Nanoparticle-Mediated Thermal Therapies." *Small* 7 (2011): 169. An excellent review of nanoparticle solutions for thermal therapy of cancer.

*Konstantatos, G., and E. H. Sargent. "Nanostructured Materials for Photon Detection." *Nature Nanotechnology* 5 (June 2010): 391–400. A review of the latest advances in technologies for enhanced sensing of light, including at the infrared wavelengths used for advanced security and night vision applications.

*Kumar, C. S. S., ed. *Nanomaterials for Cancer Therapy*. Weinheim: Wiley-VCH, 2006. A comprehensive overview of nanotechnological approaches to cancer therapy, bringing together oncology and nanotechnology.

Langer, R., and J. Folkman. "Polymers for the Sustained Release of Proteins and Other Macromolecules." *Nature* 263 (1976): 797–800. A seminal paper that laid the foundation for nano-enabled drug delivery.

Larminie, James, and Andrew Dicks. *Fuel Cell Systems Explained*. 2nd ed. Chichester: Wiley, 2003. An accessible introduction to how fuel cell technology works and how it is being incorporated into systems that enable efficient energy storage and playback.

*Lee, S.-W., C. Mao, C. E. Flynn, and A. M. Belcher. "Ordering of Quantum Dots Using Genetically Engineered Viruses." *Science* 296, no. 5569 (May 3, 2002): 892–895. A key advance at the bio-nano interface: genetically engineering viruses to customize them toward the goal of engineering specific nanostructured materials.

*Lewis, Nathan S., and Daniel G. Nocera. "Powering the Planet: Chemical Challenges in Solar Energy Utilization." *Proceedings of the National Academy of Sciences* 103, no. 43 (October 24, 2006): 15729–15735. A perspective on prospects for the field of direct solar conversion by two of the field's great names, professors at Caltech and MIT.

Maddox, Brenda. *Rosalind Franklin: The Dark Lady of DNA*. New York: HarperCollins, 2001. A fine biography for those interested in better understanding Rosalind Franklin's important contributions to the discovery of DNA structure.

*Mallouk, Thomas E., and Ayusman Sen. "How to Build Nanotech Motors." *Scientific American* 300, no. 5 (May 6, 2009): 72–77. http://research.chem. psu.edu/axsgroup/documents/research-scientificamerican20090506.pdf. An article on nanomachines, nanomotors, and nanobots by leading scientists in the field who bring a chemist's perspective to the subject.

Morton, J. G., E. S. Day, N. J. Halas, and J. L. West. "Nanoshells for Photothermal Cancer Therapy." *Cancer Nanotechnology* 624 (2010): 101. A detailed overview of the use of nanoshells for tumor ablation.

*Mouttet, Blaise. "Nanotechnology and U.S. Patents: A Statistical Analysis." *Nanotechnology Law & Business* 3, no. 3 (September 2006): 309. An overview of the nanotechnology patent landscape, depicting the intensity of commercial activity in a number of key sectors.

Nanosphere, Inc. http://www.nanosphere.us/. Web site of a company commercializing a nano approach to disease diagnosis.

*National Cancer Institute. "NCI Alliance for Nanotechnology in Cancer." http://nano.cancer.gov/. This Web site has a variety of videos, animations, and articles on the use of nanomaterials to fight cancer.

*Nelson, Jenny. *The Physics of Solar Cells (Properties of Semiconductor Materials)*. London: Imperial College Press, 2003. The canonical text that every student reads to develop a deep understanding of the physics of solar cells.

Nobelprize.org. "The Nobel Prize in Physics 1986." http://nobelprize. org/nobel_prizes/physics/laureates/1986/perspectives.html. Scientific background provided by the Nobel Prize committee on the reasons that Ernst Ruska, Gerd Binnig, and Heinrich Rohrer shared the Physics prize in 1986 for their advances.

————. "The Nobel Prize in Physics 2010." http://nobelprize.org/nobel_ prizes/physics/laureates/2010/#. See in particular "Popular Information" and "Advanced Information." An account of why the Nobel Prize in 2010 went to the discoverers of the novel physical properties of graphene, a material that holds promise in enabling new generations of transistors.

*————. "The Nobel Prize in Physics 2009." http://nobelprize.org/nobel_ prizes/physics/laureates/2009/. See in particular "Popular Information" and "Advanced Information: Scientific Background." The reasons the Nobel committee gave for awarding the 2009 prize to one of the fathers of fiber-optic communications, including an account of the innovations and their impact on the wider world.

*NOVA. "Secret of Photo 51." http://www.pbs.org/wgbh/nova/photo51/. An online look at Rosalind Franklin's contribution to the discovery of DNA structure.

*Ohta, Jun. Smart CMOS Image Sensors and Applications (Optical Science and Engineering). Boca Raton, FL: CRC Press, 2008. The technology and applications of the megapixel arrays of photodetectors that have enabled the digital photography revolution.

*Ozin, Geoffrey A., and Andre C. Arsenault. Nanochemistry: A Chemical Approach to Nanomaterials. Cambridge: Royal Society of Chemistry, 2005. A highly engaging and visual read coauthored by one of nanotechnology's pioneers, Professor Geoff Ozin.

Pearson, Helen. "Being Bob Langer." Nature 458 (March 2009): 22–24. http://www.nature.com/news/2009/090304/full/458022a.html. A profile of one of nanomedicine's most prolific leaders.

*Peer, D., J. M. Karp, S. Hong, O. C. Farokhad, R. Margalit, and R. Langer. "Nanocarriers as an Emerging Platform for Cancer Therapy." Nature Nanotechnology 2 (2007): 751. An excellent overview of nanodelivery systems for drugs.

*Perry, Tekla S. "Gordon Moore's Next Act." *IEEE Spectrum* 45, no. 5 (2008): 40–43. A long-view perspective on computing and its enablers from a pioneer of the integrated circuit and microprocessors.

*Petros, R. A., and J. M. DeSimone. "Strategies in the Design of Nanoparticles for Therapeutic Applications." *Nature Drug Delivery Reviews* 9 (2010): 615. Contains an excellent chronology of advances in drug delivery.

Poslad, Stefan. *Ubiquitous Computing: Smart Devices, Environments and Interactions*. Chichester: Wiley, 2009. Includes smart dust in a wide-ranging survey of smart devices, smart interaction between devices, and smart environments.

*Regalado, Antonio. "Reinventing the Leaf: Artificial Photosynthesis to Create Clean Fuel." *Scientific American* 303, no. 4 (October 2010): 86–89. http://www.scientificamerican.com/article.cfm?id=interactive-reinventing-the-leaf. An engaging popular magazine article in which the leaf is held up as a compelling model of a direct solar-to-chemical energy converter. The article also articulates a path forward for nanodevices inspired by the leaf.

Riehemann, Kristina, Stefan W. Schneider, Thomas A. Luger, Biana Godin, Mauro Ferrari, and Harald Fuchs. "Nanomedicine: Challenges and Perspective." *Angewandte Chemie* 48 (2009): 872. A detailed summary of frontier areas in nanomedicine.

Robinson, A. L. "Electron Microscope Inventors Share Nobel Physics Prize." *Science* 234 (1986): 821–822. An engaging article on one of the key discoveries that made nanotechnology possible: microscopes that allow visualization of matter at the nanometer-length scale.

*Ryhänen, Tapani, Mikko A. Uusitalo, Olli Ikkala, and Asta Kärkkäinen. *Nanotechnologies for Future Mobile Devices*. Cambridge: Cambridge University Press, 2010. A review by scientists at Nokia of nanotechnology's key role in the mobile handset of the future, with a special focus on new, dense, efficient, long-lived battery technologies.

*Sargent, Ted. *The Dance of Molecules: How Nanotechnology Is Changing Our Lives*. New York: Avalon, 2006. An overview of nanotechnology with a focus on its applications.

*————. "Infrared Photovoltaics Made by Solution Processing." *Nature Photonics* 3 (2009): 325–331. A review of colloidal quantum dot solar cells, one of the fastest-moving topics in solar energy, slated to unite low cost with high performance in the photovoltaics field.

Seeman, Nadrian C. "Nanotechnology and the Double Helix." *Scientific American* 290, no. 6 (June 2004): 65–75. An interesting look at how nanomaterials can be made from DNA.

Singhal, S., S. Nie, and M. D. Wang. "Nanotechnology Applications in Surgical Oncology." *Annual Review of Medicine* 61 (2010): 359. An in-depth overview of applications of nanomaterials in surgery.

*Stryer, Lubert. *Biochemistry*. New York: W. H. Freeman, 2010. The textbook many university students rely on when learning the basics of biomolecular structure and function. Revised regularly since 1988.

U.S. Department of Energy. *Basic Research Needs for Solar Energy Utilization: Report on the Basic Energy Sciences Workshop on Solar Energy Utilization, April 18–21, 2005*. http://science.energy.gov/~/media/bes/pdf/reports/files/seu_rpt_print.pdf. A report on opportunities and needs for innovation in energy capture.

*Vo-Dinh, Tuan, ed. *Nanotechnology in Biology and Medicine: Methods, Devices, and Applications*. Boca Raton, FL: CRC Press, 2007. A comprehensive text exploring cutting-edge areas of nanomedicine and nanobiotechnology.

*————. "Protein Nanotechnology: The New Frontier in Biosciences." *Methods in Molecular Biology* 300 (2005): 1–13. An overview of the protein-nano interface.

Voelcker, John. "Lithium Batteries Take to the Road: Hybrid Electric Cars Need Much Better Batteries—and A123, a Plucky Massachusetts Start-up, Says It's Got Them." *IEEE Spectrum* 44, no. 9 (September 2007): 26–31. The tale of A123, a start-up in the battery industry that went public and attracted billions of dollars in investment.

Watson, James D. *The Double Helix: A Personal Account of the Discovery of the Structure of DNA.* New York: Touchstone, 2001. First published in 1968, this personal account was written by a co-winner of the 1962 Nobel Prize for discovering the structure of DNA. For details about the award, see also: http://nobelprize.org/nobel_prizes/medicine/laureates/1962/.

Webber, M. J., J. A. Kessler, and S. I. Stupp. "Emerging Peptide Nanomedicine to Regenerate Tissues and Organs." *Journal of Internal Medicine* 267, no. 1 (2010): 71–88. A review of an interesting class of peptide-based nanomaterials that have been shown to provide an effective scaffold for the growth of a variety of tissues.

*Weinberg, Robert A. *The Biology of Cancer.* New York: Garland Science, 2007. An outstanding textbook that discusses the molecular and physiological bases and manifestations of cancer.

Weintraub, Arlene. "A Nano Drug's Giant Promise." *Bloomberg Businessweek,* April 11, 2005. http://www.businessweek.com/magazine/content/05_15/b3928059_mz011.htm. An interesting article describing the saga behind getting ABRAXANE® to market.

Whaley, S. R., D. S. English, E. L. Hu, P. F. Barbara, and A. M. Belcher. "Selection of Peptides with Semiconductor Binding Specificity for Directed Nanocrystal Assembly." *Nature* 405, no. 6787 (June 8, 2000): 665–668. Describes one of the first demonstrations that biomolecules and nanomaterials can be combined to build entirely new motifs of matter.

Wikipedia. "History of Computing Hardware." http://en.wikipedia.org/wiki/History_of_computing_hardware. A well-written perspective on computing hardware over the ages.

————. "Metamaterial." http://en.wikipedia.org/wiki/Metamaterial. An excellent overview of how scientists are designing new materials that have properties that go well beyond those of their constituents.

————. "Smartdust." http://en.wikipedia.org/wiki/Smartdust. A well-written article on ubiquitous self-powered networked sensors.

*Williams, Linda, and Wade Adams. *Nanotechnology Demystified.* New York: McGraw-Hill, 2007. A comprehensive view of applications of nanotechnology, including such topics as smart dust, diatoms, and environmental issues in nanotechnology.

*Withers, Neil. "Fuel Cells: Catalysis on the Cheap." *Nature Chemistry.* December 18, 2009. DOI:10.1038/nchem.535 (online only). An article uniting perspectives on catalysis and fuel cells, including those enabled by innovations in nanostructured materials.

Zrazhevskip, P., M. Sena, and X. Gao. "Designing Multifunctional Quantum Dots for Bioimaging, Detection, and Drug Delivery." *Chemical Society Reviews* 39 (2010): 4326. A detailed review of the use of quantum dots for *in vivo* imaging.

Notes

Notes

Notes

Notes

Notes